# A Peek Into Math of the Past

Mathematical Historical Investigations for Middle School and Pre-Algebra Students

by

Erica Dakin Voolich

DALE SEYMOUR PUBLICATIONS®
An imprint of Pearson Learning
Parsippany, NJ

*Dedication: I want to dedicate this book to my grandson Matthew and to the many middle school students who kept asking the questions about "who figured out . . . ."*

Editorial Manager: Carolyn Coyle
Senior Mathematics Editor: Nancy R. Anderson
Production/Manufacturing Director: Janet Yearian
Production/Manufacturing Manager: Karen Edmonds
Production/Manufacturing Coordinator: Lorraine Allen
Director of Design: Terry Harmon
Art Director: Jim O'Shea
Interior Design: Elaine Lopez
Cover Design: Jim O'Shea
Technical Art: Alan Noyes

Dale Seymour Publications
An imprint of Pearson Learning
299 Jefferson Road
Parsippany, NJ 07054-0480
www.pearsonlearning.com
1-800-321-3106



Acknowledgments appear on page 171, which constitutes an extension of this copyright page.

Order Number 21997
ISBN 0-7690-0828-3

1 2 3 4 5 6 7 8 9 10—ML—04 03 02 01 00

# Table of Contents

# Introduction

Often students finish school assuming that all of mathematics was "handed down along with the Ten Commandments." Some of the history of the development of mathematical ideas is interesting and accessible to middle school students. I have found that my students often ask "Who-first-discovered . . ." questions and are fascinated when I tell them stories from the history of mathematics when introducing new topics.

The Tidbits and Activities in this book are ones that I have developed for my students over the years as a middle school mathematics teacher. The Tidbits are short activities to possibly use as homework when working on related topics. The Activities are designed to take one or more class periods and can be done by groups of students. Included with some of the Tidbits and Activities are additional reproducible pages containing tables, illustrations, and teaching aids.

Teacher Notes, which are provided for each lesson, are followed by a Bibliography of materials referenced in the notes. Often it took me quite a long time to find the answers to questions that my students raised; so I have included historical background for most of the lessons. This background information, found in the Teacher Notes, is for your own use and can be shared with your students if they want more information.

Following this Introduction is a section entitled "Humanizing Your Mathematics Class." This section presents a variety of approaches to help you incorporate biographies of mathematicians into your classroom activities.

The table that follows includes information on both the mathematical and historical content of each lesson to guide you in the selection of lessons to use.

I hope you will enjoy adding the historical aspect to your teaching of middle school and pre-algebra mathematics.

| TIDBITS | Page | History | People and Places | Math Content |
|---|---|---|---|---|
| Mathematical Signs | 78 | mathematical signs and symbols, +, –, $\sqrt{\ }$, ×, ÷, π, ∞ | Widman, Rudolff, Recorde, Stevin, Oughtred, Wallis, Rahn, Pell, Leibniz, Jones, Euler, Hindus, Chinese, Moslems, al-Khwārîzmî, Fibonacci | problem solving, number theory |
| Oh, for the Good Old Days when Things Were Simpler | 80 | large numbers | Marco Polo, Chinese, Buddhists, Egyptians, Archimedes, Riese | writing large numbers, large-number names, problem solving |
| Roman-Numeral Riddle | 83 | Roman numerals, Hindu-Arabic numerals, musical catch | Europeans, Fibonacci, Purcell | Roman numerals |
| Say What You Mean and Mean What You Say | 85 | large numbers in Roman numerals | Livia, Tiberius, Galba, Romans | large numbers, Roman numerals, problem solving |
| Olden-Days Math from India | 86 | fractions | Hindus, Bakhshâlî, Mahâvirâ | fractions |
| The Egyptian Year | 87 | Egyptian calendar and myth | | multiplication and division of fractions, solar year |
| Egyptian Hours | 89 | Egyptian day | | daily papers, almanacs, arithmetic |
| The Perfect Bride | 90 | chronograms; number theory; perfect, deficient, abundant, and amicable numbers | Jews, Moslems, Greeks | primes, factors, formula substitutions, powers, patterns, primes |
| Prime-Formula Search | 92 | primes | Mersenne, Euclid, Euler, Chebyshev, Gauss, Cooper, Erdös | problem solving, number theory |
| Women in the History of Mathematics | 93 | | Kovalevskaya, Scott, Edgerton, Ladd-Franklin, Browne, Granville | |

| TIDBITS (cont.) | Page | History | People and Places | Math Content |
|---|---|---|---|---|
| "Calculators" | 96 | French Revolution | Pascal, Leibniz, de Prony, Herschel, Babbage, Lovelace | equation solving, problem solving |
| Coins | 98 | Coins, counterfeiting | | logic, problem solving |
| Firsts in Math Books | 99 | algebra, decimals, =, fractions, geometry | Mexico, Belgium, England, China, Euclid, Freyle, Stevin, Recorde, Shíshu, Suanshu, Ricci, Xú Guangqi | logic, problem solving |
| The More Things Change, the More They Stay the Same | 101 | 8th-century problems | Europe, Charlemagne, Alcuin | problem solving |
| Noah's Descendants | 102 | *The Scholar's Arithmetic* (1817) | | problem solving, exponents |
| Greenleaf's National Arithmetic; Greenleaf's National Arithmetic, the Sequel | 103, 104 | *The National Arithmetic* (1869), mathematics curriculum | | problem solving |

| ACTIVITIES | Page | History | People and Places | Math Content |
|---|---|---|---|---|
| How Large Is Your Yard?; Picky Little Details; "For All People, for All Time" | 105, 106, 107 | measurement, historical terminology, standardization, conversions, Golden Mean, S.I., French Revolution, metric system, variation on a pound, smoot, money conversion, metric prefixes | Mouton, Louis XVI, Egyptians, Penn, Jefferson, Adams | customary and metric measurement and conversions; collecting, graphing, and interpreting data |
| Circumference of Circles; Pi; Sato Moshun, Johannes, Kepler, and the Area of Circles | 109, 110, 112 | pi | Babylonians, Egyptians, Luí Hui, Archimedes, Tsu Chhung, Ptolemy, Wang Fan, Aryabhata, Fibonacci, Brahmagupta, Lambert, Viète, Newton, Leibniz, Euler, Ammei, Kohan, Nei, Ramanujan, Moshun, Kepler, Indiana | circumference and area of circles, patterns, fractions to decimals, dissection of circle |

| ACTIVITIES (cont.) | Page | History | People and Places | Math Content |
|---|---|---|---|---|
| Thales, Triangles, Playing Column, and Playing Ship | 114 | geometry theorems, congruent and similar triangles | Thales, Greece, Egypt, Babylonia | congruent and similar triangles |
| The Tile Detectives | 116 | tessellations | Jerusalem, Romans, Hadrian | tessellations, problem solving, polygons |
| A Pythagorean Puzzle | 117 | Pythagorean Theorem, $\sqrt{2}$ | Euclid, Pythagoras, Babylonians, Chinese, Hippausus | Pythagorean Theorem, comparing areas, Pythagorean triples |
| Legendary City Land Acquisition | 120 | classic Dido problem of maximizing area | Virgil, Dido, Carthage | area formulas, equation writing, substitution, Pythagorean Theorem, maximizing area, graphing calculator (optional) |
| The Sieve of Eratosthenes; Primes, Multiples, and Squares | 122, 123 | primes | Eratosthenes, Alexandria, Fermat, Euler, Goldbach, Vinogradov | primes, multiples, patterns, squares, twin primes |
| The Shapes of Numbers; The Shapes of Numbers, the Puzzle; The Shapes of Numbers, the Sums | 124, 126, 127 | figurate numbers, Pythagorean Theorem | Greeks, Gauss, Pythagoreans | numerical sequences, geometric sequences, square numbers, triangular numbers, sums of consecutive numbers (Gauss), Pythagorean triples |
| The 15 Game, Magic Squares, Constructing Odd Magic Squares, Altering Magic Squares, Concentric Magic Squares | 128, 129, 130, 132, 136 | magic squares, druids | Franklin, Chinese, Arabs, Dürer, Nigeria, Muhammad ibn Muhammad | game analysis, sums of consecutive numbers (Gauss), substitution, problem solving, patterns |

# Humanizing Your Mathematics Class

As a reader of this book, you know that there is a human aspect to the discovery and development of mathematics. However, it often has not dawned on students that the mathematics they study was developed by real people who led interesting lives. It is important that students realize that both men and women, as well as people of various nationalities and races, can and do develop mathematics. Incorporating the stories of mathematicians can be an important part of students' mathematics education.

There are many different ways to introduce mathematicians to your class. Starting could be as simple as telling the students about relevant mathematicians when the class is studying topics they developed. However, in recent years many print and internet resources have become available that make student research possible.

Various possible approaches to incorporating biographies into your mathematics class are described below. For short presentations spread out throughout the year, look at *Celebrating Birthdays* or *Mathematician Visits*. For an interdisciplinary writing activity, look at *The Rest of the Story*. For role playing, look at *TV Talk Show* or *Mathematician Visits*. In each activity, you can pick and choose the mathematicians researched. The *Selected Resources on Mathematicians*, with reading levels noted, pages 17–18, includes resources on mathematicians from ancient to modern times, men and women, and people of different races and cultures.

The activities can be adapted to different levels by your choice of resources. If you are working with fifth or sixth graders, choose mathematicians on the *Mathematicians with Middle School Resources* list, page 12. If you have students with higher reading levels, you can expand your list of mathematicians to the ones contained in the reference books and books designated for high school.

If you have the computer program Timeliner, you can make a timeline of the mathematicians studied for your classroom.

## Celebrating Birthdays

Students love excuses to celebrate, especially if food is involved. Use *Birthday List*, pages 13–16, to create two lists of mathematicians whose birthdays are spread throughout the year, one of females and one of males. Prepare strips of paper with names and birthdays of one male and one female having birthdays in both semesters, for example Evariste Galois (October 25) and Evelyn Boyd Granville (May 1). Have each student draw a strip of paper. On October 25 and May 1, the student who drew those names is responsible for preparing a short (5-minute maximum) biography presentation for the class. Afterward, everyone sings "Happy Birthday," and the presenter passes out treats (optional).

## The Rest of the Story

Paul Harvey is a radio commentator who each weekday has a short syndicated radio show called "The Rest of the Story." On it he gives the biography of a famous person with sort of an O. Henry twist. He tells about someone without fully identifying the person until the end of the story. He might use a middle name or nickname to identify the person and tell something that is not well known about that person. For example, he told of Vicky the teenager who complained about being chaperoned wherever she went (Queen Victoria), of the sailor turned pastry chef (Ho Chi Minh), and of the young child who was so sickly he was not expected to live (Scott Hamilton).

Start by reading the students a story at the end of each class for about a week, and encourage the students to listen to the syndicated stories on the local radio station—most likely ABC—that broadcasts "The Rest of the Story." Some of the stories are collected in the books by Paul Aurandt, *Paul Harvey's The Rest of the Story* (NY: Bantam Books, 1984) and *More of Paul Harvey's The Rest of the Story* (NY: Bantam Books, 1984). Assure students that you realize that the stories do not directly have something to do with mathematics, but it is important for them to think about the format.

Have students talk about Harvey's style and, as a class, summarize the details. Some things they might notice are:

- Initially, Harvey does not fully identify the individual being described. He uses nicknames and middle names instead of familiar names.
- Harvey includes dialogue that sounds realistic even though it might be ficticious.
- Harvey chooses to describe an event from the person's life that the listeners are probably not aware of. The event might make the reason he or she is famous or successful even more surprising.

Assign each student a different mathematician to research and to write a biography about using the rest-of-the-story format. Have students add a summarizing paragraph as to why this mathematician is famous, since very few students already know this about the people depicted. This is a good interdisciplinary project to do with the English teacher. A nice end-of-class activity each day is to have one student read his or her own "Rest of the Story" to the class.

## TV Talk Show[1]

Students are very familiar with the TV-talk-show format. In this activity, each student researches a mathematician and then portrays that person on the "TV Talk Show."

Assign students each a mathematician of their own gender and give them a copy of *Playing a Mathematician*, page 9, to complete while reading about the mathematician. Divide the students into groups of two or three, based on the historical period that their mathematicians lived. The advantage of using chronological order is that students often discover that they "knew" each other. For example, a group made up of Sophie Germain, Carl Gauss, and Joseph Lagrange discovered that Germain initially submitted papers to the math professor Lagrange using the pseudonym M. LeBlanc and later corresponded with Gauss initially using the same pseudonym. In their groups, students should help each other organize information and practice role playing. The culminating activity is a "TV Talk Show" where students are called up in small groups to be interviewed by their math teacher who pretends to be Oprah Winfrey while the other students make up the audience. A variation on this activity is to have students write and perform skits about their mathematicians.

This is a good activity that includes some of the ancient mathematicians who cannot be covered in activities that depend upon known birthdays.

## Mathematician Visits

It would be difficult to invite Carl Gauss or Sophie Germain to visit your mathematics class; however, students can research Gauss and Germain and role-play for a lively and informative visit. Use the following choices for mathematicians or prepare your own list based on *Birthday List,* pages 13–16, to have your students sign up for a particular presentation date.

The premade lists in *Selected Resources on Mathematicians*, pages 17–18, include mathematicians who have middle school level materials written about them. However, if you want to include more minorities or women, you should make your own list. The book *Notable Mathematicians* has indices of mathematicians by field of specialization, gender, and nationality/ethnicity. Listed resource and internet sites provide materials that are above middle school level.

After students choose their dates, give them the names of the mathematicians that they will research and portray using *Special Report Assignment*, page 11. The specific names that go with each date are given on page 8. Also, have students sign up on *Choices for Mathematicians*, page 10.

[1]The initial idea and format for the handout for this activity was based on Karen L. Tonso's workshop on "Researching Women Who Count" at the WME meeting at NCTM in April, 1992.

*Females*

*Mary Ellen Rudin, December 7*

*Julia Bowman Robinson, December 8*

*Grace Murray Hopper, December 9*

*Ada Byron Lovelace, December 10*

*Gabrielle Émilie du Châtelet, December 17*

*Mary Somerville, December 26*

*Sonya Kovalevskaya, January 15*

*Caroline Lucretia Herschel, March 16*

*Emmy Noether, March 23*

*Sophie Germain, April 1*

*Mary Gray, April 8*

*Evelyn Boyd Granville, May 1*

*Maria Gaetana Agnesi, May 16*

*Males*

*Evariste Galois, October 25*

*Benjamin Banneker, November 9*

*Norbert Wiener, November 26*

*George Pólya, December 13*

*Blaise Pascal, December 19 (June)*

*Srinivasa Ramanujan, December 22*

*Isaac Newton, December 25*

*Charles Babbage, December 26*

*John von Neumann, December 28*

*Joseph Louis Lagrange, January 25*

*Charles Lutwidge Dodgson, January 27*

*Niels Henrik Abel, February 5 (August)*

*Galileo Galilei, February 15*

*Pierre de Fermat, February 17 (August)*

*Albert Einstein, March 14*

*René Descartes, March 31*

*John Napier, April 4*

*Leonhard Euler, April 15*

*Carl Friedrich Gauss, April 30*

Mathematicians whose birthdays are in June, July, and August are assigned their "half-birthday" so they can be included during the school year. For example, Pierre de Fermat was born August 17, but is listed as February 17.

On the assigned day, the student portrays the mathematician by visiting the class for the first 5 minutes. Students can tell about the mathematician's life and work as well as share posters on the person. The posters make nice decorations for the classroom, and details about the mathematicians can become extra-credit questions on tests.

Name ______________________ Date ______________________

# Playing a Mathematician

An exciting thing is happening in class this week. You will be on a "TV Talk Show," role-playing a mathematician. The following steps will help you to prepare for your visit to the talk show.

1. Read the story about your mathematician.

2. Record the following information about your mathematician.

   a. Mathematician's name ______________________

   b. Where and when was the mathematician born?

   ______________________

   c. Where and when did the mathematician die, and at what age?

   ______________________

   d. Who was really important to the mathematician, and how did this person help?

   ______________________

   ______________________

   e. Were there any challenges in the mathematician's life? What were they?

   ______________________

   ______________________

   f. What kind of mathematics did the mathematician work on?

   ______________________

   g. What did you find most interesting about the mathematician?

   ______________________

3. Tell your partner about the life of your mathematician. Listen to your partner's story about his or her mathematician.

4. Pretend that you are your mathematician. Tell your partner about your life. Talk with your partner about his or her "life." The two of you can use the answers to the questions above to help you pretend that you are these mathematicians.

# Choices for Mathematicians

Choose one date below and sign your name on the line next to it. On this date, you will be responsible for making a presentation to the class that will involve some extra preparation. Do not worry, if we do not have school on the date you chose, you will be able to present just before or just after that date.

## Females

December 7 ____________________

December 8 ____________________

December 9 ____________________

December 10 ____________________

December 17 ____________________

December 26 ____________________

January 15 ____________________

March 16 ____________________

March 23 ____________________

April 1 ____________________

April 8 ____________________

May 1 ____________________

May 16 ____________________

## Males

October 25 ____________________

November 9 ____________________

November 26 ____________________

December 13 ____________________

December 19 ____________________

December 22 ____________________

December 25 ____________________

December 26 ____________________

December 28 ____________________

January 25 ____________________

January 27 ____________________

February 5 ____________________

February 15 ____________________

February 17 ____________________

March 14 ____________________

March 31 ____________________

April 4 ____________________

April 15 ____________________

April 30 ____________________

Name ______________________ Date ______________________

# Special Report Assignment

I am pleased to announce that we will have the pleasure of the company of a variety of mathematicians who will "visit our class this year." Through the wonders of role playing, we can even bring back such mathematicians as the inventors of calculus and the person whose research led to the building of the Eiffel Tower!

Name ______________________

The birth date of your mathematician is ______________________

For your mathematician's birthday, you need to do some research.

As you read about your mathematician, think about:

- When and where did your mathematician live?
- Who was/is an important person in this mathematician's life?
- On what kind of math problems did/does this person work?
- Did this person have any barriers or challenges when trying to do mathematics? What were they?
- What did you find particularly interesting about this person's life?

On the assigned day of this mathematician's "visit" to our class, you will be the actor or actress portraying him or her. You can use the above questions to help you prepare for your visit when you tell your classmates about "your" life.

Make a poster to hang in the classroom telling us about your mathematician. The minimum size of the poster is 18 inches by 24 inches.

# Mathematicians with Middle School Resources

Neils Henrik Abel, 1802–1829

Maria Agnesi, 1718–1799

Aryabhata al-Khwārîzmî, c. 780–850

Archimedes, 287–212 B.C.E.

Charles Babbage, 1792–1871

Benjamin Banneker, 1731–1806

Lenore Blum, 1943–

Mary Everest Boole, 1832–1916

Girolamo Cardano, 1501–1576

Emilie du Chatelet, 1706–1749

René Descartes, 1596–1650

Charles Lutwidge Dodgson, 1832–1898

Albert Einstein, 1879–1955

Euclid, c. 330–c. 275 B.C.E.

Leonhard Euler, 1707–1783

Eratostenes, c. 276–c. 195 B.C.E.

Pierre de Fermat, 1601–1665

Fibonacci (Leonardo of Pisa), c. 1170–c. 1240

Galileo Galilei, 1564–1642

Evariste Galois, 1811–1832

Carl Frederich Gauss, 1777–1855

Sophie Germain, 1776–1831

Evelyn Boyd Granville, 1924–

Mary Gray, 1939–

Heron, c. 75

Caroline Lucretia Herschel, 1750–1848

Grace Murray Hopper, 1906–1992

Hypatia, c. 370–c. 415

Omar Khayyam, c. 1048–1131

Sonya Kovalevskaya, 1850–1891

Joseph Louis Lagrange, 1736–1813

Ada Byron Lovelace, 1815–1852

Fanya Montalvo, 1948–

John Napier, 1550–1617

Florence Nightingale, 1820–1910

Emmy Noether, 1882–1935

Isaac Newton, 1642–1727

Edna Lee Paisano, 1948–

Blaise Pascal, 1623–1662

George Pólya, 1887–1985

Pythagoras, c. 560–c. 480 B.C.E.

Srinivasa Ramanujan, 1887–1920

Julia Bowman Robinson, 1919–1985

Mary Ellen Rudin, 1924–

Mary Fairfax Somerville, 1780–1872

Thales, c. 636–c. 546 B.C.E.

John Venn, 1834–1923

John von Neumann, 1903–1957

Norbert Wiener, 1894–1964

# Birthday List

## September

2 Walter S. McAfee, 1914
2 René Frédéric Thom, 1923
3 James Joseph Sylvester, 1814
7 Cheryl Praeger, 1948
8 Marin Mersenne, 1588
9 Marjorie Lee Browne, 1914
10 Charles Sanders Pierce, 1839
10 Maurice Fréchet, 1878
14 Alberto P. Calderón, 1920
14 Hans-Joachim Bremermann, 1926
15 Jean-Pierre Serre, 1926
17 Georg Friedrich Bernhard Riemann, 1826
17 Jean Taylor, 1944
18 Adrien-Marie Legendre, 1752
22 Paolo Ruffini, 1765
23 Ellen Amanda Hayes, 1851
24 Girolamo Cardano, 1501
24 Max Noether, 1844
24 Winifred Edgerton Merrill, 1862
24 Raoul Bott, 1923
28 Hilda Geiringer von Mises, 1893
28 Rhonda Hughes, 1947
30 Dirk Jan Struik, 1894

## October

3 Pierre René Delingné, 1944
4 Louis François Arbogast, 1759
4 Mary Celine Fasenmyer, 1906
6 Julius Wilhelm Richard Dedekind, 1831
6 Robert P. Langlands, 1936
7 Neils Bohr, 1885
17 Paul Bernays, 1888
18 Margaret Dusa McDuff, 1945
19 Subrahmanyan Chandrasekhar, 1910
20 William Henry Young, 1863
20 Hans Lewy, 1904
21 Martin Gardner, 1914
22 John Wallis, 1616
25 Evariste Galois, 1811
26 Shiing-Shen Chern, 1911
30 William P. Thurston, 1946
31 Karl Weierstrass, 1815
31 Ronald Lewis Graham, 1935

## November

2 George Boole, 1815
4 Johann Bernoulli, 1744
4 Andrew Mattei Gleason, 1921
6 Emma Trotskaya Lehmer, 1906
8 Moritz Pasch, 1843
8 Friedrich Ludwig Gottlob Frege, 1848
8 Felix Hausdorff, 1868
8 George Bernard Dantiz, 1914
8 Nancy Kopell, 1942
9 Benjamin Banneker, 1731
9 Hermann Weyl, 1885
12 Hugues Charles Robert Méray, 1835
15 Michel Chales, 1793

16 Eugenio Beltrami, 1835
17 Jean d'Alembert, 1717
17 August Möbius, 1790
17 Ruth Aaronson Bari, 1917
18 Lucien Marie Le Cam, 1924
19 Nina Karlovna Bari, 1901
20 Benoit Mandelbrot, 1924
25 Christian Felix Klein, 1849
26 Norbert Wiener, 1894
27 J. Ernest Wilkins, Jr., 1923

## December

1 Nikolai Ivanovich Lobachevski, 1793
1 Christine Ladd-Franklin, 1847
4 Richard Askey, (June), 1933
5 Elbert Frank Cox, 1895
5 Robin Wilson, 1943
6 Johann (Müller) Regiomontanus, (June) 1436
7 Mary Ellen Rudin, 1924
8 Caspar Wessel, (June),1745
8 Charoltte Angas Scott, (June), 1858
8 Alicia Boole Stott, 1860
8 Jacques Hadamard, (June), 1865
8 Julia Bowman Robinson, 1919
9 Grace Murray Hopper, 1906
10 Karl Gustoav Jacob Jacobi, 1804
10 Ada Byron Lovelace, 1815
11 Mary Catherine Bishop Weiss, 1930
12 Leopold Kronecker, 1823
13 George Pólya, 1887
13 John Forbes Nash, (June), 1928
14 Andrei Andreevich Markov, (June), 1856
14 Alonzo Church, (June), 1903
14 Atle Selberg, (June), 1917
14 Louise Schmir Hay, (June), 1935
15 János Bólyai, 1802
17 Gabrielle Émilie du Châtelet, 1706
17 Marius Sophus Lie, 1842
17 Mary Lucy Cartwright, 1900
18 Alice T. Schafer, (June), 1915
19 Blaise Pascal, (June), 1623
21 Kate Fenchel, 1905
22 Hermann Minkowski, (June), 1864
22 Srinivasa Ramanujan, 1887
23 Alan Turing, (June), 1912
23 David Hilbert, 1862
23 Richard Stanley, (June), 1944
24 Charles Hermite, 1822
24 Frederick Mosteller, 1916
25 Isaac Newton, 1642
26 Mary Somerville, 1780
26 Charles Babbage, 1792
26 John Horton Conway, 1937
27 Johannes Kepler, 1571
27 Jakob Bernoulli, 1654
28 Henri Lebesque, (June), 1875
28 John von Neumann, 1903

## January

1 Agner Krarup Erlang, 1878
1 Gottfried von Leibniz, (July), 1646
1 Jean Victor Poncelet, (July), 1788
2 Olga Oleinik, (July), 1925
5 Camille Jordan, 1838
7 Émile Borel, 1871
7 Chia-Chiao Lin, (July), 1916
8 Richard Courant, 1888
8 Stephen W. Hawking, 1942
10 Ruth Moufang, 1905
10 Donald Ellis Robbins, 1915
10 Donald E. Knuth, 1932
11 Vincenzo Riccati, 1707
12 Herbert Ellis Robbins, 1915
13 Gertrude Mary Cox, 1900

14 Alfred Tarski, 1901
15 Sonya Kovalevskaya, 1850
15 Stephen Smale, (July), 1930
16 Irmgard Flugge-Lotz, (July), 1903
17 Krystyna Kuperberg, (July), 1944
18 Jean Robert Argand, (July), 1768
19 Garrett Birkhoff, 1911
20 Gabor Szegö, 1895
22 Friedrich Wilhelm Bessel, (July), 1784
23 David Hilbert, 1862
23 Claribel Kendall, 1889
24 Karl Georg Christian von Staudt, 1798
25 Joseph Louis Lagrange, 1736
27 Charles Lutwidge Dodgson, 1832
28 Louis Joel Mordell, 1888
29 Daniel Bernoulli, 1700
29 Ernst Eduard Kummer, 1810
30 Marion Walter, 1928
31 Gabriel Cramer, (July), 1704
31 Sof'ja Aleksandrovna Janovskaya, 1896
31 Persi Diaconis, 1945

## February

2 Mina Speigel Rees, (August), 1902
4 William Rowan Hamilton, (August), 1805
4 John Venn, (August), 1834
4 Saunders MacLane, (August), 1909
5 Niels Henrik Abel, (August), 1802
6 Scipione Dal Ferro, 1465
7 Mary Frances Winston Newson, (August), 1869
7 Godfrey Harold Hardy, 1877
8 Ralph P. Boas, Jr., (August), 1912
9 Farkas Bolyai, 1775
9 Harold Scott MacDonald Coxeter, 1907
10 Carol Karp, (August), 1926
10 Vivienne Malone-Mayes, 1932
12 Hanna Newmann, 1914
13 George Gabriel Stokes, (August), 1819
14 Edmund Landau, 1877
15 Galileo Galilei, 1564
15 Alfred North Whitehead, 1861
16 Arthur Cayley, (August), 1821
17 Pierre de Fermat, (August), 1601
17 Ingrid Daubechies, (August), 1954
17 Ronald Aylmer Fisher, 1890
17 Rozsa Peter, 1905
18 Brook Taylor, (August), 1685
20 John Willard Milnor, 1931
20 Simon K. Donaldson, (August), 1957
21 Girard Desargues, 1591
21 Augustin-Louis Cauchy, (August), 1798
22 Adolphe Quetelet, 1796
22 Thomas Eugene Kurtz, 1928
23 Anneli Lax, 1922
23 Shige Fumi Mori, 1951
24 Bartholomeo Pitiscus, (August), 1561
24 Karen Uhlenbeck, (August), 1942
25 Johann Heinrich Lambert, (August), 1728
25 Tosio Kato, (August), 1917
27 Giuseppe Peano, (August), 1858
27 Luitzen Egbertus Jan Brouwer, 1881
30 Olga Taussky-Todd (August), 1906
30 Alexandra Bellow, (August), 1935

## March

3 George William Hill, 1838
3 Georg Cantor, 1845
3 Paul Richard Halmos, 1916
5 William Oughtred, 1574
5 Pauline Sperry, 1885
5 Vera Pless, 1931
8 Howard Aiken, 1900
8 Sylvia Young Wiegand, 1945
14 Albert Einstein, 1879
14 Waclaw Sierpinski, 1882

15 Grace Chisholm Young, 1868
16 Caroline Lucretia Herschel, 1750
16 Kunihiko Kodaira, 1915
18 Christian Goldbach, 1690
18 Jakob Steiner, 1796
18 Agnes Baxter, 1870
20 Sergei Novikov, 1938
21 Jean-Baptiste Fourier, 1768
21 George David Birkhoff, 1884
22 Irving Kaplansky, 1917
23 Pierre Simon de Laplace, 1749
23 Emmy Noether, 1882
24 Joseph Liouville, 1809
24 Sun-Yung Alice Chang, 1948
25 Richard Alfred Tapia, 1935
26 Paul Erdös, 1913
27 Karl Pearson, 1857
28 Alexander Grothendieck, 1928
29 Tullio Levi-Civita, 1873
30 Helen Abbot Merrill, 1864
30 Stefan Banach, 1892
31 René Descartes, 1596
31 Étienne Bézout, 1739

## April

1 Sophie Germain, 1776
2 Paul Joseph Cohen, 1934
4 John Napier, 1550
4 Shing-Tung Yau, 1949
7 Ivar Fredholm, 1866
8 Mary Gray, 1939
9 Élie Joseph Cartan, 1869
11 Dorothy Lewis Bernstein, 1914
11 Andrew John Wiles, 1953
12 Carl Louis Ferdinand von Lindemann, 1852
13 Ada Isabel Maddison, 1869
14 Christiaan Huygens, 1629
15 Leonhard Euler, 1707
16 Peter Apian, 1495
18 Lars V. Ahlfors, 1907
19 Richard von Mises, 1883
21 Michel Rolle, 1652
21 Michael H. Freedman, 1951
23 Sheila Scott MacIntyre, 1910
24 David Harold Blackwell, 1919
25 Andrei Nikolaevich Kolmogorov, 1903
26 Bill Gosper, 1943
28 Kurt Friedrich Gödel, 1906
29 Jules Henri Poincaré, 1854
30 Carl Friedrich Gauss, 1777
30 Claude Shannon, 1916

## May

1 Evelyn Boyd Granville, 1924
1 Peter David Lax, 1926
2 Harriet Pollatsch, 1942
5 Anna Johnson Pell Wheeler, 1883
5 Cathleen Synge Morawetz, 1923
6 André Weil, 1906
7 Alexis-Claude Clairaut, 1713
7 Pavel S. Aleksandrov, 1896
9 Gaspard Monge, 1746
11 Edna Ernestine Kramer Lassar, 1902
12 Florence Nightingale, 1820
13 Pelageya Yakovlevna Polubarinova Kochina, 1899
15 May Ida Rhodes, 1900
16 Maria Gaetana Agnesi, 1718
16 Pafunty Lvovich Chebyshev, 1821
18 Bertrand Russell, 1872
22 May Lipman Bers, 1914
25 Robert MacPherson, 1944
26 Abraham de Moivre, 1667
30 Karl Wilhelm Feuerbach, 1800
31 John George Kemeny, 1926

# Selected Resources on Mathematicians

## Internet Sites

http://www-groups.dcs.st and.ac.uk/~history/Day_files/Year.html

http://www.agnesscott.edu/lriddle/women/women.htm

## Print Materials

| | |
|---|---|
| M | Middle school or lower reading level |
| H | High school or above reading level |
| R | Reference book, good library source |
| T | Teacher source with student activities |


H R Albers, Donald J., and G.L. Alexanderson. *Mathematical People*. Boston: Birkhäuser Boston, 1985.

H *Profiles of Women in Mathematics: The Emmy Noether Lectures*. Association for Women in Mathematics. College Park, MD, 1994.

H Bedini, Silvio A. *The Life of Benjamin Banneker*. Rancho Cordova CA: Landmark Enterprises, 1972.

H Bell, E.T. *Men of Mathematics*. New York: Simon & Schuster, 1937, 1962.

M Billings, Charlene W. *Grace Hopper: Navy Admiral and Computer Pioneer*. Hillside, NJ: Enslow Publishers, Inc., 1989.

M *Celebrating Women in Mathematics and Science*. Edited by Miriam P. Cooney. Reston, VA, National Council of Teachers of Mathematics, 1996.

M T Edeen, Susan, and John Edeen. *Portraits for Classroom Bulletin Boards: Mathematicians*. Books 1 and 2. Parsippany, NJ: Dale Seymour Publications, 1988.

M T Edeen, Susan, John Edeen, and Virginia Slachman. *Portraits for Classroom Bulletin Boards: Women Mathematicians*. Parsippany, NJ: Dale Seymour Publications, 1990.

H Giles-Giron, Jacqueline. "Black Pioneers in Mathematics: Brown, Granville, Cox, Claytor, and Blackwell." *Focus* (MAA), vol. 2, no. 1, January–February, 1991.

H R Grinstein, Louis S., and Paul J. Campbell. *Women of Mathematics*. New York: Greenwood Press, 1987.

H Hawkins, William A. "Minorities and Mathematics: Overcoming the Obstacles." *Focus* (MAA), vol. 11, no. 1, January–February, 1991.

H Henderson, Harry. *Modern Mathematicians*. New York: Facts on File, 1996.

H Hoffman, Paul. *The Man Who Loved Only Numbers: The Story of Paul Erdos and the Search for Mathematical Truth*. New York: Hyperion, 1998.

H Infeld, Leopold. *Whom the Gods Love*. Reston, VA: National Council of Teachers of Mathematics, 1948, 1975.

H T Johnson, Art. *Classic Math History Topics for the Classroom*. Palo Alto, CA: Dale Seymour Publications, 1994.

H Kanigel, Robert. *The Man Who Knew Infinity: A Life of the Genius Ramanujan*. New York: Charles Scribner's Sons, 1991.

H Koblitz, Ann Hibner. *A Convergence of Lives: Sofia Kovalevskaia: Scientist, Writer, Revolutionary.* Boston: Birkhäuser, 1983.

H T Knauff, Robert E. *Short Stories from the History of Mathematics*. Burlington, NC: Carolina Biological Supply Company, 1996.

H T *Math Horizons*, a quarterly magazine published by the Mathematical Association of America that includes an article about a contemporary mathematician in each issue.

H R *More Mathematical People*. Edited by Donald J. Albers, G. L. Alexanderson, and Constance Reid. Orlando, FL: Harcourt Brace Jovanovich, 1990.

T Morrow, Jean, Connie Shrock, and Debbie Buchman. "Real People: A Fifth-Grade Class Investigates the Lives of Mathematicians." *Mathematics Teaching in the Middle School*, vol. 1, no. 4, January–March, 1995.

H Moseley, Maboth. *Irascible Genius: The Life of Charles Babbage*. Chicago: Henry Regnery, 1970.

H Muir, Jane. *Of Men and Numbers*. New York: Dodd, Mead & Company, 1966.

M *Notable Women in Mathematics: A Biographical Dictionary.* Edited by Charlene Morrow and Teri Perl. Westport, CT: Greenwood Press, 1998.

H Osen, Lynn M. *Women and Mathematics*. Cambridge, MA: MIT Press, 1974.

M *Outstanding Women in Mathematics and Science*. Windsor, CA: National Women's History Project, 1991.

H T Perl, Teri Hoch. *Math Equals*. Menlo Park, CA: Addison-Wesley, 1978.

H T Perl, Teri Hoch. *Women and Numbers*. San Carlos, CA: Wide World Publishing/Tetra, 1993.

H Reid, Constance. Julia: *A Life in Mathematics*. Washington, D.C.: Mathematical Association of America, 1996.

M Reimer, Luetta, and Wilbert Reimer. *Mathematicians Are People, Too: Stories from the Lives of Great Mathematicians*. Parsippany, NJ: Dale Seymour Publications, 1990.

M Reimer, Luetta, and Wilbert Reimer. *Mathematicians Are People, Too: Stories from the Lives of Great Mathematicians*, vol. II. Parsippany, NJ: Dale Seymour Publications, 1995.

M Reimer, Wilbert, and Luetta Reimer, *Historical Connections in Mathematics: Resources for Using History of Mathematics in the Classroom*, vols. I, II, and III. Fresno, CA: AIMS Educational Foundation, 1992, 1993, 1995.

M T Rickey, V. Frederick. *A Calendar of Mathematical Dates*. Bowling Green, OH: Bowling Green State University, 1986.

M *She Does Math! Real-Life Problems from Women on the Job*. Edited by Marla Parker. Washington, D.C.: Mathematical Association of America, 1995.

H Smith, Sanderson. *Agnesi to Zeno*. Berkeley, CA: Key Curriculum Press, 1996.

M Stonaker, Frances Benson. *Famous Mathematicians*. Philadelphia, PA: J.P. Lippincott, 1966.

H T Swetz, Frank J. *Learning Activities from the History of Mathematics*. Portland, ME: J. Weston Walch, 1994.

Voolich, Erica Dakin. "Using Biographies to 'Humanize' the Mathematics Class." *Arithmetic Teacher*, vol. 41, no. 1, September, 1993.

Voolich, Erica Dakin, and Karen Dee Michalowicz. "Happy Birthday, Great Mathematicians." *Virginia Mathematics Teacher*, vol. 17, no. 4, Fall, 1991.

H R *Notable Mathematicians: From Ancient Times to the Present*. Edited by Robyn V. Young. Detroit: Gale Research, 1998.

H Zientara, Marguerite. *The History of Computing: A Biographical Portrait of the Visionaries Who Shaped the Destiny of the Computer Industry*. Framingham, MA: CW Communications, 1981.

## Mathematical Signs, pages 78–79

Notes

To introduce the idea of the importance of our mathematical symbols, write the following problem on the board:

> Your bank pays 5.5% interest per year, compounded monthly, on savings accounts. You deposit $155. Write an equation showing how much money you will have in the account at the end of one year.

After the students have written their answers, ask them to write the same formula without using any symbols (neither numbers nor signs!).

Often students are unaware that we have not always used the same symbols to write such "simple ideas" as addition, subtraction, multiplication, and division. Initially, people needed sentences to explain what to do with various numbers. Then the directions might have been shortened to a word and then further simplified to a symbol. Sometimes two or more symbols were "invented" for the same purpose, so it often took time for mathematicians to agree on which symbol to use.

Except for the decimal point, the symbols mentioned here are generally accepted around the world and help make mathematics a universal language. When Stevin wrote his book trying to sell the idea of using decimals, he used a notation that would look very foreign to us today. Many other notations were proposed over the years. John Napier (of logarithm and Napier's Rods fame) proposed using a comma or period. Even today, some countries use a raised dot or a comma instead of a period as we do to indicate a decimal point. For a more thorough discussion of the history of decimals, see notes on *Writing Decimals Through the Years*, pages 61–63.

Most likely, writing without symbols was rather cumbersome for your students. The symbols we use to write numbers were developed in India about 600. They were derived from Brahmi symbols that date to the third century B.C.E. There is some evidence (Katz) that the Indians used a multiplicative numeration system until the seventh century. Then, possibly through Chinese influence, they combined their symbols with the Chinese base-10 system used on counting boards.

The Moslems collected and transmitted ideas to and from the lands they conquered, so ideas from such remote places as Babylonia, India, and Greece were combined and extended. People today refer to these symbols as the Hindu-Arabic numerals because the Arabs became the transmitting source of these symbols to Europe. The earliest known example of the Hindu numerals and arithmetic computations in an Islamic text was written by Muhammad ibn-Mūsā al-Khwārizmī (c. 780–850). Some Europeans did have access to his book, *Addition and Subtraction After the Method of the Indians (Kitāb al-jam'wal tafrīq bi hisāb al-Hind)* and knew about the Hindu numerals. Al-Khwārizmī also wrote an influential algebra text, *The Condensed Book on the Calculation of al-Jabr and al-Muqabala (al-kitāb al-muhtasar fī hisāb al-jabr wa-l-muqābala)*. It is from al-Khwārizmī's name that we got the word *algorithm*, and from his book title the word *algebra*.

As a child, Leonardo of Pisa, also known as Fibonacci, traveled with his father on business around the Mediterranean. His father would hire tutors for him wherever they stayed. He learned from Islamic scholars about mathematics, including the Hindu numerals. He returned to Pisa in 1200 and spent 25 years writing mathematics books. In 1202, Fibonacci wrote *Liber Abbaci*. Besides including the famous rabbit problem that gave the number sequence 1, 1, 2, 3, 5, 8, . . . the name "Fibonacci Sequence," the book formally introduced the Hindu-Arabic numerals to the Europeans. The Europeans were slow to accept the use of the "new numerals." See notes on *Roman-Numeral Riddle*, page 22.

The latest information on the earliest uses of mathematical signs and words can be found at the following web sites:

http://members.aol.com/jeff570/mathsym.html
http://members.aol.com/jeff570/mathword.html

**Answers**

| | | |
|---|---|---|
| 1. 1489 | 2. 1525 | 3. 1557 |
| 4. 1585 | 5. 1631 | 6. 1655 |
| 7. 1659 | 8. 1706 | |

**References**

Cajori, *A History of Mathematical Notations*; Katz; Smith: *History of Mathematics*, vols. I and II, *A Sourcebook in Mathematics*, vol. I

## Oh, for the Good Old Days when Things Were Simpler, pages 80–82

**Notes**

It is not unusual for people to have trouble conceiving of large numbers. If we talk about a group of 25 people, people have a sense of how many people there are; however, how do we conceive of 600,000 people? Can we distinguish between 650,000 and 600,000? *The Boston Globe* (September 11, 1985) quoted Acting Assistant Treasury Secretary John Niehenke as saying "words like trillion and quadrillion really don't exist" when Senator John Chafee asked him what came after *trillion* while discussing the mind-boggling size of the national debt.

Ask the students if they have been alive for 100, 1,000, or 10,000 days. How much difference does one zero make when talking about 1,000 or 10,000 days? A good video for bringing home the difference a zero makes is the video *Powers of Ten*. You might want to show the first half of the film when initially teaching large numbers and then show the whole video when introducing negative exponents. Give the students a copy of *Period Names in the USA*, page 82. Students love to have the names of large numbers and often are surprised to see that *zillions* is not on the list. Be sure to point out that the numbering system is different outside the United States, so actually using the exponential form could be less confusing.

Historically, people have tried to cope with understanding quantitative values of large numbers by putting them in terms they could understand. For example, the name for 10,000 in Chinese comes from *scorpion* and in Greek from *ant*; in each case these seem to represent something seemingly uncountable. When the Indian astronomers were working in China (618–907) they brought some of the Buddhist names for large numbers. They were translated into Chinese and appeared in a Chinese book in 1299:

$10^{88}$ = supreme

$10^{96}$ = the sand of the Ganges

$10^{120}$ = unimaginable

$10^{128}$ = noncountable

Egyptian hieroglyphics used a lotus flower for 1,000, a bent reed for 10,000, and a tadpole for 100,000—flowers in a field, reeds along the Nile, or tadpoles in the Nile are uncountable but 1,000, 10,000, or 100,000 could be reasonable estimates. The hieroglyph for 1,000,000 was the god of space holding up the sky—think of the numbers of stars on a clear night. The symbol originally stood for "infinitely many." At the height of Egyptian culture it stood for 1,000,000, and later it returned to its original meaning.

The book *Lalitavistara* (300 B.C.E.) tells the story of Buddha's life. It includes his naming numbers up to $10^{421}$. Buddha was competing for the hand of Gopa. Prince Dandapani, Gopa's father, put her suitors through a series of tests in writing, wrestling, archery, running, swimming, and number skills. Besides naming very large place values, Buddha also named "all of the divisions or atoms of a *yoyana* (a mile)." Buddha began:

| | atoms |
|---|---|
| 7 atoms make a very minute particle | $7^1$ |
| 7 very minute particles make 1 minute particle, and hence | $7^2$ |
| 7 minute particles make one that the wind will still carry | $7^3$ |
| 7 such particles make 1 rabbit track | $7^4$ |
| 7 rabbit tracks make 1 ram's track | $7^5$ |
| 7 rams' tracks make 1 ox track | $7^6$ |
| 7 ox tracks make 1 poppy seed | $7^7$ |
| 7 poppy seeds make 1 mustard seed | $7^8$ |

7 mustard seeds make 1 barleycorn $7^9$

7 barleycorns make 1 knuckle $7^{10}$

12 knuckles make 1 handbreadth $12 \cdot 7^{10}$

2 handbreadths make 1 ell $2 \cdot 12 \cdot 7^{10}$

4 ells make 1 bow $4 \cdot 2 \cdot 12 \cdot 7^{10}$

1,000 bows make 1 krosa $10^3 \cdot 4 \cdot 2 \cdot 12 \cdot 7^{10}$

4 krosa make 1 yoyana (mile)

One mile, therefore, contains $4 \cdot 10^3 \cdot 4 \cdot 2 \cdot 12 \cdot 7^{10} = 384{,}000 \cdot 7^{10}$ atoms. (Menninger)

In *The Sandreckoner*, Archimedes calculated the number of grains of sand that would fill a sphere the size of the universe (containing the earth, the sun, and the stars). The Greeks named numbers only up to *myrioi* (1 myriad = 10,000). Archimedes first developed a method of naming large numbers. The numbers up to a myriad of myriads (100,000,000) was called the first order of the first period. The second order was $100{,}000{,}000^{100{,}000{,}000}$. He continued naming orders up to $10^{80{,}000{,}000{,}000{,}000{,}000}$, the myriad-myriadth order of the myriad-myriadth period. Using the accepted measurements of his day for the diameter of the earth and sun and estimating the size of a grain of sand, Archimedes calculated that the universe would hold fewer than $10^{59}$ grains of sand. Interestingly, when making all of these calculations and working out the system of number naming, Archimedes noticed that the addition of the orders (what we would call exponents for 100,000,000) was the same as finding the products of the numbers. This is really the rule of exponents that is used when working with logarithms, discovered more than 1700 years later.

The use of familiar names for large numbers was first used to extend the sequence that was used by Nicolas Chuquet near the end of the fifteenth century when he wrote 745324•804300•700023•654321. "The first dot indicates a million, the second a billion, . . . trillion, . . . nonillion, and so on, as far as one may wish to go."

As different cultures have learned to write and name large numbers, there is not always agreement as to the meaning of particular terms. For example, in about 190 the Chinese mathematician Hsu Yo listed in *Shu Shu Chi I* three methods of naming numbers:

| | Upper | Middle | Lower |
|---|---|---|---|
| wan | $10^4$ | $10^4$ | $10^4$ |
| i | $10^8$ | $10^8$ | $10^5$ |
| chao | $10^{16}$ | $10^{12}$ | $10^6$ |
| ching | $10^{32}$ | $10^{16}$ | $10^7$ |
| hai | | $10^{20}$ | $10^8$ |
| tzu | | $10^{24}$ | $10^9$ |
| jang | | $10^{28}$ | |
| kou | | $10^{32}$ | |
| chien | | $10^{36}$ | |
| cheng | | $10^{40}$ | |
| tsai | | $10^{44}$ | |

Today, China uses the lower names and Japan the middle ones. This is similar to the different naming systems used by the United States and other western countries for the terms *million* and *billion*, for example.

**Answers**

1. To read the number Riese wrote, encourage the students to evaluate each section and then find the total.

   six and eighty thousand times a thousand = $86{,}000{,}000 \times 1{,}000 = 86{,}000{,}000{,}000$

   seven hundred thousand times a thousand = $700{,}000 \times 1{,}000 = 700{,}000{,}000$

   nine and eighty thousand times a thousand = $89{,}000 \times 1{,}000 = 89{,}000{,}000$

   three hundred thousand = 300,000

   five and twenty thousand = 25,000

   one hundred eight and seventy = 178

2. eighty-six billion, seven hundred eighty-nine million, three hundred twenty-five thousand, one hundred seventy-eight = 86,789,325,178

3. 86789325178
4. The initial reaction of students is to say our system is easier to read since that is what they use. See if you can get them to think beyond their own experience and to realize that ours is probably the easier to read because of its grouping by the period names.
5. The number of zeros = 3 times the Latin root + 3, or $3n + 3$.

**Bonus**

*Googol* is not derived from the Latin root of a number. When the American mathematician Edward Kasner asked his 9-year-old nephew, Milton Sirotta, for a name for a large number, the child suggested "googol." Kasner included it in his book written with James R. Newman, *Mathematics and the Imagination*, and the rest is history!

**References**

Boyer, Gullberg, Menninger, Needham

## Roman-Numeral Riddle, pages 83–84

**Notes**

Besides being something that students should be able to read, Roman numerals can be used effectively to review place value. Students often remember that you subtract when writing a number using Roman numerals; however, they often do something such as IC for 99. To prevent this problem, get them to write (think) 90 + 9 first, so 99 is written XCIX. Point out that writing the numbers 1 through 9 follows the same structure; the symbols depend upon whether you are using ones, tens, or hundreds. For example:

| | 1 | 2 | 3 | 4 | 5 | 6 | 7 | 8 | 9 |
|---|---|---|---|---|---|---|---|---|---|
| ones | I | II | III | IV | V | VI | VII | VIII | IX |
| tens | X | XX | XXX | XL | L | LX | LXX | LXXX | XC |
| hundreds | C | CC | CCC | CD | D | DC | DCC | DCCC | CM |

Today, Roman numerals are written using capital letters, but this has not always been the case. In fact, numbers were often written in script as if they formed a word. In order to keep someone from "cheating" and changing the last *i* at the end of a number such as *vi* to *viii*, for example, the final *i* would be written as a *j*, namely *viij*.

The Europeans knew about Hindu-Arabic numerals long before they were generally accepted. Leonardo of Pisa wrote the book *Liber Abaci* in 1202 introducing Hindu-Arabic numerals to the Europeans. However, change does not come easily. Italy was probably the most mathematically progressive country in Europe. However, in 1299 the city council of Florence passed a law requiring that all account books be written in Roman numerals, and in 1348 the University of Padua required that the prices of its books be given in Roman numerals. It was not until the beginning of the 16th century that the ordinary people of northern Europe made the transition to recording business transactions in Hindu-Arabic numerals. Part of the reluctance to change from Roman numerals was the fear of fraud: One could alter a *0* to look like a *9* or a *1* to look like a *4*, for example. Another part of the reluctance had to do with computation. Computing with Roman numerals was impossible with paper and pencil, as everything needed to be done on the counting board and then recorded; some masters were not anxious to share the knowledge of computation beyond their apprentices. The publication of *The Treviso Arithmetic* (1478) made computational algorithms available to the average person.

To introduce the lesson, choose a year that is important to you or has some historical significance to the students. Encode it by writing a sentence that includes all of the Roman-numeral letters in the order given, but no other Roman-numeral letters. Use your own example as the lesson introduction for the students. The example given on the students' page can be decoded by underlining all of the letters that can be used as Roman-numeral symbols and then eliminating all other letters.

My cat Max likes vans; MCMXLIV

**Extension**

A *catch* is a musical round that was popular in the seventeenth and eighteenth centuries. Some catches were bawdy and are not appropriate for a mathematics class. However, for some reason, Henry Purcell, one of the greatest English composers, wrote a catch about the Roman numerals *V* and *I*. A joint mathematics-music activity is the singing of Purcell's *Catch* about Roman numerals, page 84.

**Answers**

**1.** 1944    **2–4.** Answers will vary.

**References**

*The Catch Club or Merry Companions;* Menninger; Swetz: *Capitalism & Arithmetic*

## Say What You Mean and Mean What You Say, page 85

**Notes**

After students are familiar with writing numbers using Roman numerals, write the following symbols on the board and ask the students what they think these symbols mean.

M    ∞    (|)

These are some of the ways that the Romans wrote 1,000.

Today we use M to stand for 1,000, but M was not the generally accepted symbol for the ancient Romans. The oldest example that M was used dates from 89 B.C.E.; however, it was not in general use until the Middle Ages. In fact, the Romans did not have one symbol but many similar symbols. The Latin grammarian Priscian (c. 500) suggested that the symbol ∞ came from the Greek *x* for 1,000, but the Romans added the curves to distinguish it from the *x* they used for 10.

Write the following symbols on the board and let the students guess their values.

((|))    (((|)))

((|)) stands for 10,000 and (((|))) for 100,000.

Then ask the students to think about the symbol we use for 500 in Roman numerals today (D). Have them think about the pattern of the values of today's Roman numerals and predict what values they would expect to see besides the ones already on the board. Then have the students find the value for each of these symbols.

|))    (5,000)

((|))    (10,000)

|)))    (50,000)

(((|)))    (100,000)

If you think about writing (|), you can imagine its evolving into a D and (|) evolving into an M.

The ancient Romans did not consistently use these symbols for large numbers. Another way that they indicated large numbers was with ¯ or ⊓ over a symbol to indicate multiplication by 1,000 or 100,000, respectively.

**Answers**

**1.** 10,000    **2.** 1,000,000
**3.** 500,000    **4.** 50,000,000
**5.** 100,000    **6.** 10,000,000
**7.** 20,000    **8.** 2,000,000
**9.** 13,002,055    **10.** 300,200,100
**11.** 49,500,000 sesterces
**12.** 2.5 asses
**13.** $49{,}500{,}000 \times 2.5 \times 0.5 \div 16 =$ 3,867,187.5 pounds
**14.** $3,557,812.50

In 1998, the price of junk copper was $0.50 per pound and of raw copper was $0.92 per pound. A local junkyard can update these figures.

**References**

Cajori: *A History of Mathematical Notations*; Menninger

## Olden-Days Math from India, page 86

### Notes

The Hindus in India gave us the decimal place-value system that we use today. They also gave us the common fractions we use. These ideas were introduced initially to the Europeans by the Arabs. That is why we refer to our numeration system as the Hindu-Arabic numerals. However, the Hindus did not realize that they could extend decimal place value to include the decimal fractions as the Chinese did.

By the year 200, the Hindus wrote the common fractions as we do today, with the numerator over the denominator but without the dividing bar. For example, we write $\frac{3}{4}$, while the Hindus wrote $\begin{smallmatrix}3\\4\end{smallmatrix}$. The bar was added by the Arabs. If there were several fractions in a problem, they were separated by vertical and horizontal lines as shown on the student page. For mixed numbers the Hindus wrote the numerals vertically. For example, for $2\frac{1}{3}$ they wrote the following:

$$\begin{matrix}2\\1\\3\end{matrix}$$

To indicate subtraction, they put a dot in front of the number.

The Bakhshâlî Manuscript (c. 200) describes the Hindu algorithms for adding, subtracting, multiplying, and dividing fractions that are basically what we use today. In 830, Mahâvirâ introduced the ideas of using the least common denominator and cancellation to simplify computations.

### Answers

1. The dot means subtract.
2. Here it means $1 \div \frac{1}{3}$, but sometimes it meant $1\frac{1}{3}$. It could be confusing, and the reader was supposed to be able to tell the meaning from the context.
3. $\frac{1}{2} + (\frac{1}{4} \times \frac{1}{4}) + (1 \div \frac{1}{3}) + (\frac{1}{2} + \frac{1}{2} \times \frac{1}{2}) + (\frac{1}{3} - \frac{1}{2} \times \frac{1}{3})$
4. $4\frac{23}{48}$

## The Egyptian Year, pages 87–88

### Answers

| | | |
|---|---|---|
| **1.** $\frac{3}{32}$, T | **2.** $\frac{3}{4}$, I | **3.** $1\frac{1}{3}$, S |
| **4.** $\frac{5}{24}$, C | **5.** $\frac{27}{40}$, U | **6.** $1\frac{13}{27}$, W |
| **7.** $6\frac{2}{3}$, Q | **8.** $\frac{5}{12}$, B | **9.** $2\frac{2}{5}$, G |
| **10.** $5\frac{2}{3}$, X | **11.** 6, E | **12.** $10\frac{2}{3}$, N |
| **13.** $\frac{16}{27}$, K | **14.** $7\frac{1}{4}$, J | **15.** $\frac{8}{15}$, O |
| **16.** $\frac{8}{39}$, Y | **17.** $\frac{5}{8}$, L | **18.** 10, P |
| **19.** $3\frac{3}{5}$, A | **20.** $\frac{5}{18}$, H | **21.** $\frac{1}{24}$, Z |
| **22.** $1\frac{1}{15}$, D | **23.** $\frac{15}{16}$ | **24.** $1\frac{7}{24}$, F |
| **25.** $\frac{1}{2}$, M | **26.** 2, V | |

The decoded message:
Thoth won the dice game and as his prize made the moon give him $\frac{1}{72}$ of her light. With this light, Thoth made 5 days. These days did not appear on the calendar, but were added on at the end of the year. Nut used these days that were unknown to Re to give birth to five gods and goddesses. This is why the ancient Egyptian calendar had 12 months of thirty days with an extra 5 holidays added on at the end.

**27.** 5 days, the five holidays

**28.** 365 days

**29. and 30.** One solar year is 365.242199 mean solar days (24 hours, 3 minutes, 56.55 seconds). Initially, this seems as if the Egyptian year is close enough to the solar year. However, 100 × 365.242199 = 36,524.2199, and 365 × 100 = 36,500. This is a difference of about 24 days. If this calendar had been used for centuries, seasons would not occur at the same time on the calendar and holidays would occur in different seasons.

## Egyptian Hours, page 89

### Notes

For centuries, people have tried to measure the passage of time. Measuring time by counting sunsets or sunrises (days) or by counting full moons (months) arises out of natural phenomena.

Measuring time in hours or minutes is more artificial. Measuring the passage of time has been an important activity of people for centuries. See notes on *Exploring the Perpetual Calendar*, pages 68–71. Often students have not given much thought to how the day is changing around them, and this activity highlights the fact that the length of the day changes with the time of the year. During the vernal and autumnal equinoxes, the day and night are approximately the same length of time; at the winter solstice, the day is the shortest and at the summer solstice, it is the longest. How long the daylight will be is determined by your location on the earth and the day of the year. Students can find information on the length of a day in an almanac.

**Answers**

**1.–6.** Answers will vary.

## The Perfect Bride, pages 90–91

**Notes**

This lesson relates numbers to various properties that students might not associate with numbers. It begins with chronograms and ends with amicable numbers. *Chronogram* is the term used to describe the expression of a date of an event within a meaningful phrase or word. (Ifrah)

Students will need to use what they know about finding factors of numbers. If students need help finding all of the factors of a number, you can teach them the trick of finding the square root of the number and then checking all of the factors less than or equal to the square root; be sure they include the factor pairs. For example, to find the factors of 1,184, take its square root: $\sqrt{1,184} \approx 34$. You need check only the numbers up to 34 to find all of the factors of 1,184: 1 and 1,184, 2 and 592, 4 and 296, 8 and 48, 16 and 74, 32 and 37.

Problems 3, 4, and 5 can be used for bulletin boards. If more than two people in the class have the same numerical value, you could challenge the class to figure out who the pairs are.

**Extension**

Students can explore these interesting patterns using perfect numbers. (Gullberg).

**A.** Perfect numbers seem to be the sum of consecutive odd cubes:

$28 = 1^3 + 3^3$ and $496 = 1^3 + 3^3 + 5^3 + 7^3$

Is this true for the other perfect numbers? (Yes, for perfect numbers other than 6)

Is the converse true? That is, if a number is a sum of consecutive odd cubes, will it be a perfect number? (No)

**B.** What is the final sum of the digits in perfect numbers? (1, for perfect numbers other than 6)

For example, for 28: 2 + 8 = 10, 1 + 0 = 1

Is the converse true? That is, if the final sum of the digits of a number is 1, will it be a perfect number? (No)

**C.** What is the sum of the reciprocals of all of the factors of perfect numbers? (2)

For example, for 28:
$\frac{1}{1} + \frac{1}{2} + \frac{1}{4} + \frac{1}{7} + \frac{1}{14} + \frac{1}{28} = 2$

**Answers**

**1. and 2.** Answers will vary.

**3.** Possible answer: fuzzy–2,606

**4.** Possible answer: abaca–8

**5.** Possible answers: sty, wetter, and yu–1,000

**6.** 28; 1 + 2 + 4 + 7 + 14 = 28

**7.** Abundant (A): 30 and 36; deficient (D): 31, 32, 33, 34, 35, 37

**8.** A prime cannot be abundant because its only proper factor is 1.

**9.** It seems that most numbers are deficient. There are about 30 perfect numbers known today; interestingly, they are all even. No one has proven whether or not there is an infinite number of perfect numbers. When you think about how many factors are necessary for a number to be abundant, most are probably deficient.

10. Answers will vary.

11. Amicable means *friendly*.

12. The perfect number for a bride would be 220, and her name might be *Poline*. The perfect-number pair used here, 284 and 220, is said to have been known by the Pythagor-eans who were very interested in the patterns that could be attributed to numbers. For many years this was the only known pair, until 1636 when Pierre de Fermat (yes, the same Fermat as in Fermat's Last Theorem) found 17,296 and 18,416. In 1638 René Descartes discovered the pair 9,363,584 and 9,437,056. Leonhard Euler found 60 pairs. (Gullberg)

**References**

Chonograms: Ifrah; amicable and perfect numbers: Gullberg

## Prime-Formula Search, page 92

**Notes**

The only number in Problems 1–3 that is *not* prime is 15.

Initially, it looks as if these formulas often generate primes as long as $n$ is prime. However, $2^n - 1$ generates more composites than primes. When substituting the first four primes in $2^n - 1$, you get primes, but the fifth prime, 11, gives 2,047 = $23 \times 89$. This is an important formula, however; whenever $n$ is prime and $2^n - 1$ is prime, then $(2^n - 1)(2^{n-1})$ is a perfect number. For more information, see notes on *Mersenne Primes and Perfect Numbers*, pages 66–67.

The formula $n^2 + n + 17$ breaks down when $n = 16$, and $n^2 + n + 41$ breaks down when $n = 40$. A little algebra explains why:

| $n^2 + n + 17$: | $n^2 + n + 41$: |
| --- | --- |
| $16^2 + 16 + 17$ | $40^2 + 40 + 41$ |
| $16(16 + 1) + 17$ | $40(40 + 1) + 41$ |
| $16(17) + 17$ | $40(41) + 41$ |
| $(16 + 1)(17)$ | $(40 + 1)(41)$ |
| $(17)(17)$ | $(41)(41)$ |

Even though these break down, they do generate primes; in fact, the only values of $n$ less than 100 that do *not* generate primes in $n^2 + n + 41$ are 40, 41, 44, 49, 56, 65, 76, 81, 82, 84, 87, 89, 90, and 96. A computer at Los Alamos, *Maniac II*, checked all of the values for $n$ up to 10 million and found that this formula generated primes 47.5% of the time.

Mathematicians have searched for primes for many years. Karl Gauss started studying primes when he was 15. A prime search became a way to pass the time in solitary confinement in Iran for journalist Roger Cooper who calculated all of the primes less than 5,000 during several years of imprisonment in the 1980s.

**Extension**

Have the students investigate Chebyshev's theorem: For any number $n > 1$ and its double $2n$, there is always at least one prime number between $n$ and $2n$. Pafnuty Lvovich Chebyshev proved this in 1850. Later, 18-year-old Paul Erdös came up with a more elegant proof, leading to this rhyme:

> Chebyshev said it, and I say it again.
> There is always a prime between $n$ and $2n$.

**Answers**

1. **a.** 3 **b.** 7 **c.** 15
   **d.** 31 **e.** 63 **f.** 127
   **g.** 2, 3, 5, and 7 **h.** 2,047; no; 23 and 89
2. **a.** 19 **b.** 23 **c.** 29
   **d.** 37 **e.** 47 **f.** 59
   **g.** 73 **h.** All values of $n$
   **i.** 289; no; 17 and 17
3. **a.** 43 **b.** 47 **c.** 53
   **d.** 61 **e.** 71 **f.** 83
   **g.** 97 **h.** All values of $n$
4. Possible answers: 40, 41, 44, 49, 56, 65, 76, 81, 82, 84, 87, 89, 90, 96

## Women in the History of Mathematics, pages 93–95

**Answers**

| | | |
|---|---|---|
| A. 1874 | B. 1876 | C. 3 |
| D. 22 | E. 1894 | F. 1880 |
| G. 50 | H. 8 | I. 1886 |
| J. 1926 | K. 78 | L. 44 |
| M. 1949 | | |

## "Calculators," pages 96–97

**Notes**

My middle school students are always amazed when I tell them I did not own a calculator until adulthood, and that in high school we used slide rules to do calculations. I have brought in slide rules (extras purchased at yard sales) to show the students how we multiplied using scientific notation. Often they are surprised at the "inaccuracy," since they seem to think that a 10-digit display of decimals on their calculator is the norm and necessity for accuracy in an answer. Relevant significant digits is a hard concept for middle school students.

You could tell your students that Babbage was interested not only in accurate computation of mathematical tables, but also in their readability. The tables he published in 1826 were considered the most accurate available at that time. Before publishing the tables, he experimented with different typefaces, paper colors, and ink colors. Initially he tried printing one page on 140 different colored sheets using 10 different ink colors. He even tried black on black and red on red. Then he tried three metallic inks and 11 other paper colors. His samples were bound into 21 volumes. Have your students figure out how many possible combinations Babbage could have made (1963) and how many more than his original color experiments this was (563). You might ask the students to think about whether he changed the paper color or ink color between each printing and why one would have been more efficient. Babbage was very interested in efficiency in manufacturing and his study of the English postal system resulted in the introduction of the penny post.

Many of the persons mentioned in this story have made other significant mathematical contributions. There are age-appropriate activities and biographical information on Lovelace in Perl (1993 and 1978) and on Pascal in Reimer (1992). Stories about Pascal are in Reimer (1990), and about Babbage and Lovelace in Reimer (1995).

**Answers**

| | | |
|---|---|---|
| $a = 1642$ | $b = 19$ | $c = 10$ |
| $d = 15$ | $e = 1672$ | $f = 30$ |
| $g = 2$ | $h = 1794$ | $i = 6$ |
| $j = 8$ | $k = 80$ | $l = 2$ |
| $m = 2$ | $n = 17$ | $o = 1835$ |
| $p = 140$ | $q = 40$ | $r = 3700$ |
| $s = 1822$ | $t = 1823$ | $u = 1832$ |
| $v = 1833$ | $w = 10$ | $x = 10$ |
| $y = 5$ | $z = 2$ | |

**References**

Augarten; Babbage; Cajori: *A History of Mathematics*; Moseley; Perl: *Math Equals*, *Women and Numbers*; Reimer: *Mathematicians Are People, Too*, *Mathematicians Are People, Too*, vol. two, *Historical Connections in Mathematics*; Williams

## Coins, page 98

**Notes**

Students probably have not given much thought to the idea of coins. They have them and use them, but no one questions their exchange values. If you take 100 pennies to the bank, you will get a dollar. With the debasing of coins, in the past you might have had your coins weighed to see that there really was a pound of silver, for example. We do have trouble with counterfeit bills today. If counterfeiters are caught today they go to jail; but in Venice in the fourteenth century, a woman caught minting coins had her nose cut off and a man was blinded.

Today as you travel between countries, you need to exchange money. You might have the students think about what it would be like to own a small general store in colonial America. You needed to be able to convert between currencies of various colonies as well as the countries that settlers had come from. Students will be better able to understand why one thing the young United States needed to do was to establish their own monetary system. For more information, see notes on "*For All People, for All Time,*" pages 33–36.

**Answers**

1. 1424, Switzerland
2. 1448, Germany
3. 1478, Sweden
4. 1485, France
5. 1534, Italy
6. 1549, Scotland
7. 1551, England
8. Two good reasons to not buy the coin are:

- If it really dated from XLIX B.C.E., the year would not be written like that. People living before Christ did not know that they were living 59 years before he was born.
- 51 years before 1424 is 1373, and 1373 is the earliest Roman numeral-dated coin.

**References**

*The New Encyclopaedia Britannica*, s.v. "coin"; Swetz: *Capitalism & Arithmetic*

## Firsts in Math Books, pages 99–100

**Notes**

Your students might be interested in knowing more about these remarkable books.

Juan Diez Freyle, *Summario de las Quentas de Plata y Ore (Brief Summary of Reckoning),* 1556

The interest in mathematics during the colonization period was to solve practical problems. This book "contained extensive tables relating to gold and silver exchange, among other monetary affairs, as well as arithmetic problems relating to the tables and some elementary algebra. In general the earliest mathematics texts elsewhere in Latin America also contained very practical material, especially including material useful for military purposes." (Katz)

Simon Stevin, *La Thiende* (*The Art of Tenths*), 1585

Stevin's book gave the Europeans the first well-thought-out description of computation with decimals with rules that sound very familiar to us today. This was an idea that was new to the Europeans who used common fractions (or sexigesimals for astronomy) for their computations. It took another 200 years for decimals to come into common use, namely when the French government, following the French Revolution, had mathematicians develop what we know as the metric system. For a translation of Stevin's introduction to his book, in which he tried to convince readers of the usefulness of decimal numbers, see notes on *Writing Decimals Through the Years*, pages 61–63.

Robert Recorde, *The Whetstone of Witte*, 1557

Recorde was a physician who wrote four successful mathematics books. Recorde's ideas were not really new mathematical ideas, since they were based on German textbooks by Stifel and Rudolff. However, *The Whetstone of Witte* was the first algebra textbook in England and was used for many years. When introducing the = symbol for equality, Recorde said "To avoid the tedious repetition of these words—is equal to—I will set as I do often in work use, a pair of parallels, or gemow [twin] lines of one length, thus =, because no 2 things can be more equal." (Katz) It took 100 years before his sign for equality was generally accepted. He wrote his books in the format of a dialogue between a master and a pupil, carefully explaining each step in the process. Recorde published this book a year before he died in prison. He was falsely accused of treason, imprisoned, and then released. Later, he lost a libel suit and could not pay the fine, dying in prison.

Suànjing Shíshu, *Ten Mathematical Manuals*, 656

During the Han dynasty (206 B.C.E.–220) specialized mathematical manuals were written. These manuals had practical problems applicable to the different needs of civil servants, for example, tax collection, weights and measures, currency, construction of dikes and canals, land and river transport, and so on. During the Tang dynasty (618–907) the *Ten Mathematical Manuals* was the text adopted for the mathematical part of the education of civil servants. In 1230, mathematics was eliminated from the required education of civil servants.

Jiuzhang Suanshu, *Nine Chapters on the Mathematical Art*, 1084

"*Nine Chapters on the Mathematical Art* is a compilation of 246 problems loosely grouped in nine chapters. Some of its material predates the great book-burning and burial-alive of scholars of 213 B.C. It is believed that the *Nine Chapters* were put in their final form sometime before 100 A.D." (Straffin) It is considered the earliest known mathematics writing in China that still exists today. In 1084, it was mass-printed using woodcut printed pages. It is not known who authored this text. Most likely it is the "collective effort and wisdom of mathematicians of several centuries and that it was only after re-editing and augmenting by a number of people that it received its final form." (Yan) It is the earliest known book in the world to show how to compute with fractions and probably the first to solve systems of linear equations. It also treats such topics as positive and negative numbers, geometric calculations, calculation of roots, the Pythagorean Theorem, and proportions.

Euclid, *Elements* (Jihe Yuanben), 1607

"The most important mathematical text of Greek times, and probably of all times, the *Elements* of Euclid, written about 2,300 years ago, has appeared in more editions than any other work than the *Bible*. It has been translated into countless languages and has been continuously in print in one country or another nearly since the beginning of printing." (Katz) We do not have the original work by Euclid; however, copied manuscripts do exist. The *Elements* covers both geometry and number theory and is a compilation of mathematical knowledge in Euclid's day. At the end of the sixteenth century, the Jesuit missionaries came to China. They realized that mass conversions to Christianity were not possible, so they became conversant in the Chinese language and sought to seek high-level dialogues in areas of mathematics and calendar calculations. Matteo Ricci was the first Jesuit in China. He translated books such as Euclid's *Elements* by explaining the contents of the original work to the Christian convert and high-level public official, Xu Gúangqi, who wrote everything down. In Chinese it is called *Jihe Yuanben*. It is still used in China, Japan, and Korea today.

**Answers**

1. Juan Diez Freyle, *Summario de las Quentas de Plata y Ore*, 1556
2. Simon Stevin, *La Thiende*, 1585
3. Robert Recorde, *The Whetstone of Witte*, 1557
4. *Ten Mathematical Manuals*, 656
5. *Nine Chapters on the Mathematical Art*, 1084
6. Euclid, *Elements*, 1607

**References**

Boyer; Katz; Martzloff: *A History of Chinese Mathematics*; "π in the Sky"; Straffin; Yan

## The More Things Change, the More They Stay the Same, page 101

**Notes**

When Charlemagne was the ruler of what is now France, Western Germany, parts of Austria, and Italy (the Holy Roman Empire), he decided that education of the clergy and government workers was important. Around 789, Charlemagne appointed Alcuin of York his educational advisor. Alcuin developed schools in abbeys and monasteries all over the empire, as well as in Charlemagne's own palace. The curriculum was made up of the quadrivium (arithmetic, geometry, astronomy, and music) and the trivium (grammar, rhetoric and logic). Most Europeans were uneducated at the time, so Alcuin wrote textbooks for these subjects including the math book *Propositions for Sharpening Youthful Minds*. Unfortunately, people in the clergy and government service saw more need for literacy than for numeracy, so the mathematics part of education was often neglected. This was not a time of general education of everyone. This brief educational renaissance occurred during the Dark Ages in Western Europe (fifth to eleventh centuries).

Diagrams or manipulatives are useful in Problems 1 and 2. Diagrams help keep straight who is where. For example,

| 1. | 2. |
|---|---|
| C, W —G→ | M, F —S, D→ |
| C, W ←G | M, F ←S— D |
| C—W→ G | F —S, M→ D |
| C←G— W | F ←S— M, D |
| G—C→ W | S —F→ M, D |
| G← C, W | S ←D— F, M |
| —G→ C, W | —S, D→ F, M |

Alcuin also had another crossing problem that in today's terms sounds rather sexist: "Three men and their sisters having to cross a river in a boat holding only two people, where it is assumed that to be safe each girl must have no other companion than her brother." (Burton) An extension might be to give a less sexist version: There are three men and each has his own dog. These men and their dogs need to cross a river. There is one boat that can only hold one man and one dog. The dogs get along with each other but none of the dogs can be left with another man without his owner present. How many trips does it take to get all three pairs to the other side? Predict and then figure out how many trips it would take to get four pairs across the river.

**Answers**

1. The man takes the goat across and goes back and brings the wolf across. He leaves the wolf and takes the goat back to the original side. He leaves the goat and picks up the cabbage and takes it across and leaves it with the wolf. He goes back and gets the goat and brings it across.
2. The son and daughter cross and the son returns with the boat. The son and mother cross and the son returns with the boat. The father crosses and the daughter returns with the boat. The son and daughter cross. In this solution, the son and daughter can switch roles.
3. 20 pieces of licorice for 25¢; 12 pieces of licorice for 15¢, 3 lollipops for 5¢, and 5 cinnamon bears for 5¢; 4 pieces of licorice for 5¢, 6 lollipops for 10¢, and 10 cinnamon bears for 10¢
4. There are 7 solutions; however, Alcuin listed only one*. Do not expect your students to find more than one solution.

2 men, 30 women, 68 children

5 men, 25 women, 70 children

8 men, 20 women, 72 children

*11 men, 15 women, 74 children

14 men, 10 women, 76 children

17 men, 5 women, 78 children

20 men, 0 women, 80 children

In a follow-up discussion, you might write these three solutions on the board:

8 men, 20 women, 72 children

11 men, 15 women, 74 children

14 men, 10 women, 76 children

Ask the students to look for any patterns that might lead to finding the other four solutions. Hopefully, they will notice that the first column goes up by 3 each time, the second column goes down by 5, and the third column goes up by 2. They can work both forward and backward from the solutions given.

There is a less obvious pattern in Problem 3. If you think of groups of each kind of candy, lollipops come in groups of 3, licorice in groups of 4, and cinnamon in groups of 1. Rewriting as groups:

0 lollipops, 5 licorice, 0 cinnamon

1 lollipop, 3 licorice, 5 cinnamon

2 lollipops, 1 licorice, 10 cinnamon

Similar sequences exist here.

**References**

1983 problems: Dolan; Alcuin's Problem 1: Katz; Alcuin's Problem 4: Martzloff: *A History of Chinese Mathematics*; Alcuin information: Burton

## Noah's Descendants, page 102

**Notes**

This is a good problem to do after students have seen exponents. Some students will start by repeatedly doubling and continue until arriving at the solution. Sometimes the students double the wrong number of times because they do not start with the year zero.

You can save the student-composed problems and then give them as homework. Students enjoy having their problems "published," even if only on homework sheets.

**Answers**

1.

| Year | Population |
|---|---|
| 0 | 6 |
| 20 | 12 |
| 40 | 2 |
| . | . |
| . | . |
| . | . |
| 500 | 201,326,592 |

Encourage students to think about what process they are using and how they might denote that process. They are actually multiplying 6 by 2 by 2 by 2 . . . to 25 times. Repeated multiplication by the same number is denoted using exponents: $6 \times 2^{25} = 201,326,592$.

2. Answers will vary.

## Greenleaf's National Arithmetic; Greenleaf's National Arithmetic, the Sequel, pages 103–104

**Notes**

The full title of this book is *The National Arithmetic, on the Inductive System, Combining the Analytic and Synthetic Methods; Forming a Complete Course of Higher Arithmetic.* The second page tells the reader that "This Work is an authorized Text-Book for the Public High Schools of the City and County of Philadelphia. Also for the Public Schools of New York City." After the students have solved the problems, you can point out that this was the high school textbook used by my great-grandmother. When folks talk about what people knew in the olden days, you can point out that for today's students their great-great-great grandparents' high school mathematics was similar to today's pre-algebra.

To see how the mathematics curriculum has changed over the years, consider Harvard University. Originally, arithmetic was still taught in the senior year of college; then in 1807 arithmetic became an admissions requirement. In 1820 algebra became an admissions requirement. If you look at old textbooks, you will find that even though there are some interesting problems, there is a great deal of drill and practice and very little development of concepts.

Just in case your students should ask how to compute the tonnage of a ship, here is what Greenleaf tells his students to do:

"FOR SINGLE-DECKED VESSELS. Take the length on deck from the forward side of the main stem to the after side of the stern post, and the breadth at the broadest part above the main wales; take the depth from the under side of the deck plank to the ceiling of the hold; and deduct from the length three fifths of the breadth; multiply the remainder by the breadth, and the product by the depth; and divide the last product by 95.

FOR DOUBLE-DECKED VESSELS. Proceed as with single-decked vessels, except for the depth take half the breadth."

Answers

*Greenleaf's National Arithmetic*

1. George $1,346, James $1,596, Edwin $1,756
2. 52 of each animal
3. 14 bins, each holding 6 bushels
4. $24
5. Total: $13,459.56; James $3,364.89; William $4,486.52; Mary $1,121.63; Wife $4,486.52

***Greenleaf's National Arithmetic, the Sequel***

1. 1,252, 1,352, 1,452, and 1,552 pairs of shoes
2. $2\frac{7}{9}$ days if you presume it is the same depth; however, the answer given by Greenleaf assumed the original cellar was 6 by 6 by 6 and the new one 10 by 10 by 10. In that case, it would be $4\frac{17}{27}$ days.
3. $30 and $40
4. He worked 75 days and was idle 15 days.
5. 80 scholars
6. He had 7 children and an estate of $5,000.

## How Large Is Your Yard?; Picky Little Details; "For All People, for All Time," pages 105–108

### Notes

When you start a unit on measurement, ask the students where our units of measure came from. Initially, length units were based on parts of the body. The students will most likely think of the *foot*. They might have heard of a *hand* used to measure horses; now a hand is 4 inches, but originally it was the width of a hand. If students have seen cloth being measured in a store, they might remember that a *yard* is the distance from the nose to the tip of the longest finger. Here are other lengths that were based on body parts:

*finger*—width of index finger; *cubit*—length from elbow to longest finger tip; *fathom*—distance from fingertip to fingertip with outstretched arms; *span*—thumb to baby fingertip on stretched hand; *mile*—1,000 double paces

Ask your students whether they think most adults have a foot that is about a foot long, a yard that is a yard long, and an inch that is an inch long. After the students have done *How Large Is Your Yard?* for homework, choose one or more of the units to make a frequency chart of the adult data. If you do this activity with more than one class, combine the data. You should get a distribution resembling a normal distribution. Compare the standard length with the median and mean of your measurements. Ask your students what they think would have happened if they had included children in the data. You can use the students' self-measurements to find the class mean *foot* and *yard* or *cubit*. Presuming that a person's fathom is approximately equal to his or her height, only people about 6 feet tall actually have a personal yard close to 36 inches, so do not be surprised if your class mean is less than the standard-sized foot and yard.

The Egyptians were one of the earliest people to standardize measurement. They needed to be able to determine boundaries annually after the flooding of the Nile. The Egyptian *cubit* dates to about 3000 B.C.E.; a black granite royal cubit (524 mm = 20.62 in.) was used as a standard at regular intervals. The correlations between the individual cubits and the royal cubit were quite accurate, for example, sides of the Great Pyramid of Giza vary by only 0.05% from the mean side length.

One of the problems with using body parts or other common references of measure is lack of consistency as one goes from one place to another. An arithmetic textbook from 1856 (Ray. *The Principles of Arithmetic, Analyzed and Practically Applied*. Cincinnati: Winthrop B. Smith & Co., 1856.) lists weights and measurement systems for 43 international cities from Alexandria, Egypt, to Vera Cruz, Mexico. In a few examples, the text says these cities have officially accepted the French system (metric) and gives the old system in case some old measurements are still in use.

One pound avoirdupois (lb av) is what we call a *pound*. Other countries also used *pound* as a measure of weight; but, confusingly, 1 pound was not the same amount throughout the world in the mid-1800s. Here are Ray's examples of *pound* for use when doing conversions:

Amsterdam, Holland—(French since 1820),
old: 1 lb = 1.08923 lb av

Antwerp, Belgium—(French since 1816),
old: 1 lb = 1.03 $\frac{1}{3}$ lb av

Barcelona, North of Spain—
1 lb = 0.88215 lb av

Bremen—1 lb = 1.098 lb av

Cadiz, South of Spain—1 lb = 1.015 lb av

Copenhagen, Denmark—1 lb = 1.1025 lb av

Dantzic, East Prussia—1 lb = 1.033 lb av

Genoa, Sardinia—
1 lb peso sottile = 0.6989 lb av
1 lb peso grosso = 0.76875 lb av

Hamburg—1 lb = 1.068 lb av

Leghorn, Tuscany—1 lb = 0.74864 lb av

Lisbon, Portugal—
1 lb or arratel = 1.10119 lb av

Port-au-Prince, Haiti— Measures same as France, weights same as England but 8 percent heavier

Riga, Russia— 1 lb = 0.9217 lb av

Stockholm, Sweden—
1 lb or pund = 0.9375 lb av

St. Petersburg, Russia— 1 lb = 0.9026 lb av

Trieste, Austria— 1 lb = 1.236 lb av

Venice, Lombardy—
1 lb peso sottile = 0.66428 lb av
1 lb peso grosso = 1.05286 lb av

Before assigning *Picky Little Details*, you might want to read some of these examples to your students to demonstrate how one seemingly "obvious" unit of measure can vary. After your students complete *How Large Is Your Yard?*, you can tell them about the *smoot*, a regional nonstandard unit of measure. In 1958, as a joke, a group of MIT students used Oliver Smoot as the unit of measure to measure the Massachusetts Avenue bridge connecting Cambridge with Boston near the college campus. They marked the sidewalk with paint every 10 smoots. They found that the bridge was "364.4 smoots plus one ear" long. For years the students repainted the marks semiannually. Then in 1989, the bridge was repaired and the old smoot-marked sidewalk was taken up. The question became whether to remark the bridge in smoots as before or to measure the bridge using Stephen Smoot, Oliver's son, an MIT student. The new smoot would have been 4 inches longer. Luckily, some students marked the smoots on a quarter-mile-long string before the sidewalk was destroyed. So the original markings could be replaced once construction was finished.

Ray's book includes an even more local example of need for conversion in the 1800s—money. Today, we encourage tourism between states, because it helps local businesses. However, in the mid-1800s, states' individual currency was still in use even though Congress had adopted the following decimal currency 70 years before, on August 8, 1786.

**Federal or United States Money**

10 mills (m) make 1 cent (ct)

10 ct make 1 dime (d)

10 d make 1 dollar ($)

$10 make 1 eagle

A shopkeeper would need to be able to make change for a variety of currencies and might not wish for too many out-of-state customers. In his 1856 text, Ray points out:

"Before our present currency was established, our accounts were kept in pounds, shillings and pence. In many states, the denominations shillings and pence are still retained, but not with the same values.

In New Hampshire, Massachusetts, Rhode Island, Connecticut, Virginia, Kentucky, and Tennessee,

12 d = 1 shilling (s) = $16\frac{2}{3}$ cents

6 s = $1 = 100 cents

In New York, North Carolina, and Ohio,

12 d = 1 shilling = $12\frac{1}{2}$ cents

8 s = $1 = 100 cents

In New Jersey, Pennsylvania, Delaware, and Maryland,

12 d = 1 shilling = $13\frac{1}{3}$ cents

7 s 6 d or 90 d = $1 = 100 cents

In South Carolina and Georgia,

12 d = 1 shilling = $21\frac{3}{7}$ cents

4 s 8 d or 56 d = $1 = 100 cents

In Canada and Nova Scotia,

12 d = 1 shilling = 20 cents

5 s = $1 = 100 cents"

Historically, units of measure generally have not developed in a systematic fashion. The units related to whatever the need for measurement was and who used or made the measurement. For example, originally an *acre* was the amount of land an ox could plow in a day. The Babylonian *talent* was the weight of a cubic foot of rainwater. The English *grain* was the weight of one barleycorn, and an *inch* was *x* barleycorns laid end to end. In 1686, William Penn's land agreement with the Indians was called the "Walking Purchase" because it extended as far as a man could walk in a day and a half, about 30 miles. Everyone involved, both settlers and Indians, understood what the land-deal agreement was and there were no conflicts about land until 1737. Thomas Penn, who wanted to defraud the Indians out of land, arranged for athletes to make the walk after a path had been cleared for them. This time the men "walked" closer to 60 miles, actually they ran, and the trust between the settlers and the Indians was breached.

Adults, not just students, prefer to use whole numbers. Over the years, if one unit of measure were too large, for instance, foot, then a smaller one such as an inch was developed so that fractions would not be necessary. The metric system and the ancient Chinese system are counterexamples. See notes on *Chinese Rod Numerals*, pages 53–54.

When the United States of America considered how to handle all the various nitty-gritty issues of establishing a country, they developed the monetary system based on tens using *mills, cents, dimes, dollars*, and *eagles*. Secretary of State Thomas Jefferson suggested adopting a decimal measurement system based on an unchanging standard that related weight, length, and volume to each other. He could have been describing the metric system that France adopted in 1799 and made the only legal measurement system in France in 1837. Unfortunately for us today, the English system was adopted, even though Secretary of State John Quincy Adams encouraged acceptance of the metric system in 1821. The motto adopted in France for the metric system, "For all people, for all time," is a bit ironic, as the metric system is for just about everyone in the world except citizens of the United States.

Introduce the metric system by reading the following quote and have the students guess when it was written.

> "GREENLEAF'S NEW PRACTICAL ARITHMETIC, appears to me, to be an improvement on the Common School Arithmetic, which has been in use in this school for many years, in general arrangement, in the presentation of the Metric System of Weights and Measures, and in a very varied set of examples in Mensuration. *The introduction of the Metric System has my warm approval; I envy the school-master of thirty years hence, who by it will be relieved of that stupefying incubus—Dominate Numbers*; and I can almost hear the children of the next generation wondering that we of today should have wandered in such wilderness so many weary years. No Arithmetics, in my opinion, have kept for so long a time a more deserved share of public favor than Greenleaf's.
>
> DAVID B. SCOTT, Principal."

This was dated November 26, 1866. It is included in Benjamin Greenleaf's *The National Arithmetic on the Inductive System, Combining the Analytic and Synthetic Methods; Forming a Complete Course of Higher Arithmetic*. After students guess the date, you can tell them that on July 28, 1866, Congress approved, but did not mandate, the use of the metric system as a legal system of weights and measures in the U.S.A.

Once you have introduced the metric units given in *"For All People, for All Time"* and students realize that conversion is just a matter of multiplying or dividing by a power of 10, point out the conversion chart in the activity.

| kilo- | hecto- | deka- | gram<br>liter<br>meter | deci- | centi- | milli- |
|---|---|---|---|---|---|---|
| | $\leftarrow \div 10$ | | | | $\times 10 \rightarrow$ | |

For each space moved to the right, multiply by 10; for each space moved to the left, divide by 10. So to go from kilometers to centimeters, multiply by 10 five times, or by 100,000.

You may want to review with students the abbreviations for both customary and metric units, as well as the conversion factors among and between the two systems of measurement.

**Extensions**

- Have students investigate whether their own inch and hand relate to their foot in the same way that the standardized measures of inch and hand relate to the standard foot.
- The classical Greek vision of the perfect person had the navel located such that the ratio of the height of the person to the height of the navel from the floor was the Golden Mean [ $\frac{1 + \sqrt{5} - 1}{2}$, ≈ 1.618033988]. Have your students take measurements of all of their family members and then divide the height by the height of the navel. If you make three frequency graphs (adult, adult and children, children), you will find the distribution of each is very close to the Golden Mean even though the process of measuring was not particularly accurate.
- Samuel Clemens took the pseudonym Mark Twain, a phrase learned when working on a riverboat on the Mississippi River. Have the students find the meaning of *mark twain* and its relationship to measurement.

**Answers**

***How Large Is Your Yard?***

Answers will vary.

***Picky Little Details***

Answers will vary.

***"For All People, for All Time"***

1. 12 in. = 1 ft; 3 ft = 1 yd, 1,760 yd = 1 mi,
 10 mm = 1 cm, 10 cm = 1 dm,
 10 dm = 1 m, 10 m = 1 dkm,
 10 dkm = 1 hm, 10 hm = 1 km
2. Answers will vary.
3. **a.** 23 cm = 230 mm = 0.00023 km
 **b.** 3.5 L = 3,500 mL = 0.035 hL
 **c.** 0.002 kg = 2 g = 0.00002 Mg
 **d.** 42.5 m = 42,500,000,000 nm = 4.25 dkm
4. **a.** Before you criticize someone, walk 1.61 kilometers in that person's shoes.
 **b.** 0.473 liter is 0.453 kilogram the whole world round.
 **c.** Give him 2.54 centimeters and he'll take 1.61 kilometers.
 **d.** *805 Kilometers*
 **e.** *14,496 Kilograms*
 **f.** *I Love You 44.050 Liters*
 **g.** 37.85-liter hat
 **h.** 2.54 centimeter worm
 **i.** 1.61-kilometer-long hot dog

**Extension**

Have students use at least one prefix or measurement name and accurately incorporate it into an equation. Several examples follow. Have students share their equations with the class.

1,000,000 phones = 1 megaphone; 453.6 gram crackers = 1 pound cake; 10 cards = 1 dekacards

**References**

Brinkworth; Eves; Gaines; Menninger; *The New Encyclopaedia Britannica*, 15th ed., s.v. "systems of weights and measures, in measurement and observation"; Newman; Ray

## Circumference of Circles; Pi; Sato Moshun, Johannes Kepler, and the Area of Circles, pages 109–113

**Notes**

Students often just memorize the various formulas connected to circles, without real understanding. The activities *Circumference of Circles* and *Sato Moshun, Johannes Kepler, and the Area of Circles* not only demonstrate why the formulas work, but introduce students to how the formulas developed historically.

When the students measure the circumference of circles and check out the four expressions in *Circumference of Circles*, they should find that

$C \div d$ is a little greater than 3. The follow-up discussion in class should give this special ratio the name of *pi* ($\pi$). Tell students that pi is actually an irrational number that never repeats, regardless of how many decimal places are computed. Use *Pi* as the follow-up activity to *Circumference of Circles*. Ideally, this assignment would fall on "Pi Day," March 14.

When discussing *Pi*, explain that a circle's circumference has to be less than the perimeter of a polygon circumscribed around it and greater than the perimeter of a polygon inscribed in it. For many years, the value of pi was approximated with the method used by Archimedes and Luí Hui. Called the *method of exhaustion*, it allows one to find an upper and lower value for pi. Archimedes used this method with polygons of 6, 12, 24, 48, and 98 sides. Ask students to think about why he might have chosen polygons with those numbers of sides.

Instead of assigning students to work independently on *Sato Moshun, Johannes Kepler, and the Area of Circles*, you might want to have students actually cut out a circle and work through the steps with them, demonstrating how to find the area of a circle. It turns out that the base of the "parallelogram" is equal to one-half the circumference $[(\frac{1}{2})2\pi r = \pi r]$ and the height is the radius $r$, so the area $= \pi r^2$. In the second method, the base of the large triangle is equal to the circumference $2\pi r$ and the height is the radius $r$, so the area of the triangle is $(\frac{1}{2})(2\pi r)(r) = \pi r^2$. You might want to tell students about Leonardo da Vinci's method of finding the area of a circle: Take a wheel that has a thickness equal to half the radius of the wheel. Roll the wheel one complete revolution. The area of the track equals the area of the circle. Why does this work?

Read the following to your students about the attempt to legislate the value of $\pi$:

*Not everyone who claims to be a mathematical expert actually is one. On January 18, 1897, Dr. Edwin J. Goodwin of Solitude, Indiana, convinced his state representative, Taylor Record, to introduce House Bill #296 concerning Goodwin's "new mathematical truth." In his bill, Goodwin gave a convoluted, incoherent explanation which possibly meant that the value of* $\pi = \frac{16}{\sqrt{3}}$, *approximately 9.2376. Goodwin was willing to let Indiana use this value of* $\pi$ *for free, while everyone else would have to pay royalties. The legislators probably had no clue as to what the bill was saying, but as in* The Emperor's New Clothes, *did not want to appear ignorant, so the bill was referred to the Committee on Swamp Lands which quickly passed it on to the Committee on Education. The Committee on Education recommended that it pass. The House of Representatives passed it unanimously (67–0) on February 5, 1897. The local newspaper, the* Indianapolis Journal *wrote about the strangest bill ever passed in the House of Representatives in Indiana. The bill went to the state senate, and was referred to the Committee on Temperance, which reported it out with the recommendation that it be passed. Meanwhile, C.A. Waldo, a mathematics professor at Purdue University was in the state capitol to make sure that the funding for the university was taken care of. The senate passed the bill and then Professor Waldo clued the senators into the folly of this bill. On February 12, 1897, the senate decided this was not an appropriate topic for legislation and voted to indefinitely postpone discussion of this legislation. It has yet to come up for reconsideration.*

Blatner's book *The Joy of* $\pi$ is appropriate for middle school students who want to know more about $\pi$. His web site, http:\\www.joyofpi.com, has many wonderful links to other sites on practically any aspect of pi you can think of!

**Answers**

*Circumference of Circles*

**1.–5.** Answers will vary.

**6.** $C \div d$

*Pi*

1. Answers will vary depending upon how many digits students' calculators display.
   - **a.** 3.160493827
   - **b.** 3.1459292
   - **c.** 3.142857143; 3.140845070

d. 3.141666666

e. 3.155555556

f. 3.14

g. 3.1416

h. 3.16227766

i. 3.141818182

2. Tsu Chhung's

3. $\frac{1}{9} - \frac{1}{11}$

4. $\frac{1^2 \cdot 3^2 \cdot 5^2 \cdot 7^2}{4 \cdot 6 \cdot 8 \cdot 10 \cdot 12 \cdot 14 \cdot 16 \cdot 18} + \frac{1^2 \cdot 3^2 \cdot 5^2 \cdot 7^2 \cdot 9^2}{4 \cdot 6 \cdot 8 \cdot 10 \cdot 12 \cdot 14 \cdot 16 \cdot 18 \cdot 20 \cdot 22}$

5. $\frac{5!}{3 \cdot 5 \cdot 7 \cdot 9 \cdot 11} + \frac{6!}{3 \cdot 5 \cdot 7 \cdot 9 \cdot 11 \cdot 13}$

6. $\frac{(1 \cdot 3 \cdot 5 \cdot 7)(4 \cdot 6 \cdot 8 \cdot 10)}{5 \cdot 7 \cdot 9 \cdot 11 \cdot 13 \cdot 15 \cdot 17 \cdot 19 \cdot 21} - \frac{(1 \cdot 3 \cdot 5 \cdot 7 \cdot 9)(4 \cdot 6 \cdot 8 \cdot 10 \cdot 12)}{5 \cdot 7 \cdot 9 \cdot 11 \cdot 13 \cdot 15 \cdot 17 \cdot 19 \cdot 21 \cdot 23 \cdot 25}$

7. $\frac{10,395}{13 \cdot 46,080} + \frac{135,135}{15 \cdot 645,120}$

When completing these patterns, students need to be careful to include all of the factors. For example, in Problems 4 and 6, it is easy to assume that one factor has been added each time, when actually it is two factors. In Problem 7, if the students get stuck, ask them to think about multiplying: "What do I multiply 2 by to get 8? 8 by to get 48?"

***Sato Moshun, Johannes Kepler, and the Area of Circles***

1. a. Parallelogram

   b. Base: $\frac{1}{2}$ the circumference, or $\frac{1}{2}(2\pi r) = \pi r$; height = $r$

   c. $\pi r(r) = \pi r^2$

2. The base is $2\pi r$ and the radius is $r$, so its area is $\frac{1}{2}(2\pi r)(r) = \pi r^2$.

**References**

Beckmann; Berggren; Blatner; Boyer; Katz; Meyer; Peterson: *Islands of Truth*; Smith: *A History of Japanese Mathematics*; Yan

## Thales, Triangles, Playing Column, and Playing Ship, pages 114–115

**Notes**

You may need to direct the two role-playing activities presented here. Provide students with masking tape so that they can mark their points. It is nice to have groups of three students work on each activity. Since the activities take quite a bit of space, you may want to have students work in the hallway or gym or on the playground. If space is a problem, you might have several students play the part of a given student and have groups of students check the accuracy of the role-playing students' positions.

After students have finished *Playing Column*, ask them to explain why the method works. (The shadow is created by the sun's rays, which form the same angle at the top of the column as at the top of the stick in the ground.)

Students' explanations should indicate that what they have done is to construct two congruent right triangles: $AB = BC$, angles $A$ and $C$ are right angles, and angles $ABC$ and $CBD$ are vertical angles.

**References**

Bunt; Smith: *A History of Mathematics*, vol. I; van der Waerden: *Geometry and Algebra in Ancient Civilizations* and *Science Awakening I*; *Notable Mathematicians: From Ancient Times to the Present*

## The Tile Detectives, page 116

**Notes**

This is a good activity to use when introducing students to tessellating patterns. By using pattern blocks to create their patterns, they use regular polygons. Mathematicians classify tessellations made with regular polygons as *regular*, *semiregular*, and *demiregular* tessellations. A regular tessellation uses only one regular polygon to tessellate the plane and the only three regular polygons that tessellate are equilateral triangles, squares, and hexagons. A semiregular tessellation uses a combination of regular polygons, but every vertex has the same polygons in the same order encircling the vertex.

For example, Problem 1 has 3 triangles followed by 2 squares at each vertex. Semiregular tessellations are named by the regular polygons at each vertex, so Problem 1 is named 3.3.3.4.4.

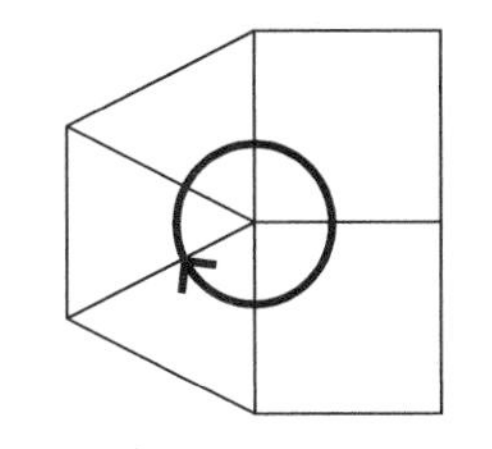

A demiregular tessellation uses a combination of regular polygons, and there are either two or three different vertex patterns. For example, the Bonus, which has two solutions, with the same vertex patterns, is named 3.3.3.3.3.3/3.3.4.3.4; the slash indicates the division between the vertex patterns. The names for the other tessellations are:

**2.** 3.6.3.6 **3.** 3.4.6.4

**4.** 3.3.3.3.6 **5.** 3.3.4.3.4

You can explain this number-naming system and have students name each of their tessellation solutions. There are more semiregular and demiregular tessellations; but, because they use regular octagons and dodecagons which are not pattern blocks, they were not included here. For more information see Bezuszka, et al., (1977).

The tessellation in the burned house in Jerusalem (the activity example) did not use equilateral triangles, so it is not a semiregular tessellation.

Tessellations provide a nice application of different symmetries: translation, rotation, and reflection. The master of applying these symmetries to transforming tessellating polygons was M.C. Escher. To learn how to make Escher-like tessellations, see Ranucci and Britton. If you look carefully at many of Escher's drawings, you can see the original tessellating polygons.

### Answers

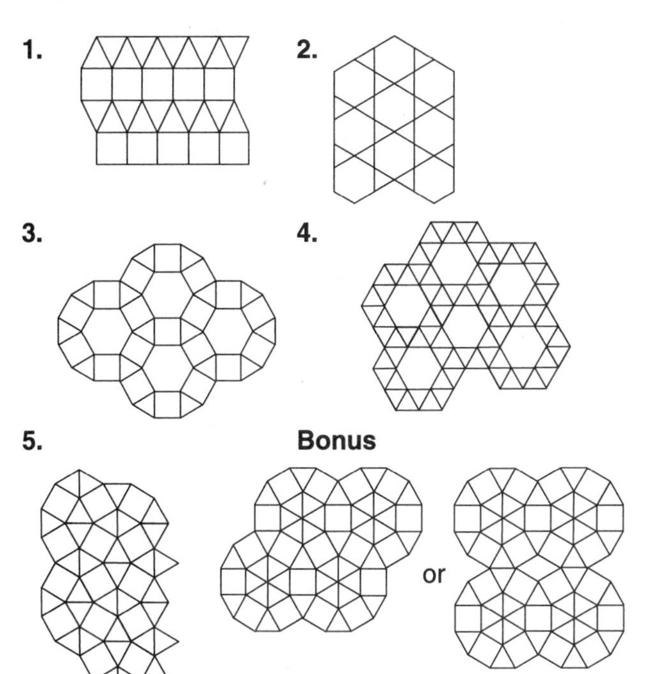


### Extension

Have students look at quilt pattern books to find designs that are regular, semiregular, and demiregular tessellations. They can design their own quilts using pages from wallpaper books. Many of the traditional patchwork quilt patterns are semiregular and demiregular tessellations. Some quilts use the same underlying tessellating pattern; but by making adjoining pieces the same color, the quilters get different overall visual designs. My great-grandmother sewed many tessellating patterns, but I suspect no one in the ladies' church quilt group discussed the mathematics of her beautiful quilts!

### References

Armstrong; Bezuszka; Britton; Ranucci; Seymour: *Introduction to Tessellations*

## A Pythagorean Puzzle, pages 117–119

**Notes**

Often students memorize $a^2 + b^2 = c^2$ and think of it as only a relationship between the side lengths of a right triangle. There is historical evidence that ancient mathematicians, including Euclid, thought of the formula as a relationship between the areas of squares on the sides of a right triangle. This activity illustrates the latter relationship.

Make copies of *Pythagorean Puzzle Pieces A* and *B* on different colors of paper, for example, the *A Pieces* on green paper and the *B Pieces* on yellow paper. Give each student a right triangle with sides labeled *a*, *b*, and *c*, and a strip containing two rectangles made up of squares and triangles labeled a, b, and c. If you prefer, you can make copies on white paper and have students color the diagrams accordingly.

After students agree that the two rectangles have equal areas, tell them that they need to remember this for later use. They can verify the equality by counting grid squares. Be sure students glue their triangle in the center of their paper.

Students may need a little help making the squares out of the c pieces. So you might want to circulate throughout the classroom giving direction and explanations, such as the following:

- Yes, all of the c pieces must be used.
- Yes, a square can be made using all of the c pieces.
- No, you cannot pile pieces on top of each other or have gaps.

When someone figures out how to get the c pieces together, you might have that person arrange a set of pieces on the overhead for the other students to see. The goal of this activity is not to solve the problem of how to put together those five pieces to make a square, but to discover the Pythagorean Theorem.

While students work to glue their squares to the single triangle, it is important that they recognize that the triangle has side lengths *a*, *b*, and *c*; and that the area of the square on side *a* is $a^2$, the area of the square on side *b* is $b^2$, and the area of the square on side *c* is $c^2$. Have them recall the relationship between the a, b, and c pieces given in Problem 2.

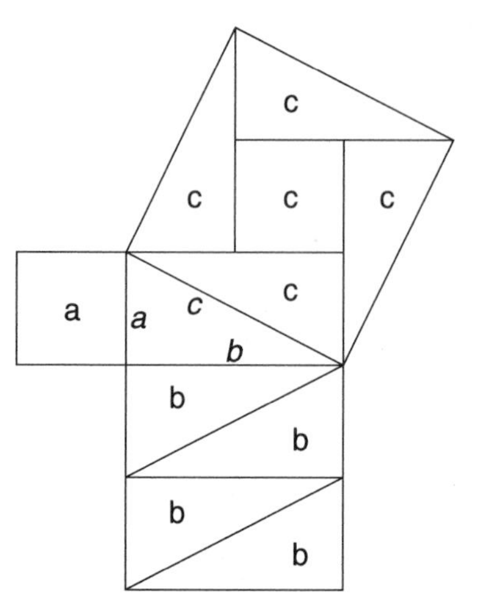


Give your students time to summarize in their own words what this demonstrates. Most likely, *theorem* is not a word they have heard before. You might tell them it is similar to *theory*, but a theorem is a theory that has been proven to always be true. You can tell them this theorem has been proven for one particular triangle on their papers; later, in algebra or geometry, they will see proofs that this theorem is valid for all right triangles.

For another example of Pythagorean mathematics see notes on *The Shapes of Numbers*, pages 45–47.

When your students study irrational numbers, you can remind them of the Pythagoreans, this theorem, and the Pythagorean belief that whole numbers or their ratios could explain everything mathematical. This theorem eventually led to the realization that numbers such as $\sqrt{2}$ were *not* rational. There are various forms of the legend about Hippausus of Metapontum, a Pythagorean, who disclosed the existence of what they called "incommensurable magnitudes," that is, irrational numbers. One version of the legend is that Pythagoras had Hippausus's tombstone erected as if he were already dead. Another version of the legend is that Hippausus was thrown overboard at sea. This legend is an example of when mathematics can be hazardous to your health!

**Extension**

Let students work in groups and use calculators to search for *Pythagorean triples*—three whole numbers $a$, $b$, and $c$, such that $a^2 + b^2 = c^2$. Have them check their list to see which are *primitive triples*. Primitive triples are not multiples of another triple, such as $2a$, $2b$, and $2c$, which is a Pythagorean triple but not a primitive one. Compile the list on the board and then ask how many Pythagorean triples exist: 100? 1,000?

Actually there is an infinite number of Pythagorean triples. You can show the students two of the formulas that will always generate Pythagorean triples. Since there is no greatest number to substitute in the formulas, the number of triples is infinite. Have students think about what kind of numbers you can substitute in order to generate primitive triples in each case.

(a) Choose two numbers $x$ and $y$ with $x > y$. Let $a = x^2 - y^2$, $b = 2xy$, and $c = x^2 + y^2$.

(b) Choose one number $z$. Let $a = 2z$, $b = z^2 - 1$, and $c = z^2 + 1$.

Formula (b) for generating Pythagorean triples is attributed to Pythagoras.

**Answers**

1. Yes
2. The area of the a square plus the area of the b square equals the area of the c square.
3. $a^2$, $b^2$, $c^2$
4. Answers will vary.

**References**

Pearcy; van der Waerden: *Geometry and Algebra in Ancient Civilizations*

## Legendary City Land Acquisition, pages 120–121

**Notes**

This is a good activity to use near the end of the year in a pre-algebra class. It includes area formulas, writing formulas and equations, substituting in equations, reversing formulas, the Pythagorean Theorem, order of operations, and correctly keying into a calculator.

Many students have worked on the problem of how much area a certain amount of fencing can enclose. If the restrictions are that they must have a rectangular figure, then the square (or the shape closest to a square, if whole numbers are required for dimensions) is the solution. If, however, they are using flexible fencing, then the greatest area will be enclosed by a circle. When students initially look at this problem, they may assume that this is the same problem.

However, there is one other significant piece of information that changes the problem, namely, that one edge is the coastline.

According to the legend, Dido chose the most efficient shape, which just happens to be the semicircle. However, that may not be your students' solution. It is important for the students to actually try various shapes and play with the possible dimensions and areas before the class discusses the results. Middle school students are not ready for solutions derived using calculus; however, they can use trial and error. If you have access to graphing calculators, they can come up with quite accurate solutions. In the examples that follow, I use a length of 28 meters for the length of the reconstructed hide, since that is the longest that a group of my students were able to construct from their sheet of 8.5"-by-11" paper. The solutions that follow probably are not the solutions that students might suggest. The students will most likely come up with specific triangles, not general solutions. Have the groups share their solutions with the class and use their examples of rectangles, for example, to lead into the discussion of rectangles in general and finding the largest rectangle. You will need to allow two to three class periods for the groups to cut up their "hides," design the geometric shapes, make the calculations, and have a class discussion of the results. Depending upon the level of abstract development of your students, some may need to take their long strip and lay out the geometric shapes on the hall floor before doing any calculations, while others will do their designing with paper and pencil.

Consider a rectangle with one side being the shore. You have 28 meters for the other three sides. So $x$ must be less than 14.

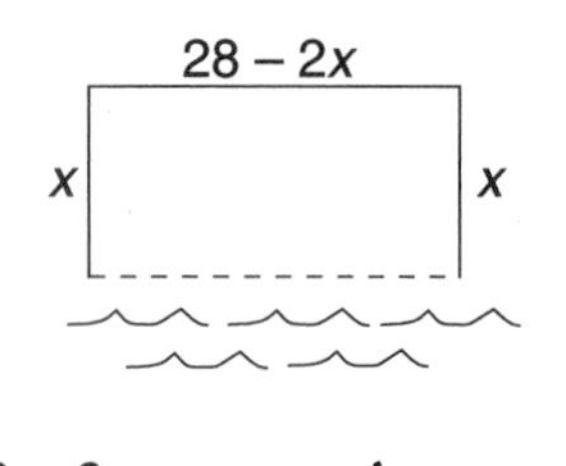


| $x$ | $28 - 2x$ | Area |
|---|---|---|
| 1 | 26 | 26 |
| 2 | 24 | 48 |
| 3 | 22 | 66 |
| 4 | 20 | 80 |
| 5 | 18 | 90 |
| 6 | 16 | 96 |
| 7 | 14 | 98 |
| 8 | 12 | 96 |

If students stop at 6 or 7 for $x$, they might assume that as $x$ increases, the area will increase; so it is important to try enough values to see the values for the area peak and then decline. This is the simplest example for this problem of what would be a maximum point if the students were able to graph the polynomial. If students have graphing calculators, they may graph Area = $x(28 - 2x)$ and better visualize the increase and decrease in the area. They can also find that the maximum is at 7. Have students can develop the rectangle formula in a whole-class discussion. Before you have the students put the equation into the calculator, discuss what they think the graph will look like and, based on the data in the chart, what should be the maximum and minimum values for $x$ and $y$ on the graph.

Closely related to the rectangle is the square. If the border is 28 meters, then each side will be $\frac{28}{3}$ and the area $(\frac{28}{3})^2 \approx 87.1$.

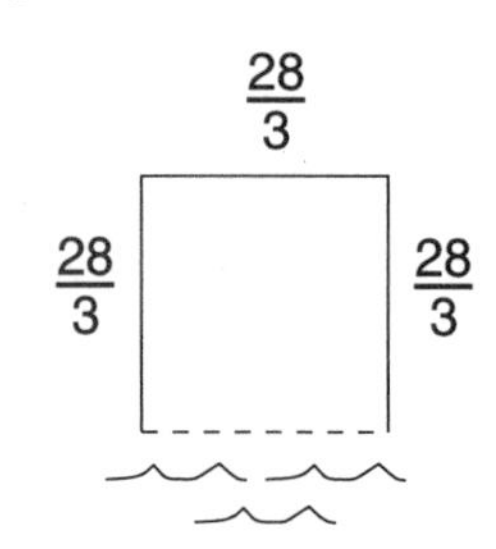


The triangle that is the easiest to investigate is the right triangle that uses the coastline for the hypotenuse. This is actually the simplest triangle to investigate, since the area is just $\frac{(28-x)x}{2}$.

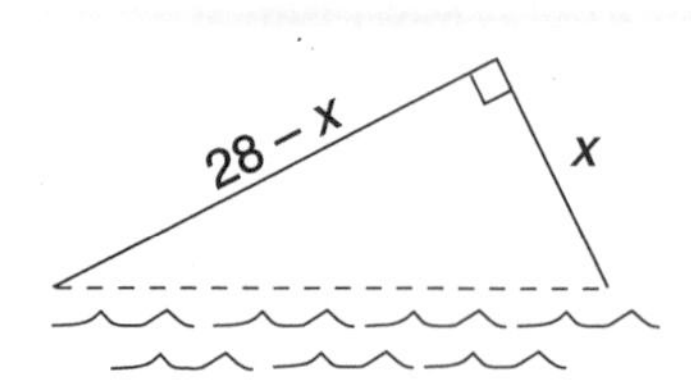


| $x$ | $28 - x$ | Area |
|---|---|---|
| 1 | 27 | 13.5 |
| 2 | 26 | 26 |
| 3 | 25 | 37.5 |
| 4 | 24 | 48 |
| 5 | 23 | 57.5 |
| . | . | . |
| . | . | . |
| . | . | . |
| 12 | 14 | 84 |
| 13 | 15 | 97.5 |
| 14 | 14 | 98 |
| 15 | 13 | 97.5 (repeats from here) |

As with the rectangle, the area increases and then decreases as the length of the base of the triangle increases. Students can graph Area = $\frac{(28-x)x}{2}$ on the calculator.

This next example is a good one to try with groups who have some algebra. Consider a right triangle with the base along the coastline. Again you have 28 meters to build the other two sides, each of which must be less than 28 meters.

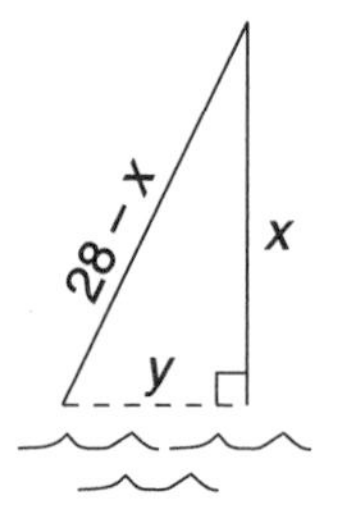


By the Pythagorean Theorem, $y^2 + x^2 = (28 - x)^2$; solving for $y$ gives $y = \sqrt{(28 - x)^2 - x^2}$. If you have students graph the area formula, parentheses are particularly important. Area = $\frac{x(\sqrt{((28-x)^2-x^2)}}{2}$.

| $x$ | $y$ | Area |
|---|---|---|
| 1 | ≈26.98 | ≈13.49 |
| 2 | ≈25.92 | ≈25.92 |
| 9 | ≈16.73 | ≈75.30 |
| 10 | ≈14.97 | ≈74.83 |

Let the students discover there is a maximum value for $x$. Using trial and error, the students will find that the greatest area (≈75.389) is for $x \approx 9.53$. The graph of this formula clearly illustrates the maximum value for $x$.

Consider an equilateral triangle with the coastline as one side.

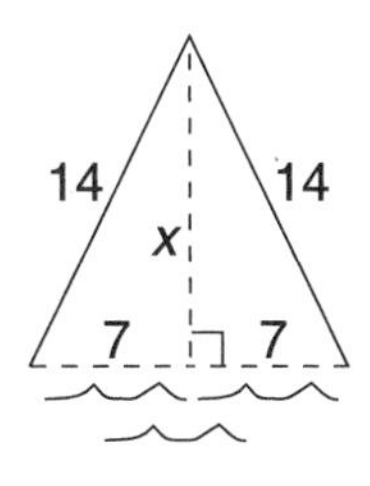


The students can find the height using the Pythagorean Theorem: $7^2 + x^2 = 14^2$, $x \approx 12.12$; this then gives an area ≈ 84.87.

Examine an isosceles triangle with the coastline for its base, a problem similar to that for the equilateral triangle. You have 28 meters for the other two sides, so they must each be 14 meters.

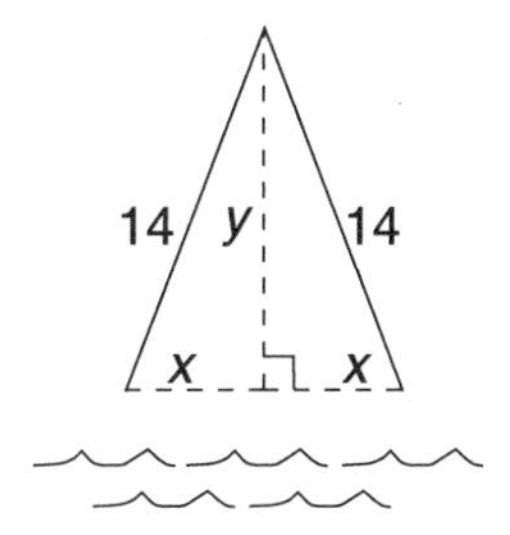


Now, students can try different bases along with the Pythagorean Theorem to find the height. $y^2 + x^2 = 14^2$; $y = \sqrt{14^2 - x^2}$. Then, using that information, they can find the area of the triangle. I have students multiply the value of $y$ shown on the calculator (more digits than displayed here) by $x$ to get the area.

| $x$ | $y$ | Area |
|---|---|---|
| 1 | ≈13.9642 | ≈13.9642 |
| 5 | ≈13.0877 | ≈65.3834 |
| 6 | ≈12.6491 | ≈75.8927 |
| 9 | ≈10.7238 | ≈96.5142 |
| 10 | ≈9.7980 | ≈97.9796 |

Trial and error is a good technique to use at this point. Try letting $x$ = 10.1, 9.5, and 9.9, for example. To one decimal place for $x$, 9.9 gives the greatest value for the area, 97.9999. As you can see, the area of the right isosceles triangle with sides of 14 is just slightly more than the area of the isosceles triangle with height of 9.9 and sides of 14.

So far, the greatest areas we have found are those of the rectangle with dimensions of 7 and 14 and the right isosceles triangle with sides of 14. Each had an area of 98 square meters. But is this the greatest area possible? From the traditional area-enclosure problem, we know that a circle is the most efficient; but a circle does not have a straight side as rectangles and triangles do. What about a semicircle? With 28 as half the circumference of a circle, the area of a circle with a circumference of 56 is ≈249.55. This gives a semicircle with area of ≈124.8 square meters. This is the maximum area that can be contained within 28 meters of perimeter. Dido used a semicircle to gain the maximum land for the city of Carthage. The process of going from the circumference of a semicircle to the area of the semicircle is a good experience for the students in reversing a process.

To answer the final question in the activity, if we convert the original dimensions of the paper hide (8.5" by 11") into meters using 2.54 centimeters = 1 inch, we get 0.2159 meters by 0.2794 meters for an area of ≈0.06 square meter. The semicircle is about 2,080 times as large as the original hide. That was quite a clever solution that Dido came up with!

**Answers**

1.–3., 5. Answers will vary.

4. A semicircle

**References**

Dunham

## The Sieve of Eratosthenes; Primes, Multiples, and Squares, pages 122–123

**Notes**

When circling the multiples of 11 in *The Sieve of Eratosthenes*, students should find that all of the multiples of 11 have already been crossed out. It turns out that you need to actually cross out multiples only up to the square root of the number you are checking. In this case, $\sqrt{100} = 10$; 9 was crossed out with multiples of 3, and 8 and 10 were crossed out with multiples of 2. So 7 finished the job. If you wanted to find the primes up to 200, you would need to check up only through 14 ($\sqrt{200} \approx 14.14213$), and really only up through 13 because 14 is composite.

Eratosthenes was born in Cyrene, was educated in Plato's school in Athens, and was the tutor for King Ptolemy II's son. He was one of the outstanding scholars in Alexandria and was the chief librarian at The Museum for 40 years. Eratosthenes studied and wrote in many fields; however, only fragments of his work remain. The two areas for which he is most noted are mathematics and geography. As mentioned in the activity, Eratosthenes not only figured out how to generate a list of primes, but he also successfully measured the circumference of the earth. In his book *Geographica*, he recognized that the earth is spherical, used a grid similar to that with lines of longitude and latitude, and suggested it might be possible to sail from Spain to India. A picture of Eratosthenes' map of the world is in Burton.

The Library was actually a university that its founder Ptolemy I wanted to be the intellectual center of the Greek world. "The aim of the Library was to collect the entire body of Greek literature in the best available copies and to organize it systematically. Ship captains who sailed from Alexandria were instructed to bring back scrolls from every port they touched until their return. The story is told that Ptolemy III, who reigned from 247–221 B.C.E., borrowed the authorized texts of the playwrights Aeschylus, Sophocles, and Euripides from Athens, against a large deposit. But rather than return the originals, he returned only copies. He was quite willing to forfeit the deposit. The Library ultimately contained over 500,000 volumes in every field of knowledge. Although parts of the library were destroyed in various wars, some of it remained intact until the fourth century." (Katz)

A follow-up activity to finding the primes is to have students notice some of the patterns with primes in *Primes, Multiples, and Squares*. The 100 charts are rearranged to emphasize the multiples of 4 and the multiples of 6. Have students look at the multiples-of-6 chart and ask which column could be extended to ensure that no new primes would be found. [The 3 column]

**Extension**

Have students look for *twin primes*; these are primes that have a difference of 2, for example, 5 and 7. Or have them find examples of Goldbach's Conjectures. Christian Goldbach (1690–1764) noticed patterns that have neither been proven true and for which no counterexamples have been found. Two of Goldbach's Conjectures are the following:

- Every even integer greater than 2 can be written as the sum of two primes. For example, $4 = 2 + 2$ and $8 = 3 + 5$.
- Every integer greater than 6 can be written as the sum of three primes. For example, $7 = 2 + 2 + 3$ and $10 = 2 + 3 + 5$.

**Answers**

***The Sieve of Eratosthenes***

5, 5; 7, 7; 11, 11; primes less than 100: 2, 3, 5, 7, 11, 13, 17, 19, 23, 29, 31, 37, 41, 43, 47, 53, 59, 61, 67, 71, 73, 79, 83, 89, and 97

***Primes, Multiples, and Squares***

Students should circle the primes less than 100; see *The Sieve of Eratosthenes*.

1. Possible answer: For primes > 2, each is either 1 more or 1 less than a multiple of 4.
2. Possible answer: For primes > 3, each is either 1 more or 1 less than a multiple of 6.
3. $5 = 2^2 + 1^2$ ; $13 = 3^2 + 2^2$; $17 = 4^2 + 1^2$ ; $29 = 5^2 + 2^2$; $37 = 6^2 + 1^2$; $41 = 5^2 + 4^2$; $53 = 7^2 + 2^2$; $61 = 6^2 + 5^2$; $73 = 8^2 + 3^2$; $89 = 8^2 + 5^2$; $97 = 9^2 + 4^2$
4. Possible answer: These primes are all the primes that are 1 greater than a multiple of 4. Pierre de Fermat (1601–1665) studied integers that could be represented in the form $x^2 + y^2$. In 1751 Leonhard Euler (1707–1783) stated that every prime of the form $4n + 1$ could be represented as the sum of two squares in exactly one way. So your students should not be able to find more than one representation for these primes, nor should they be able to find a similar representation for any other primes. The converse is not true, however. Just because a number can be written as the sum of two squares does not mean that the number is a prime of the form $4n + 1$. For example, $34 = 3^2 + 5^2$. In 1937, Ivan Vinogradov (1891–1983) proved that every odd integer greater than 6 can be written as the sum of three primes.

For another activity on primes, see *Mersenne Primes and Perfect Numbers*, pages 157–158. You could also have students check out this web site:

www.utm.edu/research/primes/largest.html

## The Shapes of Numbers; The Shapes of Numbers, the Puzzle; The Shapes of Numbers, the Sums, pages 124–127

Notes

More than 2,500 years ago, the Pythagoreans studied what we call *figurate*, or *polygonal,* numbers. The Pythagoreans formed a secret society whose belief was that everything could be explained by numbers. The members of the society spent a great deal of time searching for patterns. Triangular and square numbers are the easiest to visualize. One way to demonstrate the numbers is with tiles; another way is with spider drawings.

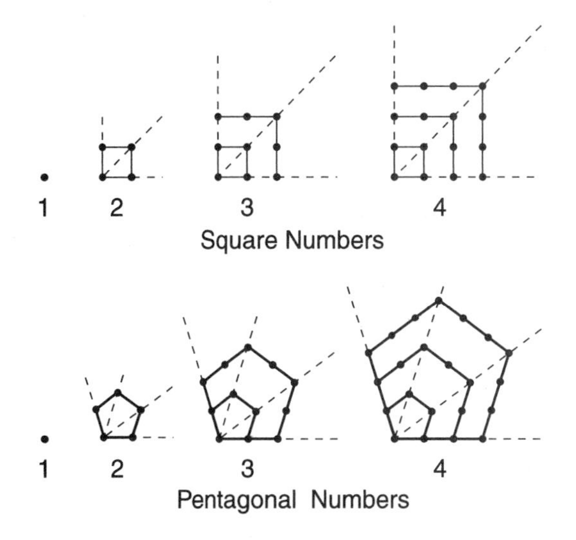


You may want to have tiles, cubes, or disks available for your students to use when working on these activities.

For *The Shapes of Numbers, the Puzzle*, assign each group of students a different triangular number and have them build 8 copies. In order to have enough cubes, you can assign groups on opposite sides of the room the same number. Once the 8 copies are built, have students take an additional cube and then put everything else away. Encourage the students to build each copy of their triangular number using a different color. When the groups finish building, they should each have copies of their triangular number in 8 different colors. If you do not have linking cubes, students can use $\frac{1}{2}$"-square graph paper. They can color and cut out copies of their triangular number.

No matter which triangular number the groups were assigned, they should be able to make a square by putting 2 triangles together to make a rectangle and then placing the rectangles around a square.

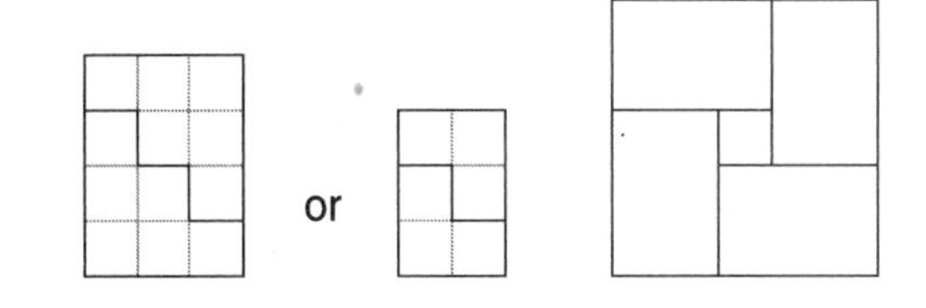

In the follow-up class discussion, ask which triangular number each group used and what square number they built. Organize the information in a table and see if students can predict what square would be built from the 100th and the $n$th triangular numbers.

| Triangular Number | Square Number |
|---|---|
| 2nd | 5th |
| 3rd | 7th |
| . | . |
| . | . |
| . | . |
| $n$th | $(2n + 1)$th |

*The Shapes of Numbers, the Sums* can be used as a culminating assignment after students complete *The Shapes of Numbers* and *The Shapes of Numbers, the Puzzle*

**Answers**

*The Shapes of Numbers*

**1.**

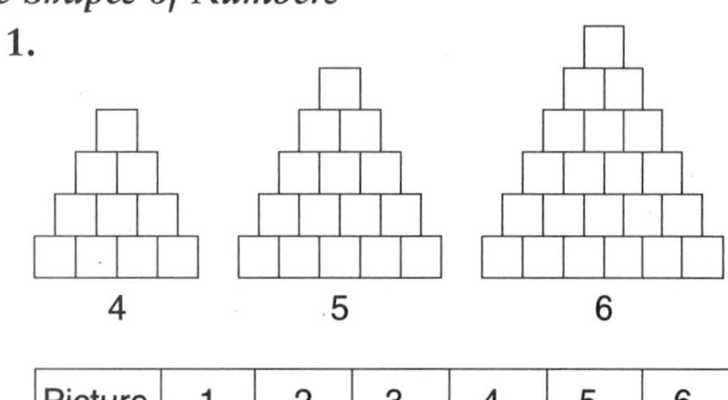

| Picture | 1 | 2 | 3 | 4 | 5 | 6 |
|---|---|---|---|---|---|---|
| Blocks | 1 | 3 | 6 | 10 | 15 | 21 |

**2.**

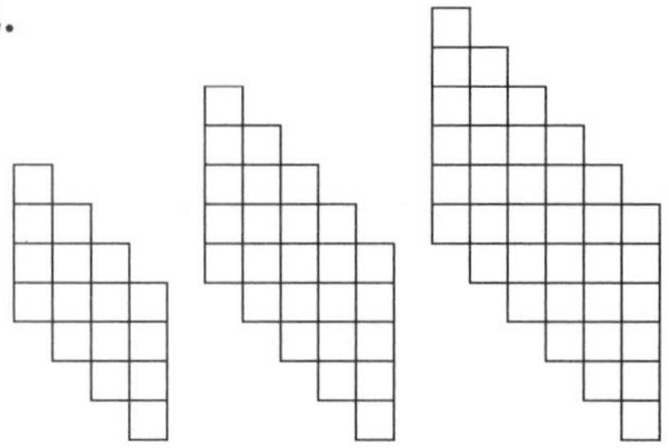

4 5 6

| Picture | 1 | 2 | 3 | 4 | 5 | 6 |
|---|---|---|---|---|---|---|
| Blocks | 1 | 4 | 9 | 16 | 25 | 36 |

**3.** Possible answer: At each stage, add 3 more than you added the stage before.

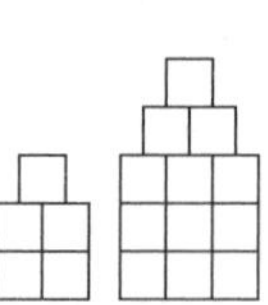

**4.** 35 blocks; 51 blocks

**5.** Answers will vary.

**6.**

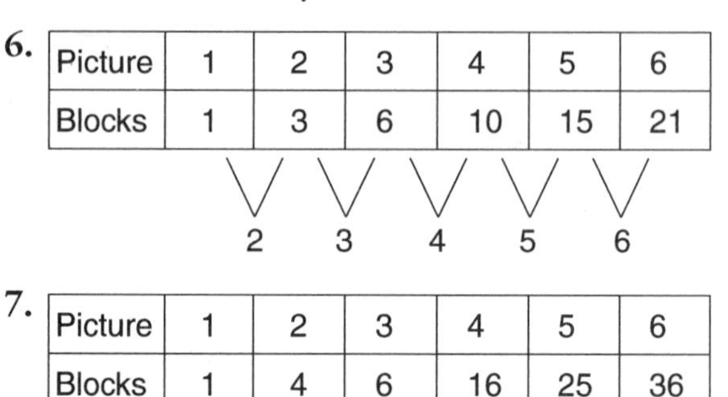

| Picture | 1 | 2 | 3 | 4 | 5 | 6 |
|---|---|---|---|---|---|---|
| Blocks | 1 | 3 | 6 | 10 | 15 | 21 |

Differences: 2 3 4 5 6

**7.**

| Picture | 1 | 2 | 3 | 4 | 5 | 6 |
|---|---|---|---|---|---|---|
| Blocks | 1 | 4 | 6 | 16 | 25 | 36 |

Differences: 3 5 7 9 11

**8.**

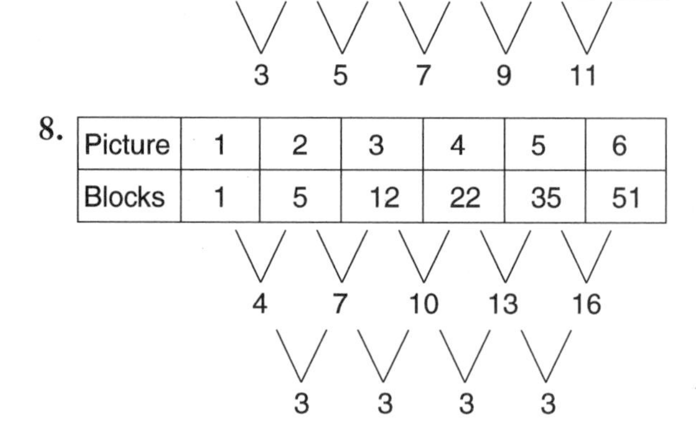

| Picture | 1 | 2 | 3 | 4 | 5 | 6 |
|---|---|---|---|---|---|---|
| Blocks | 1 | 5 | 12 | 22 | 35 | 51 |

Differences: 4 7 10 13 16

Second differences: 3 3 3 3

**9.** Answers will vary.

**10.**

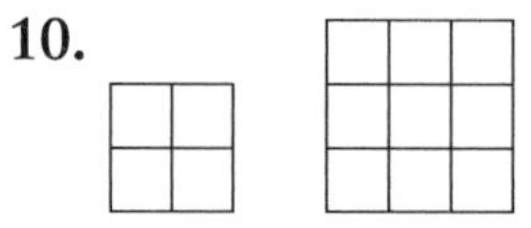

**11.** Answers will vary.

**12.** A square number

Asking students to figure out why this happens is a lead-in to *The Shapes of Numbers, the Puzzle.* To demonstrate that this always works, use linking cubes to build various triangular numbers, using one color for the first triangular number, another color for the second, and so on. Then put consecutive triangular numbers together to make a square.

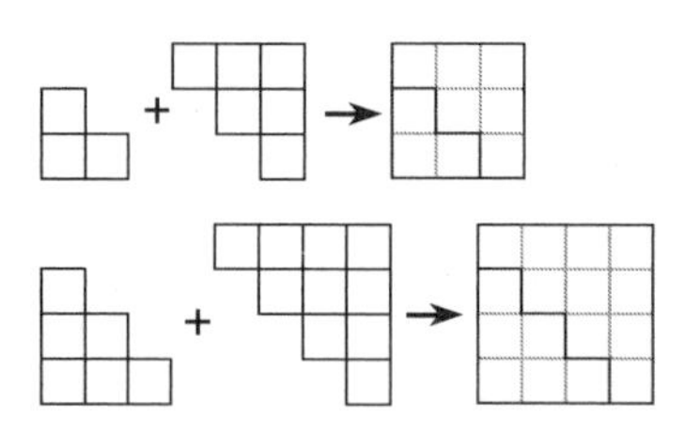

*The Shapes of Numbers, the Sums*

**1.a.** $1 = 1$

$1 + 2 = 3$

$1 + 2 + 3 = 6$

$1 + 2 + 3 + 4 = 10$

$1 + 2 + 3 + 4 + 5 = 15$

$1 + 2 + 3 + 4 + 5 + 6 = 21$

**b.** square

**2.** $100 + 1 = 101$, $99 + 2 = 101$, $98 + 3 = 101$; 101; 50; 5,050; Gauss multiplied $101 \times 50 = 5{,}050$.

**3.** 5,050

**4.** Add 1 to the final number and multiply the sum by half the number of terms.

This rule can be modified to work for any arithmetic series, and you might want to do this with your students. An arithmetic sequence has the same difference between consecutive terms. To find the sum, add the first and last terms and multiply the sum by half the number of terms.

**5.a.** $1 = 1$

$1 + 3 = 4$

$1 + 3 + 5 = 9$

$1 + 3 + 5 + 7 = 16$

$1 + 3 + 5 + 7 + 9 = 25$

**b.** square

**6.** 2,500; Here are two possible strategies: 1) The sum of the first 50 odd numbers is $1 + 3 + 5 + \ldots + 95 + 97 + 99$; using Gauss's pattern, there must be 25 sums of 100, for 2,500. From Part a, for an odd number of terms, the sum is the square of the middle term; for an even number of terms, the sum is the square of the number between the two middle terms, which is 50, for $50^2 = 2{,}500$.

When discussing this pattern with the class, it is nice to model with linking cubes or on graph paper using the *gnomon* model:

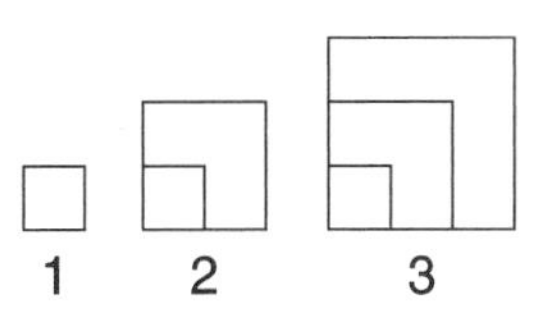


In the class discussion, have the students figure out why each of the gnomons represents an odd number.

With students who already know the Pythagorean Theorem, you could point out that this pattern of the sums of consecutive odd numbers demonstrates a way to generate Pythagorean triples. For example, with $1 + 3 + 5 + 7 + 9 = 25 = 5^2$, note that $1 + 3 + 5 + 7 = 16 = 4^2$ and $9 = 3^2$.

So $1 + 3 + 5 + 7 + 9 = (1 + 3 + 5 + 7) + 9 = 4^2 + 3^2 = 5^2$.

No matter what the first numbers in the series are, their sum will be a square number, as will the final sum. So, if you start with a series whose final addend is a square number (9, 25, 49, . . .), you will have a Pythagorean triple.

For advanced students who are interested in exploring the algebraic patterns in the figurate numbers, let them try generating the algebraic rules not only for the square and triangular numbers, but also for the pentagonal, hexagonal, heptagonal, and octagonal numbers. There are some interesting relationships among the formulas.

## The 15 Game; Magic Squares, pages 128–129

### Notes

Magic squares have fascinated people for centuries. Many students have seen the 3-by-3 magic square. There is a wealth of mathematics in the study of magic squares that we have only hinted at in these activities. If you want to investigate them further, refer to some of the books in the bibliography.

Start the first class by having partners play *The 15 Game* for a few minutes. Then have groups of students answer the questions. Give each group a different set of questions to be responsible for in a class presentation. Have Group A report on their discussion. Hopefully with some guidance, everyone will notice that there are 8 legal ways to get a sum of 15, each of which can be put in 6 different orders and in 8 different places in the 3-by-3 square. This gives $8 \times 6 \times 8 = 384$ different ways to win this game.

Assign *Magic Squares* for homework. Many students have seen magic squares before, but they may not remember exactly how to arrange the numbers. The activity does not say that the magic sum is actually 15. If someone asks, a hint might be, "What game were you playing today?" Tell students that they will discuss the Lo Shu magic square during the next class period.

You can begin the second class period by having the rest of the groups share their solutions to the questions in *The 15 Game*. Tell the students that magic squares have fascinated people from all over the world for centuries. Ben Franklin claimed to be able to "fill the cells of any magic square, of reasonable size, . . . as fast as" he could write them down.

Refer students to the Lo Shu magic square. Tell them that Chinese legend is that this magic square was a gift from a turtle from the River Lo to the engineer-Emperor Yu probably around 4,000 years ago. The *yin* numbers, which are black, are the numbers of the earth, while the *yang* numbers, which are white, are the numbers of the heavens. Have students translate the Lo Shu magic square into our numerals, and have students tell the class about the patterns they found when looking at the magic square. Hopefully they noticed that the sum of the diagonal corner number pairs is 10 and the sum of the opposite number pairs is also 10. Someone might also claim to have a "different" 3-by-3 square. If so, write it on the board and compare it with the Lo Shu square. There are actually 8 different solutions, but they all have a 5 in the center and the same numbers together on sides. They come from various rotations and reflections of the Lo Shu square. Continue with *Constructing Odd Magic Squares*, pages 130–131.

**Answers**

**1.** Sample square: **2.** Patterns will vary.

| | | |
|---|---|---|
| 6 | 1 | 8 |
| 7 | 5 | 3 |
| 2 | 9 | 4 |

**3.** Yin: even numbers; Yang: odd numbers

**References**

Andrew; Benson; Fults; Gardner: *The 2nd Scientific American Book of Mathematical Puzzles & Diversions*; Moran; Needham; Olivastro; Pappas: *The Joy of Mathematics*, *More Joy of Mathematics*; Peterson: "Games Mathematicians Play"; Zaslavsky

## Constructing Odd Magic Squares, pages 130–131

**Notes**

This activity continues from the introduction to magic squares in *The 15 Game*. Remind the students that a 3-by-3 magic square uses the numbers 1 through 9 and has a magic sum of 15. The sum of the digits is $1 + 2 + 3 + 4 + 5 + 6 + 7 + 8 + 9 = 45$. Ask students how these numbers are related. $[45 \div 3 = 15]$

The ask students the following questions:

- What numbers do you think you will need for a 5-by-5 magic square? [1 to 25]
- What is the sum of $1 + 2 + 3 + \ldots + 25$? [325]

At this point you might want to talk about Gauss's trick for adding consecutive numbers:

$$\begin{array}{l} 1 + 2 + \ldots + 9 \\ \underline{9 + 8 + \ldots + 1} \\ 10 + 10 + \ldots + 10 \end{array}$$

There are 9 sums of 10, so the total is $9 \times 10 = 90$; but each number is added twice, so you need to divide the answer by 2: $1 + 2 + 3 + \ldots + 9 = (9 \times 10) \div 2 = 45$

- If the sum 1 + 2 + 3 + . . . + 25 = 325, what do you think the magic sum is going to be? [325 ÷ 5 = 65, since there are 5 rows and 5 columns each with the same sum.]

Then have students predict the magic sum of a 7-by-7 magic square using the numbers 1–49. [(49 × 50) ÷ 2 = 1,225; 1,225 ÷ 7 = 175]

Show the students how to construct the 3-by-3 magic square using the pyramid method described below. Then have them use this method to complete *Constructing Odd Magic Squares* for homework.

The pyramid method for constructing magic squares works only for magic squares with odd dimensions. This is not the only method to construct magic squares, and other methods might give different arrangements of the same numbers which also work. To make a 3-by-3 square, construct numbered "pyramids" on each side of the square as shown.

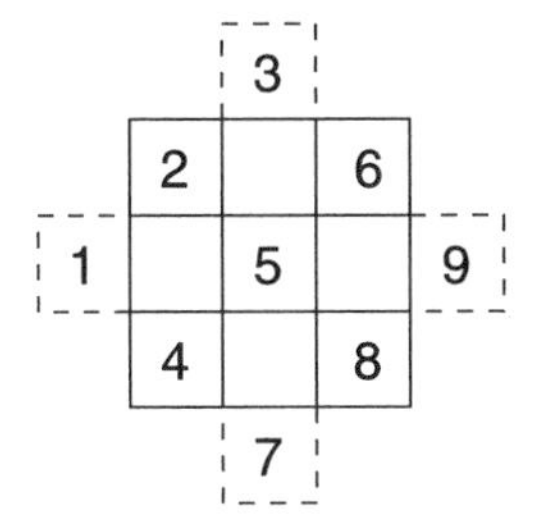

Place the number in the left pyramid in the square in the right side.

| 2 |  | 6 |
|---|---|---|
|  | 5 | 1 |
| 4 |  | 8 |

Place the number in the right pyramid in the square in the left side.

| 2 |  | 6 |
|---|---|---|
| 9 | 5 | 1 |
| 4 |  | 8 |

Place the number in the top pyramid in the square in the bottom side, and the number in the bottom pyramid in the square in the top side.

| 2 | 7 | 6 |
|---|---|---|
| 9 | 5 | 1 |
| 4 | 3 | 8 |

Similarly, for a 5-by-5 square, place the numbers in the left pyramid in the right side of the square. Place the numbers in the right pyramid in the left side of the square. Place the numbers in the top pyramid in the bottom and the numbers in the bottom pyramid in the top.

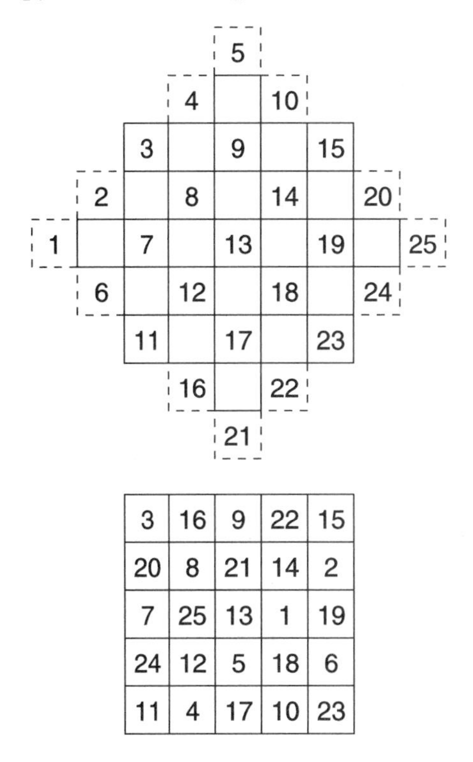

| 3 | 16 | 9 | 22 | 15 |
|---|---|---|---|---|
| 20 | 8 | 21 | 14 | 2 |
| 7 | 25 | 13 | 1 | 19 |
| 24 | 12 | 5 | 18 | 6 |
| 11 | 4 | 17 | 10 | 23 |

Start the activity in class and let the students finish it for homework as well as look for patterns in the magic squares they have constructed.

During the next class, copy the 5-by-5 and 7-by-7 magic squares on the board. Point out that we predicted sums of 65 and 175 for these magic squares; then ask if this held true for the ones constructed. Ask students what they noticed about their magic squares. Hopefully someone will point out that diametrically opposed pairs of numbers have the same sum. If no one noticed this, ask what the sum of the diagonally opposite corners is in each square and then where can you find other pairs of numbers with the same sum. Also inquire how this sum relates to the center number. [The sum is 2 times the center number.]

Complete this table with the class:

| Dimensions of Square | Center Number | Magic Sum |
|---|---|---|
| 3 by 3 | | |
| 5 by 5 | | |
| 7 by 7 | | |

Ask students what number they would multiply times the center number to get the magic sum. [The length of the side of the square]

Interestingly, in each example, the center number of the magic square is also the middle number if you were to list the numbers consecutively.

Then have students predict what would happen if they were to create a 27-by-27 magic square.

- What numbers would you use? [1–729]
- What would be the center number? [365]
- What would be the magic sum? [9,855]

Show a copy of *C.A. Browne Jr.'s Fabulous 27-by-27 Composite Magic Square* on the overhead. Did Browne do what you expected? This magic square is actually made up of 81 smaller (9-by-9) magic squares. If students inquire how this was done, you can explain that the 729 numbers were divided into 9 groups of 81 consecutive numbers. Then a 9-by-9 magic square was constructed from each of these 81 numbers. Each of these 9 magic squares was treated as if it contained the numbers 1–9 placed in a 3-by-3 magic square. The dark lines indicate each of these squares. This same process can be used to make smaller magic squares and might be something for students to investigate further on their own if they are especially interested in magic squares.

**Answers**

**1. and 2.** See completed squares in notes.

**3.**

| | | | | | | |
|---|---|---|---|---|---|---|
| 4 | 29 | 12 | 37 | 20 | 45 | 28 |
| 35 | 11 | 36 | 19 | 44 | 27 | 3 |
| 10 | 42 | 18 | 43 | 26 | 2 | 34 |
| 49 | 17 | 41 | 25 | 9 | 33 | 1 |
| 16 | 48 | 24 | 7 | 32 | 8 | 40 |
| 47 | 23 | 6 | 31 | 14 | 39 | 15 |
| 22 | 5 | 30 | 13 | 38 | 21 | 46 |

**4.** Answers will vary.

## Altering Magic Squares; Concentric Magic Squares, pages 132–137

**Notes**

Assign *Altering Magic Squares* for homework after completing the discussion on *Constructing Odd Magic Squares*. Students should find that they can add, subtract, multiply, or divide each number in a magic square by the same number and in each case create a new magic square. You can use this fact to make magic-square puzzles for review of fractions and/or decimals. Students should discover that squaring each number does not create another magic square.

If students have had some algebra, you can ask them to "prove" why any or all of these altered squares will be magic squares, and why the new magic sum will be 3 times the altered center number. For example, for adding a number, let $x$ be the number added:

| | | |
|---|---|---|
| 4 | 9 | 2 |
| 3 | 5 | 7 |
| 8 | 1 | 6 |

becomes

| | | |
|---|---|---|
| $4 + x$ | $9 + x$ | $2 + x$ |
| $3 + x$ | $5 + x$ | $7 + x$ |
| $8 + x$ | $1 + x$ | $6 + x$ |

The sum of any original row, column, or main diagonal was 15, and the sum of the new rows, columns, and main diagonals is $15 + 3x = 3(5 + x)$. The other alterations can be similarly demonstrated. You might want to assign a different demonstration to each group to present to the class.

During the next class period, you can introduce the class to other interesting magic squares. Historically, people thought magic squares had special powers. Ninth-century Arabic astrologers used magic squares when calculating horoscopes. In the sixteenth century, the German artist Albrecht Dürer included a magic square in his engraving *Melancholia*, because fourth-order magic squares were considered to be an antidote to depression. Display *Melancholia* on the overhead. The specific year Dürer created the print is in the square, shown below. Have students find it. [1514]

| 16 | 3 | 2 | 13 |
|---|---|---|---|
| 5 | 10 | 11 | 8 |
| 9 | 6 | 7 | 12 |
| 4 | 15 | 14 | 1 |

Dürer's magic square has an interesting property. Have the students square each number to make a new square and then find the sums of the individual rows and columns. The sums of the first and last rows are equal. The sum of the middle columns are equal. Also, the sum of the numbers on the two main diagonals equals the sum of the first two rows as well as the sum of the numbers in the last two columns.

A recent translation of a fifth-century magic charm has led to a whole new kind of magic square. This charm was used by Druid priests and had a runic inscription. Display *Alphamagic Squares* on the overhead. This rune is interesting in that it is a magic square in which the number of letters in the names of each of the numbers in the square also forms a magic square both in the original language and in English. To demonstrate this, use an overhead marker to circle the first four symbols, which spell "five" in the runic language. For example:

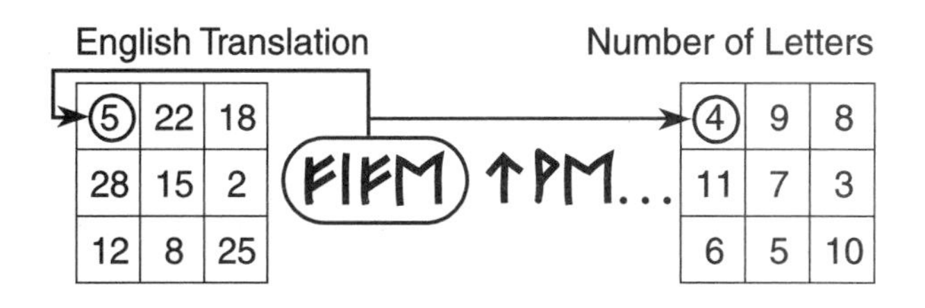


In the early eighteenth century in Katsina, which is now northern Nigeria, Muhammad ibn Muhammad wrote about constructing magic squares and told his students to "work in secret and privacy. The letters are in God's safekeeping. God's power is in his names and his secrets, and if you enter his treasury you are in God's privacy, and you should not spread God's secrets indiscriminately." (Zaslavsky) Display *Muhammad ibn Muhammad*, on the overhead.

Another interesting kind of magic square that Muhammad ibn Muhammad wrote about is a *concentric* magic square. Display the following magic square on the overhead.

| 7 | 8 | 22 | 25 | 3 |
|---|---|---|---|---|
| 24 | 12 | 17 | 10 | 2 |
| 5 | 11 | 13 | 15 | 21 |
| 6 | 16 | 9 | 14 | 20 |
| 23 | 18 | 4 | 1 | 19 |

Ask students what the word *concentric* means, and how a magic square could be concentric.

This magic square is actually 2 magic squares. It is a 5-by-5 magic square with a 3-by-3 magic square in the middle. What is the magic sum of the 3-by-3 square? [39] What is the magic sum of the 5-by-5 square? [65] Give students a chance to look for patterns in the square and to see whether the patterns they saw before still hold true here. If someone does not notice it, have them check the sums of the diagonal corners and then look for other pairs with the same sums. Assign *Concentric Magic Squares*. You may need to assure students that their second magic square might have duplicate numbers, depending upon how they choose their numbers for substitution.

**Answers**

### *Altering Magic Squares*

1. Yes; 33

| 10 | 15 | 8 |
|---|---|---|
| 9 | 11 | 13 |
| 14 | 7 | 12 |

2. Answers will vary. Samples are given for $A = 4$, $B = 5$, $C = 3$, and $D = 2$.

a. Yes; 27

| 8 | 13 | 6 |
|---|---|---|
| 7 | 9 | 11 |
| 12 | 5 | 10 |

b. Yes; 0

| –1 | 4 | –3 |
|---|---|---|
| –2 | 0 | 2 |
| 3 | –4 | 1 |

c. Yes; 45

| 12 | 27 | 6 |
|---|---|---|
| 9 | 15 | 21 |
| 24 | 3 | 18 |

d. Yes; $7\frac{1}{2}$

| 2 | $4\frac{1}{2}$ | 1 |
|---|---|---|
| $1\frac{1}{2}$ | $2\frac{1}{2}$ | $3\frac{1}{2}$ |
| 4 | $\frac{1}{2}$ | 3 |

e. Yes; 81

| 22 | 47 | 12 |
|---|---|---|
| 17 | 27 | 37 |
| 42 | 7 | 32 |

f. No

| 16 | 81 | 4 |
|---|---|---|
| 9 | 25 | 49 |
| 64 | 1 | 36 |

3. Problem 2f does not.

**Bonus**

A. 15

| –2 | 3 | 14 |
|---|---|---|
| 21 | 5 | 11 |
| –4 | 7 | 12 |

B. Answers will vary. Samples are given for $X = 10$, $Y = 3$, and $Z = 4$. 30

| 7 | 9 | 14 |
|---|---|---|
| 17 | 10 | 3 |
| 6 | 11 | 13 |

C. Yes; the sum of the first row is $(X - Y) + (X + Y - Z) + (X + Z) = 3X$; similarly, the sum for each other row, each column, and each diagonal is also $3X$, which is 3 times the middle number, $X$.

### *Concentric Magic Squares*

1. a. 37 b. 37 c. 74 d. 111

| 31 | 10 | 28 | 8 | 33 | 1 |
|---|---|---|---|---|---|
| 2 | 23 | 18 | 22 | 11 | 35 |
| 3 | 13 | 20 | 16 | 25 | 34 |
| 32 | 12 | 21 | 17 | 24 | 5 |
| 7 | 26 | 15 | 19 | 14 | 30 |
| 36 | 27 | 9 | 29 | 4 | 6 |

Answers for Problems 2 and 3 will vary. Samples are given for $A = 6$, $B = 5$, $C = 3$, $D = 2$, and $E = 1$.

2.

| 8 | 9 | –1 | 9 | 5 |
|---|---|---|---|---|
| 1 | 1 | 8 | 9 | 11 |
| 7 | 14 | 6 | –2 | 5 |
| 7 | 3 | 4 | 11 | 5 |
| 7 | 3 | 13 | 3 | 4 |

3. a. 18 b. 30 c. 12
d. It is twice the center number. e. 12
f. It is twice the center number.

4. a. Yes; the sums of the diagonal corners of the 3-by-3 square is $(A - B) + (A + B) = 2A$ and $(A - C) + (A + C) = 2A$ and of the 5-by-5 square is $(A + D) + (A - D) = 2A$ and $(A + E) + (A - E) = 2A$.

b. Yes; the sum of each row, column, and diagonal of the 3-by-3 square is $3A$, for example, $(A - B) + A + (A + B) = 3A$; the sum of each row, column, and diagonal of the 5-by-5 square is $5A$, for example, $(A + D) + (A - B) + A + (A + B) + (A - D) = 3A$.

**References**

Andrew; Benson; Fults; Gardner: *The 2nd Scientific American Book of Mathematical Puzzles & Diversions;* Moran; Needham; Olivastro; Pappas: *The Joy of Mathematics* and *More Joy of Mathematics;* Peterson: "Games Mathematicians Play"; Zaslavsky

## Chinese Rod Numerals, pages 138–140

### Notes

Chinese rod numerals provide a nice vehicle for reviewing the idea of place value in decimals, while having students "play detective" a bit to figure out how they work.

For this activity you will need about 30 toothpicks, preferably flat ones, for each pair or triple of students unless the students are abstract thinkers. Before passing out the activity, you might write the following on the board without any explanation:

1 chi = 10 cun

1 cun = 10 fen

1 fen = 10 li

1 li = 10 fa

1 fa = 10 hao

1 chi, 3 cun, 5 fen, 5 li

Ask students, "What is this?" Most likely they will tell you that it is some kind of conversion table based on tens that they have never seen before. It is actually a conversion table for units of measure that the Chinese adopted about 170 B.C.E. The chi was probably a bit smaller that 1 foot since 6 chi = 2 paces. During the third century, Liu Hui would write "1 chi, 3 cun, 5 fen, 5 li" for 1.355 feet. This is the same as 1 foot, 3 tenths, 5 hundredths, 5 thousandths.

In the eighth century, Han Yan dropped the individual place-value names and wrote the digits followed by the measurement term as we would write 1.355 feet today.

Chinese did their computations with little sticks on a board that looked something like a large checkerboard. To multiply 32.5 by 1.42 they multiplied 325 by 142 and then applied their rules, called *bu qu*, to place the decimal point, in a manner similar to ours. You might tell the students about bu qu.

When the students translate the number triangle they will actually be translating the triangle we know as Pascal's Triangle. Long before Blaise Pascal was born, the triangle was known in China as a means of determining the coefficients in binomial expansion. It was even known in Europe 100 years before Pascal published it; it appeared on the title page of Peter Apianus's *Arithmetic* (1527) and in Michael Stifel's *Arithemetica Integra* (1544). Stifel used this triangle to determine coefficients. In the 1650s, Pascal used what he called the *arithmetical triangle* to solve probability problems. Besides using the triangle for binomial expansion and probability combinations, you may find many different patterns in the triangle. You might want to put a copy of the triangle on a bulletin board with the patterns that the students found. As the year goes on, when they notice any new patterns, add them. When you get into number theory, you can find the triangular numbers and the Fibonacci numbers, as well as interesting patterns if you look for various multiples.

Some of the patterns in Pascal's Triangle that the students might not notice are the *powers of 2* (the sum of each row), *1 less than the powers of 2* (sums of rows), *the powers of 11* (Read the rows as place values, multiply each entry by its place value, and add.), the *Star of David pattern* (Choose any number, connect every other number that surrounds it, and then connect the alternate numbers forming a Star of David. The two products of the connected numbers are equal.), and the *circle pattern* (Choose any number, find the product of the six surrounding numbers, and the product is a square number.). For a list of books with activities related to Pascal's Triangle, see references for Pascal's Triangle. For books that will give biographical information on Pascal, an interesting personality to tell students about, see references for biographies, page 17. For another activity that uses Pascal's Triangle, see *The World Series and Pascal*, page 141.

When the students have finished *Chinese Rod Numerals*, you can tell them that even though the Chinese were probably the first to use decimal fractions, the news did not spread to the rest of the world. The Arabs were probably the first to reinvent decimals after adopting the Hindu numerals. Probably the first Arab to do so was al-Uqlidīsī, who wrote 163'35 for 163.35 (952–953), but he did not know the algorithms that make decimal computations easy. In the early fifteenth century, al-Kāshī, the Royal astronomer in Samarkand (north of Afghanistan), not only understood how to write with decimals but how to compute with them.

Even though Hindu numerals spread to Europe by way of the Arabs, the idea of decimal fractions did not seem to reach Europe. Decimals had to be reinvented yet again. Just as Europeans had to reinvent Pascal's Triangle, they also reinvented decimals almost 200 years after the Arabs and 800 years after the Chinese were computing with decimals! For a more thorough discussion of the development of decimals, see notes on *Writing Decimals Through the Years*, pages 61–63.

**Answers**

1. | stands for 1 and ‾ stands for 5.
2. ||| stands for 3 and ‾ stands for 5.
3. 𝍫, 𝍬, 𝍭
4. 𝍰, 𝍱
5. 𝍮𝍦, 𝍰𝍧
6. **a.** Hundreds and ten-thousands
   **b.** Thousands and hundred-thousands
7. [illegible]
8. Answers will vary.
9. [illegible]
10. **a.** ○; ○ **b.** Answers will vary.
11. Sample answer: You would never know whether the decimal point or the zero comes first, so the number could be 10 times as great as it should be or $\frac{1}{10}$ of what it should be.
12. The tens
13. Sample answers: 70, 7,000, 700,000, 0.7, 0.007, 0.00007
14. [illegible]
15. 1; 1, 1; 1, 2, 1; 1, 3, 3, 1; 1, 4, 6, 4, 1; 1, 5, 10, 10, 5, 1; 1, 6, 15, 20, 15, 6, 1; 1, 7, 21, 35, 35, 21, 7, 1; 1, 8, 28, 56, 70, 56, 28, 8, 1; 1, 9, 36, 84, 126, 126, 84, 36, 9, 1
16. Sample patterns: The sum of the numbers in each row is twice the sum of the numbers in the preceding row. The sum of the numbers in each row is a power of 2; the power of 2 is the same as the row number. The numbers in each diagonal row differ by the number between them and up to the left or right. The numbers in the third diagonal rows are triangular numbers.

**References**

al-Daffá; *Ancient China's Technology and Science*; Ifrah; Katz; Yan; Needham; Swetz: "The Evolution of Mathematics in Ancient China"
Japanese triangle: Smith: *A History of Japanese Mathematics*; Chinese triangle: Temple; Pascal's Triangle: Colledge; Kenny; Seymour: *Visual Patterns in Pascal's Triangle*

## The World Series and Pascal, page 141

**Notes**

The problem proposed to Pascal by the Chevalier de Méré more than 340 years ago is closely related to the problem of finding the probability of winning the World Series. The students should realize that in a best-of-7 series you need to win 4 games and that you could play as few as 4 games or as many as 7 games to win the tournament. Even if you are down 3 games to 1, it is possible to win the series.

Have students work in pairs to quickly collect the data. Then combine the pairs' data into a whole-class list. First have each group report how many times Hypatia's Hot Hitters won and how many times they lost. They should find that Hypatia's Hot Hitters won far more games than they lost, since the theoretical probability of winning is $\frac{7}{8}$. Do not tell the students this, because they will figure that out for themselves in the following discussion.

Ask students to list the possible series of 3 coin tosses to model the completion of the series. If they have not used a tree diagram to find all possible solutions, demonstrate one:

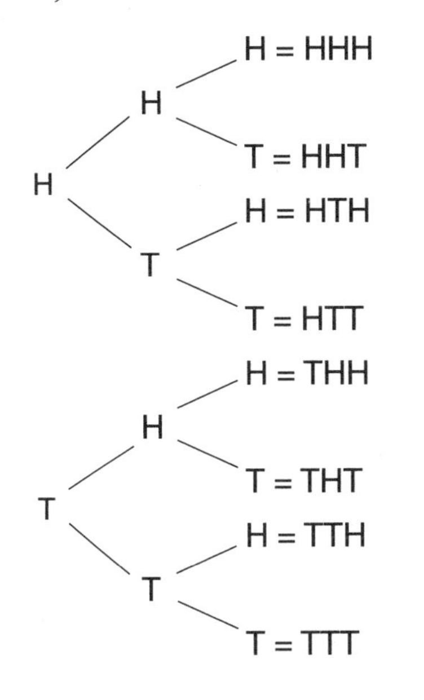


In the first 4 outcomes above (HHH, HHT, HTH, HTT), Hypatia's team would not actually play the last 2 games, because by winning (getting a head on) the first toss, her team won the series. In the next 2 outcomes (THH, THT), her team won by the second toss. In TTH, they did not win until the last toss. In TTT, Hypatia's team lost. There are actually 8 possibilities; Hypatia's team won 7 of the 8 times, so the probability that Hypatia's Hot Hitters won the World Series is $\frac{7}{8}$.

Compare the class totals and have students figure out the fraction of the time that Hypatia's Hot Hitters won. Point out that this is *experimental probability*, whereas the *theoretical probability* is $\frac{7}{8}$. The experimental and the theoretical probabilities may not be equal, but that is not surprising. Often students will think that tossing a coin will come up tails exactly 50% of the time. You can tell them the story of John Kerrich, a British mathematician who was a prisoner of war in Germany during World War II. To pass the time, he tossed a coin 10,000 times and kept track of the results. His results were:

| Number of Tosses | Percent Heads |
|---|---|
| 10 | 40% |
| 20 | 50% |
| 30 | 57% |
| 5,000 | 50.7% |
| 10,000 | 50.7% |

The question of the tournament prize is closely related to the probability of Hypatia's team's winning. When Pascal dealt with this problem, he corresponded with Fermat in 1654 discussing his solution. A few years later in his book *Treatise on the Arithmetical Triangle* (*Traité du Triangle Arithmétique*), he used his famous triangle to answer such questions. He concluded that in this case, $\frac{7}{8}$ of the prize would be awarded to the leader when the game was interrupted and $\frac{1}{8}$ to the competitor. However, his explanation was somewhat different from that above. Imagine you have played 4 games and to win you need to win 1 game out the next 3. Pascal assumed each competitor should get part of the prize. If you were going to play only 1 round and you could each win the series by winning that game, your chance of winning the next game is 50%, so you should get half of the $80 prize, $40. Now, imagine instead that you need 1 game to win and your opponent needs 2 games to win. You are entitled to the $40 you could win in the first round plus half of the $40, $20, from the second, for a total of $60. In the case we initially considered, you need 1 game to win, and your opponent needs 3 games to win. Now you are entitled to $40 ($\frac{1}{2}$ of $80 for the first round) + $20 ($\frac{1}{2}$ of $40 for the second round) + $10 ($\frac{1}{2}$ of $20 for the third round) for a total of $70. Again, the prize is divided $\frac{7}{8}$ to $\frac{1}{8}$ between the competitors.

What is known today as Pascal's Triangle was developed in the process of solving this problem. However, Pascal was not the first to develop this triangle. While he was probably the first to use it to solve probability problems, the Chinese developed the same triangle to find polynomial coefficients in a binomial expansion. See notes on *Chinese Rod Numerals*, pages 53–54. Pascal arranged the numbers in the arithmetical triangle this way:

| | | | | | | | | | |
|---|---|---|---|---|---|---|---|---|---|
| 1 | 1 | 1 | 1 | 1 | 1 | 1 | 1 | 1 | 1 |
| 1 | 2 | 3 | 4 | 5 | 6 | 7 | 8 | 9 | |
| 1 | 3 | 6 | 10 | 15 | 21 | 28 | 36 | | |
| 1 | 4 | 10 | 20 | 35 | 56 | 84 | | | |
| 1 | 5 | 15 | 35 | 70 | 126 | | | | |
| 1 | 6 | 21 | 56 | 126 | | | | | |
| 1 | 7 | 28 | 84 | | | | | | |
| 1 | 8 | 36 | | | | | | | |
| 1 | 9 | | | | | | | | |
| 1 | | | | | | | | | |

Today the triangle is usually arranged like this:

```
Row 0                  1
Row 1                1   1
Row 2              1   2   1
Row 3            1   3   3   1
Row 4          1   4   6   4   1
Row 5        1   5  10  10   5   1
Row 6      1   6  15  20  15   6   1
Row 7    1   7  21  35  35  21   7   1
Row 8  1   8  28  56  70  56  28   8   1
Row 9 1  9  36  84 126 126  84  36   9   1
```

Pascal realized that if you have an interrupted series and you need to win 1 of 3 games, the initial series could be 4 out of 7, 5 out of 8, 5 out of 9, and so on. What is important is how many games you must win out of how many games are left. To use this arithmetical triangle to solve this problem, go to row 3, because you need to win some number *out of 3 games*. Row 3—1, 3, 3, 1—lists the number of ways you can win 0 out of 3 (1 way: TTT), 1 out of 3 (3 ways: HTT, THT, TTH), 2 out of 3 (3 ways: THH, HTH, HHT), and 3 out of 3 (1 way: HHH). There are 8 (1 + 3 + 3 + 1) different results possible when tossing 3 coins or playing 3 games. If you need to win 1 game out of 3, winning 1, 2, or 3 games will satisfy the situation, so the probability is $\frac{(3 + 3 + 1)}{8} = \frac{7}{8}$.

### Extensions

- Give the students other game situations to analyze; for instance, what is the probability of winning a series if you need to win

  1 out of the next 4 games? ($\frac{15}{16}$)

  2 out of the next 5 games? ($\frac{26}{32} = \frac{13}{16}$)

  3 out of the next 5 games? ($\frac{16}{32} = \frac{1}{2}$)

- Get a pizza-toppings menu from a local pizza delivery business. Choose 4 toppings and have the students figure out how many different pizzas they could order with any or all of the toppings. The possibilities should look like the row 4 of Pascal's Triangle. Do the same for 5 toppings, and then have the students predict the possibilities for 6, 7, and 8 toppings.

- Have the students investigate the mathematicians in this year's World Series game: Hypatia and the Bernoulli family. Have them tell how Jacques Bernoulli was connected to probability.

### Answers

**1.** 4 games, 7 games

**2.** Answers will vary.

**3.** 1 toss; 4 tosses

**4. a.** 1 more win **b.** 3 more wins

**5. and 6.** Answers will vary.

**7.** The fairest way, based on probabilities, is $70 for your opponent and $10 for you.

**8.** The distribution is based on the chances of winning when you are in a best-of-7 series, with 4 games (3–1) completed. The probabilities are $\frac{7}{8}$ that the person (team) with 3 wins will win the series and $\frac{1}{8}$ that the person (team) with 1 win will win the series.

### References

Katz; Moore; Colledge; Kenny; Seymour: *Visual Patterns in Pascal's Triangle*

## Math Detective: How Did They Do That?, pages 142–144

**Notes**

This activity is designed for group work. Give each group a different multiplication algorithm to decode and present to the class. As the groups finish, give them a piece of overhead laminate and an overhead pen so they can project their example while explaining it to the class. Arrange the student presentations so that the Egyptian and Russian peasant presentations are one after another and that the Sacchieri and Bhāskara presentations are one after another. There are some interesting similarities for the students to notice.

Students are often surprised that there is more than one way to multiply and might find another method easier than the one they learned.

Our multiplication algorithm was included in the *Treviso Arithmetic* (1478), the earliest known dated and published arithmetic book. However, it was not the only multiplication method included because there were various algorithms in use at that time. Pacioli's *Sūma* was published in 1494 and included eight different multiplication algorithms. The Sacchieri and Bhāskara algorithms are similar to ours. At that time, addition and subtraction also looked pretty much like ours.

Prior to the Europeans' acceptance of Hindu-Arabic numerals and computational algorithms, most computation was done on a counting board, moving counters around somewhat like moving beads on an abacus. The results were recorded using Roman numerals. The *Treviso Arithmetic* was a step toward making computation available to the average middle-class Italian merchant with all the intermediary computations visible and checkable.

The lattice method, probably the easiest to use, was developed in India and was used extensively from China to Europe during the fourteenth to eighteenth centuries. The Italian writers called it *gelosia* because it looked like the lattices on windows. However, it was hard for printers to set type for it in a book, so it fell out of favor. The method is easy to use, and because of the lattice students have an easy time of keeping everything lined up properly for summation.

The Egyptian and Russian peasant algorithms have the same subproducts and are each related to writing numbers in base 2. The Egyptian algorithm is elegant in its simplicity. You do not need to know all the multiplication facts, but only be able to double numbers. The Egyptians used the same method when multiplying mixed numbers. The Egyptians understood—as did the Babylonians with their base-60 system which included sexigesimals similar to our decimals—that one algorithm for multiplication worked for all numbers. For example, if you want to multiply 29 by 17 or 29 by $4\frac{1}{2}$, you use the same method. This is the same point that Simon Stevin tried in 1585 to use to convince the Europeans to use decimals. Stevin pointed out that if you use decimals instead of fractions, then you needed only one algorithm for multiplying both whole numbers and decimals.

**Extensions**

Students might want to investigate how the Egyptians did division. The Egyptian approach to division was different from ours. The question asked was not "What is 1,596 divided by 42?" but rather "What times 42 equals 1,596?" By framing the question in that way, one can do division as the inverse of multiplication, using the multiplication algorithm.

Start by making the table the same way as you would for multiplication:

| ? × 42 = 1,596 | |
|---|---|
| 1 | 42 |
| **2** | **84** |
| **4** | **168** |
| 8 | 336 |
| 16 | 672 |
| **32** | **1,344** |

Now instead of looking for numbers in the left column as you did for multiplication, look in the right column for numbers that sum to 1,596. You should find that 1,344 + 168 + 84 = 1,596. Add the corresponding numbers on the left: 32 + 4 + 2 = 38. Hence, 38 × 42 = 1,596.

This method also works for quotients that are mixed numbers; however, besides doubling, you need to look for fractional parts of 42. For example, think of the pairs of factors of 42: 1 and 42, 2 and 21, 3 and 14, 6 and 7. Each of these pairs generates fractional parts:

$\frac{1}{42}$ of 42 is 1.

$\frac{1}{2}$ of 42 is 21 and $\frac{1}{21}$ of 42 is 2.

$\frac{1}{3}$ of 42 is 14 and $\frac{1}{14}$ of 42 is 3.

$\frac{1}{6}$ of 42 is 7 and $\frac{1}{7}$ of 42 is 6.

Now try 784 ÷ 42.

| ? × 42 | = 784 |
|---|---|
| 1 | 42 |
| **2** | **84** |
| 4 | 168 |
| 8 | 336 |
| **16** | **672** |
| 32 | 1,344 |
| $\frac{1}{42}$ | 1 |
| $\frac{1}{2}$ | **21** |
| $\frac{1}{21}$ | 2 |
| $\frac{1}{3}$ | 14 |
| $\frac{1}{14}$ | 3 |
| $\frac{1}{6}$ | **7** |
| $\frac{1}{7}$ | 6 |

Looking at the right column, we find
$672 + 84 + 21 + 7 = 784$, so $16 + 2 + \frac{1}{2} + \frac{1}{6} = 18\frac{2}{3}$.
Therefore, $18\frac{2}{3} \times 42 = 784$.
The Egyptians used unit fractions and probably would have left the answer as $18 + \frac{1}{2} + \frac{1}{6}$.

Students might also want to explore Napier's Rods (Bones). John Napier, who is credited with the invention of logarithms, introduced the notation we use for decimals today. Recall that Stevin tried to popularize the idea of decimal computation, and many different notations were tried. Napier also marketed a computational aid for multiplication that is closely related to the lattice method of multiplication.

The rods, or *bones* since they were sometimes made from ivory or bone, were basically the multiplication tables arranged in column form. They could be used to find partial products and then totaled as in lattice multiplication. Let the students make their own set and see if they can figure out how to compute using them.

| 1 | 2 | 3 | 4 | 5 | 6 | 7 | 8 | 9 | |
|---|---|---|---|---|---|---|---|---|---|
| /1 | /2 | /3 | /4 | /5 | /6 | /7 | /8 | /9 | 1 |
| /2 | /4 | /6 | /8 | 1/0 | 1/2 | 1/4 | 1/6 | 1/8 | 2 |
| /3 | /6 | /9 | 1/2 | 1/5 | 1/8 | 2/1 | 2/4 | 2/7 | 3 |
| /4 | /8 | 1/2 | 1/6 | 2/0 | 2/4 | 2/8 | 3/2 | 3/6 | 4 |
| /5 | 1/0 | 1/5 | 2/0 | 2/5 | 3/0 | 3/5 | 4/0 | 4/5 | 5 |
| /6 | 1/2 | 1/8 | 2/4 | 3/0 | 3/6 | 4/2 | 4/8 | 5/4 | 6 |
| /7 | 1/4 | 2/1 | 2/8 | 3/5 | 4/2 | 4/9 | 5/6 | 6/3 | 7 |
| /8 | 1/6 | 2/4 | 3/2 | 4/0 | 4/8 | 5/6 | 6/4 | 7/2 | 8 |
| /9 | 1/8 | 2/7 | 3/6 | 4/5 | 5/4 | 6/3 | 7/2 | 8/1 | 9 |

**Answers**

**1b.–5b.** Answers will vary.

**1. a.** Ancient Egyptian Multiplication

Start with the two factors, 129 and 1,482, with a space for a column under each. It is not required, but it is easier if the smaller factor is listed on the left.

| **129** | × **1,482** |
|---|---|
| 1 | 1,482 |
| 2 | 2,964 |

Your first row is: 1 1,482. To get the next row, double each of these numbers.

| **129** | **1,482** |
|---|---|
| **1** | **1,482** |
| 2 | 2,964 |
| 4 | 5,928 |
| 8 | 1,1856 |
| 16 | 23,712 |
| 32 | 47,424 |
| 64 | 94,848 |
| **128** | **189,696** |

Continue the process by repeatedly doubling, until the number in the left column would be greater than 129 if doubled again.

Now look in the left column for the numbers that sum to 129 (1 + 128).
Add the corresponding numbers from the right column (1,482 + 189,696). The sum, 191,178, is the product of 129 times 1,482.

The columns are really a multiplication table for 1,482 ($1 \times 1{,}482 = 1{,}482$ and $128 \times 1{,}482 = 189{,}696$). You might want to point out that this method works because of the distributive property:

$1{,}482 \times 129 = 1{,}482(1 + 128) =$
$1{,}482 + 189{,}696$

2. a. Russian Peasant Multiplication

Start with the two factors, 129 and 1,482, with a space for a column under each. The first entry in each column are these factors.

| 129 × | 1,482 |
|---|---|
| 129 | 1,482 |
| 64 | 2,964 |
| 32 | 5,928 |
| 16 | 11,856 |
| 8 | 23,712 |
| 4 | 47,424 |
| 2 | 94,848 |
| 1 | 189,696 |

Take half of the number in the left column. (Round down, keeping no remainders.) Double the number in the right column. Repeat the process until the number in the left column is 1.

| 129 × | 1,482 |
|---|---|
| 129 | 1,482 |
| ~~64~~ | ~~2,964~~ |
| ~~32~~ | ~~5,928~~ |
| ~~16~~ | ~~11,856~~ |
| ~~8~~ | ~~23,712~~ |
| 4 | ~~47,424~~ |
| ~~2~~ | ~~94,848~~ |
| 1 | 189,696 |

Cross out all even numbers in the left column as well as the corresponding numbers in the right column. Add the remaining numbers in the right column (1,482 + 189,696). The sum (191,178) is the product of 129 and 1,482.

3. a. Lattice Multiplication

This method involves placing multiplication facts into the grid and then adding on the diagonal using the lines as a guide.

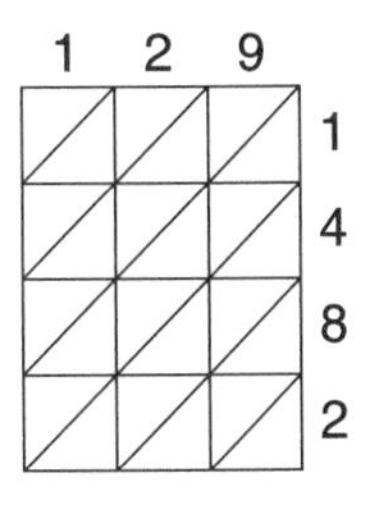


Begin by placing the two factors around the outside. The first factor goes on top and the second vertically down the right side of the grid, beginning with the greatest place value on top.

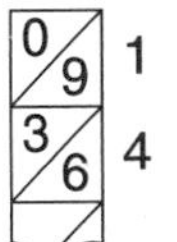


Insert the products in the boxes where the rows and columns intersect. For example, $1 \times 9 = 9$ and $4 \times 9 = 36$.

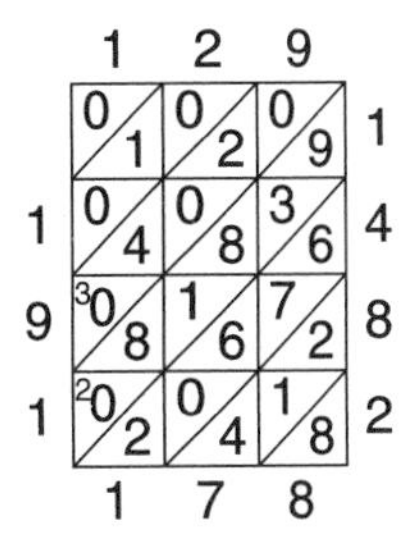


Complete the grid by filling in all of the products. Starting in the lower right corner, add along each diagonal, carrying if necessary.

Read the answer by starting at the upper left corner and read the number in a counter-clockwise direction.
$129 \times 1{,}482 = 191{,}178$

4. a. Sacchieri Multiplication

This method is very similar to our own algorithm. The placing of factors helps keep the subproducts positioned correctly for summation.

```
    1 2 9
        /2
       /8
      /4
     /1
```

Begin by placing the two factors, one on top and the other on the vertical diagonal with the greatest place value at the bottom.

Multiply, recording the subproducts.

```
      1 2 9
      2 5 8 /2  ←  2 × 129
   1 0 3 2 /8  ←  8 × 129
    5 1 6 /4  ←  4 × 129
   1 2 9 /1  ←  1 × 129
```

```
      1 2 9
      2 5 8 /2
   1 0 3 2 /8
    5 1 6 /4
   1 2 9 /1
   1 9 1 , 1 7 8
```

Total each vertical column as we do in our algorithm.

5. a. Hindu Multiplication

This method of multiplication is similar to our algorithm, except that the subproducts are found in a different order. What we would consider the multiplicand and the multiplier have reversed positions.

```
   1,4 8 2
 1 2 9
 1 2 9  ←  1 × 129
   5 1 6  ←  4 × 129
  1 0 3 2  ←  8 × 129
     2 5 8  ←  2 × 129
 1 9 1,1 7 8
```

**References**

Katz; Smith: *History of Mathematics*, vol. II;
Swetz: *Capitalism & Arithmetic*

## Egyptian Unit Fractions; Eye of Horus Fractions, pages 145–147

**Notes**

The ancient Egyptians had a culture that involved various calculations; for example, they surveyed and collected taxes. Most of what we know about the Egyptians' mathematics comes from the Rhind Papyrus, named for the Englishman who found it, rather than the scribe Ahmes who wrote it. The Egyptians used a unit system for writing fractions. In order to simplify the explanation for students, the activity does not mention that there were special symbols for $\frac{1}{2}$, $\frac{1}{4}$ and $\frac{2}{3}$, namely,

To introduce the concept of unit fractions, you may want to pose this problem to the students: Imagine you lived a long time ago and the only kind of fractions you knew how to write were those that had numerators of 1. What would be different in your family's life?

Sometimes students are surprised that there is another way to write and calculate with fractions. After working on writing our fractions as unit fractions, students might think that computations must be difficult. However, there is some indication that the Egyptians understood something about what we would call common denominators and equivalence. For example, they would write the following fractions with the four numbers underneath.

In our notation, this set of numbers is:

| $\frac{1}{2}$ | $\frac{1}{10}$ | $\frac{1}{16}$ | $\frac{1}{32}$ |
|---|---|---|---|
| 80 | 16 | 10 | 5 |

Notice that the numbers below the fractions are the numerators if we write all the fractions with their least common denominator, 160.

Multiplication and division with fractions and mixed numbers were done by the same method as with whole numbers. It is not difficult; and if you want to learn how to multiply and divide with unit fractions, see Bunt.

**Answers**

***Egyptian Unit Fractions***

1. a. $\frac{1}{20}$ b. $\frac{1}{5} + \frac{1}{7} = \frac{12}{35}$
   c. $\frac{1}{3} + \frac{1}{20} = \frac{23}{60}$ d. $\frac{1}{25} + \frac{1}{15} = \frac{8}{75}$
   e. $\frac{1}{2{,}000} + \frac{1}{1{,}000} = \frac{3}{2{,}000}$
   f. $\frac{1}{40{,}022} + \frac{1}{2} = \frac{20{,}012}{40{,}022}$
   g. $\frac{1}{11{,}000} + \frac{1}{2} = \frac{5{,}501}{11{,}000}$

2. a. b.
   c. d. $\frac{1}{3} + \frac{1}{8}$
   e. $\frac{1}{2} + \frac{1}{9}$ f. $\frac{1}{8} + \frac{1}{9}$

3. Possible answers: $\frac{5}{12} = \frac{1}{3} + \frac{1}{12}$; $\frac{5}{12} = \frac{1}{4} + \frac{1}{6}$

**Bonus**

A. $\frac{7}{24} = \frac{1}{4} + \frac{1}{24}$ B. $\frac{17}{36} = \frac{1}{3} + \frac{1}{9} + \frac{1}{36}$

***Eye of Horus Fractions***

1. $\frac{1}{64}$
2. a. $\frac{3}{4} = \frac{1}{2} + \frac{1}{4}$
   b. $\frac{3}{16} = \frac{1}{8} + \frac{1}{16}$
   c. $\frac{5}{32} = \frac{1}{8} + \frac{1}{32}$
   d. $\frac{3}{32} = \frac{1}{16} + \frac{1}{32}$
   e. $\frac{5}{8} = \frac{1}{2} + \frac{1}{8}$

f. $\frac{3}{64} = \frac{1}{32} + \frac{1}{64}$

g. $\frac{5}{16} = \frac{1}{4} + \frac{1}{16}$

h. $\frac{5}{64} = \frac{1}{16} + \frac{1}{64}$

i. $\frac{7}{8} = \frac{1}{2} + \frac{1}{4} + \frac{1}{8}$

j. $\frac{11}{16} = \frac{1}{2} + \frac{1}{8} + \frac{1}{16}$

**Bonus**

No; if you look at any fraction with a denominator that has a factor other than 2, such as $\frac{1}{3}$, and then use the J.J. Sylvester method adjusted to use the Eye of Horus denominators, you get $\frac{1}{3} = \frac{1}{4} + \frac{1}{12}$. To check, you need to find a common denominator, which in this case is 12. This common denominator will have to have a factor of 3 in order for $\frac{1}{3}$ to be converted to it.

**References**

Boyer, Bunt, Chase, Gillings, Ifrah, Knorr, Menninger

## Writing Decimals Through the Years, pages 148–149

**Notes**

Have students listen carefully while you read them the following two paragraphs. Do *not* give students copies of this material.

Years ago when we did not have radio, television, and numerous magazines and newspapers to advertise new books, an author would put a tantalizing description in the beginning of the book or on the title page. This description was more of an advertisement than you might see on a book jacket today. The following is from the preface of the book *La Thiende*, written in 1585 by Simon Stevin in Flemish. It was translated into English in 1608. Listen while I read this. Try to figure out what he is selling.

"We will speak freely of the great utility of this invention; I say great, much greater than I judge any of you will suspect, and this without at all exalting my own opinion . . . , for the astronomer knows the difficult multiplications and divisions which proceed from the progression with degrees, minutes, seconds and thirds . . . , the surveyor, he will recognize the great benefit which the world would receive from this science, to avoid . . . the tiresome multiplications in Verges, feet and often inches, which are notably awkward, and often the cause of error. The same of the masters of the mint, merchants, and others. . . . But the more that these things mentioned are worthwhile, and the ways to achieve them more laborious, the greater still is the discovery *****, which removes all these difficulties. But how? It teaches (to tell much in one word) to compute easily, without fractions, all computations which are encountered in the affairs of human beings, in such a way that the four principles of arithmetic which are called addition, subtraction, multiplication, and division, are able to achieve this end, causing also similar facility to those who use the casting-board (jetons). Now if by this means will be gained precious time; . . . if by this means labor, annoyance, error, damage, and other accidents commonly joined with these computations, be avoided, then I submit this plan voluntarily to your judgement."

What Simon Stevin was selling in 1585 was the idea of computing with decimals, or what he called *disme*. If your students do not immediately guess decimals, do not tell them. Ask them to think about problems this invention could solve. Remind them that the invention could be had by reading a book, so it was not a calculator as many students often guess. This reading makes a good introduction to the study or review of decimals and a way to make computations with fractions easier. You can add that since not all fractions are terminating decimals, for the sake of accuracy they still need to know about fractions.

After discussing Stevin's idea, give students *Writing Decimals Through the Years*, or display a copy of the activity on the overhead. See how many of the numbers the students can decipher. If you use a transparency, you may wish to fill in the last column and cover it up, displaying the answer only after students have had time to make suggestions. Some are more obvious than others. Discuss which notation students think is the clearest and easiest to use for computations. A photocopy of the table can be hung on the wall as a poster.

Prior to 1585, a few mathematicians in the western world understood the decimal concept, but no one ever put all of the ideas together in a coherent fashion they way Stevin did. From *Chinese Rod Numerals*, pages 138–140, you know that the Chinese understood the concept of extending the integral place values to include the fractions based on the powers of 10. Similarly, the Babylonians extended the sexagesimal place values to include the fractions based on the powers of 60. The decimal concept developed independently in the West.

The Arabs adopted Hindu numerals, and there is evidence that abu al-Hasan, Ahmad ibn Ibrahim al-Uqlidisi of Damascus, used decimals in a work dating from 952–953. *In Kitab Al-Fusul Fi Al Hisab Al-Hindi*, al-Uqlidisi wrote 16'35 in the middle of a computation to stand for 163.35. He did some computations but not with our modern algorithms. At one point, he multiplied a decimal by an integer by multiplying the decimal part and the integer part separately and adding the results.

In the early 15th century, al-Kāshī, the royal astronomer of Ulugh Beg in Samarkand, may have been the first to really understand decimals. He computed pi to a high degree of accuracy in sexagesimals and then converted his answer into decimals which he claimed to have invented:

sah-hah

3    141592635898732

He did not use a decimal point, but instead wrote *sah-hah* which means *integer* and left a space to separate the integer from the decimal part. Sometimes he wrote numbers in chart form:

| Integers | First Tenths | Second Tenths |
|---|---|---|
| 17 | 2 | 8 |

or

| Integers | Decimal Fractions |
|---|---|
| 17 | 28 |

At other times he used the Hindu notation:

17
02
08

Al-Kāshī understood multiplication as we do today. He solved $14.3 \times 25.07$ by multiplying $143 \times 2507$ and then determining the position of the decimal point. Unfortunately, when mathematical ideas were brought to Europe by the Arabs, the news about decimals was left behind. Decimals had to be reinvented.

Simon Stevin did not invent decimals; he just realized the possibilities and popularized the idea. Stevin's notation was somewhat awkward. For example, Stevin wrote 3.45 as 3⓪4①5②. To add two decimals, he labeled the columns vertically.

|  | ⓪① ②③ |  |  |
|---|---|---|---|
| He wrote | 2 4 7 8 4 1 | for | 247.841 |
| and | + 2 3 0 7 | for | + 2.307 |
|  | 2 5 0 1 4 8 |  | 250.148 |

After Stevin's compilation and popularization, a more useful notation still needed to be developed. John Napier used the notation we use today in his book on logarithms published in 1619. Interestingly, over 400 years later we still do not have standardization of notation; today you will find the dot, the raised dot, or a comma to indicate a decimal point, depending upon where in the world you are.

The Chinese and the Arabs had some knowledge of decimals. Many Europeans came close to discovering decimals but did not appreciate the significance of what they had written. Many who came close were dealing with square roots. Up until the sixteenth century, one method of computing the square root of a number began with multiplying by 1,000,000 and then taking the root and saying the new answer was 1,000 times too great. François Viète (1540–1603) realized the significance of decimals. In 1579 he recommended against using sexagesimals and instead encouraged using "hundredths and hundreds, tenths and tens." Francesco Pellos (1450–1500) foreshadowed the idea of decimals when he used a dot to indicate a that number was divided by a power of 10. (*Compendio de lo Abaco*)

Pellos's dot was not a decimal point. The first use of the period as a decimal point was by either G.A. Magini (1555–1617) in *Deplanis Triangulis* (1592) or Christoph Clavis (1537–1612) in a sine table published in 1593. John Napier popularized the use of decimals when he introduced logarithms. Napier suggested using either a period or a comma saying, "Whatever is written after the period is a fraction." *(Constructio,* 1619) In 1696, Samuel Jeake wrote a description of the many ways that decimals can be written but did not include the decimal point as an option!

**References**

Bag; Boyer; Bunt; Cajori: *A History of Mathematical Notations;* Chase; *Ancient China's Technology and Science;* Datta; Dedron; Gillings; Ifrah; Karpinski; Katz; Knorr; Menninger; Needham; Neugebauer; Popp; Saidan; Smith: *A History of Mathematics,* vol. II; *A History of Japanese Mathematics;* Swetz: *Capitalism & Arithmetic;* Temple; van der Waerden: *Science Awakening I;* Yan

**Answers**

**1.** 163.35 **2.** 0.75

**3.** 3.141592635898732 **4.** 393.75

**5.** 141,421.35624

**6.** 314,159.26536 **7.** 3.14

**8.** 123.459872 **9.** 8.00798 **10.** 0.17

**11.** 13.00024 **12.** 1,994.9160

**13.** 0.01414 **14.** 141.4

**15.** 3.22916 **16.** 5.9321 **17.** 6.93

**18.** 1.532 **19.** 39.063 **20.** 2.5

**21.** 0.25 **22.** 16.7249 **23.** 3.04

**24.** 58.5 **25.** 31.008

**26.** 25.80079 **27.** 12.345

**28.** 92.123345 **29.** 22.3

**30.** 272.097792 **31.** 645.879 **32.** 30.24

**33.** 0.9985 **34.** 4.2005 **35.** 32.634

**36.** 0.00002677 **37.** 2.5 **38.** 2.5

## To Repeat or Not Repeat, That Is the Question; Divide Like a Babylonian, pages 150–151

**Notes**

Students can easily convert fractions to decimals by dividing the numerator by the denominator on their calculators. The only potential difficulty with this activity of which you should be aware is that some calculators round to the last digit instead of truncating. If a student's calculator rounds, the student might think that $\frac{1}{24}$ is nonterminating, The display might be 0.041667, for example, whereas if their calculator had truncated at the right end of the display, it would show 0.041666. You might want to precede this activity by having students convert $\frac{2}{3}$ by long division and then with a calculator to see who has a final digit of 7 (rounded) and who has a final digit of 6 (truncated). One fraction that might give a difficulty if the calculator rounds is $\frac{1}{7}$, depending upon how many digits are displayed.

When students find the prime factored form of the denominators, they should find that the denominators of fractions that do *not* repeat have only 2s and/or 5s as factors. Some of the repeating ones have 2s and/or 5s, but they have at least one other number as a factor. Students might not recognize the rule in its entirety, so this is a good point for class discussion after they have completed and have come up with their theories. The reason for this is that we use a base-10 number system. One way to convert a fraction to a decimal is to write the fraction with a denominator of 10, 100, 1,000, and so on. The only such fractions are those whose denominators have only 2s and/or 5s as factors.

Problem 7 asks students to find the prime-factored form of 60. This question leads into a discussion about the Babylonians who developed a sexigesimal (base-60) number system possibly 5,000 years ago. Base 60 might seem at first a bit foreign to us, but a legacy of the Babylonians is our division of time and angle measurement into units of 60 that were preserved over the centuries in astronomical measurements and calculations. But why use base 60 when base 10 seems so much simpler? We do not know for sure, but if you consider which fractions would be nonrepeating in base 60, namely, all the fractions with factors of only 2s, 3s, and/or 5s in the denominators, there are far more nonrepeating sexigesimals than there are nonrepeating decimals. The Babylonians did make astronomical calculations that used fractional parts. These were written in a form similar to our decimal fractions rather than to our common fractions, so calculations were very easy. Addition and subtraction could be done by grouping the place values—or, as we would say "by lining up the decimal points"—and multiplication could be done as with whole numbers and determination of the "sexigesimal" point afterward. As an extension, assign *Divide Like a Babylonian* after the discussion on why the Babylonians chose base 60.

**Answers**

***To Repeat or Not Repeat, That Is the Question***

1. $\frac{1}{2} = 0.5$, $\frac{1}{3} = 0.333\ldots$, $\frac{1}{4} = 0.25$, $\frac{1}{5} = 0.2$, $\frac{1}{6} = 0.1666\ldots$, $\frac{1}{7} = 0.14285714\ldots$, $\frac{1}{8} = 0.125$, $\frac{1}{9} = 0.111\ldots$, $\frac{1}{10} = 0.1$, $\frac{1}{11} = 0.0909\ldots$, $12 = 0.08333\ldots$

   Nonrepeating: $\frac{1}{2}, \frac{1}{4}, \frac{1}{5}, \frac{1}{8}, \frac{1}{10}$

   Repeating: $\frac{1}{3}, \frac{1}{6}, \frac{1}{7}, \frac{1}{9}, \frac{1}{11}, \frac{1}{12}$

2. $\frac{1}{2}$: 2; $\frac{1}{3}$: 3; $\frac{1}{4}$: $2 \times 2$; $\frac{1}{5}$: 5; $\frac{1}{6}$: $2 \times 3$; $\frac{1}{7}$: 7; $\frac{1}{8}$: $2 \times 2 \times 2$; $\frac{1}{9}$: $3 \times 3$; $\frac{1}{10}$: $2 \times 5$; $\frac{1}{11}$: 11; $\frac{1}{12}$: $2 \times 2 \times 3$

3. They have only 2s and/or 5s as factors.

4. **a.** Repeating; 0.0666 . . .

   **b.** Nonrepeating; 0.0625

   **c.** Nonrepeating; 0.05

   **d.** Repeating; 0.041666 . . .

   **e.** Repeating; 0.0333 . . .

   **f.** Nonrepeating; 0.025

5. Sample answer: If the denominator of a fraction has prime factors other than 2 and/or 5, the fraction will be a repeating decimal.

6. Sample answer: When the numerator of a fraction is 1, you find the decimal by dividing 1.0, 1.00, 1.000, and so on, by the denominator. The only prime factors of 10 are 2 and 5. So when the numerator is divided by 2s and/or 5s from the denominator, the answer does not have a remainder and the decimal does not repeat. When the numerator is divided by any other prime factors of the denominator, the answer does have a remainder and the decimal repeats.

7. $2 \times 2 \times 3 \times 5$

***Divide Like a Babylonian***

1. **a.** 0.5 **b.** 0.25 **c.** 0.125 **d.** 0.1 **e.** 0.04 **f.** 0.2 **g.** 0.008

2. Answers will vary.

3. $2{,}745 \div 25 = 2{,}745 \times 0.4 = 109.8$

4. $3{,}257 \div 50 = 3{,}257 \times 0.2 = 651.4$

5. $18{,}848 \div 8 = 18{,}848 \times 0.125 = 2{,}356$

## An Old-Time Toy: The Tower Puzzle, pages 152–156

**Notes**

There are many patterns for your students to find when investigating the Tower Puzzle. It is best if they work with partners, so that someone can record what is happening. If you do not have any Tower Puzzles, make or buy one as a model for demonstration. Make copies of *The Tower Puzzle Disks A* in one color and *The Tower Puzzle Disks B* in another color. Give pairs of students a strip of each color and have them cut out the 5 circles. Alternatively, students can cut appropriate-sized disks out of two colors of plastic foam. Students can divide a sheet of paper into thirds to use as the puzzle board.

The answers given are not the only answers that students might give. Be sure to check their observations; if they are not what you expected, you might find some other interesting patterns.

The number of moves to transfer $n$ disks is $2^n - 1$. Students might not initially recognize their answers in Problem 1 as 1 less than a power of 2. During the class discussion, which you should have before assigning Problems 9 and 10, you lead students to this conclusion after they have seen the powers of 2 that show up in Problems 5 and 6. Some students might see the answers as the sums of powers of 2, or notice that the differences between the terms are the powers of 2, or "doubles."

The Tower Puzzle is a toy that has been around since 1883, when the French mathematician Edouard Lucas (1842–1891) marketed it as created by "Prof. Claus of the College of Li-Sou-Stain," which was really an anagram for Prof. Lucas of the College of Saint Louis. Lucas was a number theorist who was interested in Mersenne primes. *Mersenne primes* are numbers of the form $2^n - 1$, where $n \geq 1$. Interestingly, as we saw in the investigation of the Tower Puzzle, the minimum number of moves necessary to transfer $n$ disks from one tower to another is $2^n - 1$. Sometimes, we see the same patterns in what seem to be very different problems. The numbers of the form $2^n - 1$ are an example of this.

As an extension, assign *Mersenne Primes and Perfect Numbers*, pages 157–158.

**Answers**

1. **a.** 0 moves **b.** 1 move **c.** 3 moves
   **d.** 7 moves **e.** 15 moves **f.** 31 moves
   **g.** 1,023 moves
2. Answers will vary.
3. For the least number of moves, never place a disk of one color directly on a disk of the same color.
4. **a.** A **b.** ABA
   c. ABACABA **d.** ABACABADABACABA
   e. ABACABADABACABAEABACABAD ABACABA
   f. ABACABADABACABAEABACABAD ABACABAFABACABADABACABAE ABACABADABACABA
5. The letters are symmetric around a center letter that happens to be the largest disk. For example, for 2 disks: A<u>B</u>A and for 3 disks: ABA<u>C</u>ABA

   If students do not just record the moves but think about what is happening when solving the puzzle, they might see the following:

   To move 4 disks, you first need to move 3 disks, which is done by ABACABA. Then, you need to move disk D, after which you need to move the original 3 disks on top of D. So for 4 disks: ABACABA<u>D</u>ABACABA. Martin Gardner (1967) pointed out that this pattern shows up when writing numbers in base 2 and when tracing the paths for Hamiltonian circuits on polyhedrons.

6.

| A | B | C | D | Total |
|---|---|---|---|---|
| 8 | 4 | 2 | 1 | 15 |

7.

| A | B | C | D | E | Total |
|---|---|---|---|---|---|
| 16 | 8 | 4 | 2 | 1 | 31 |

8. The number of moves for each disk is a successive power of 2.
9. To transfer a tower of an odd number of disks, then place the first disk on the tower that you want the finished tower to be located; to transfer a tower of an even number of disks, place the first disk on the tower you do *not* want the finished tower to be located.
10. You can relax. There are $2^{64} - 1 =$ 18,446,744,073,709,551,615 moves. Students should recognize that the number of moves is $2^{64} - 1$ but may not initially realize how large this number really is. If they are using a scientific calculator, they will realize that it is a 20-digit number. Now, if those priests work around the clock, moving one disk every second, then in a 365-day year they move 31,536,000 disks. This may seem like too many moves, but if you do a little bit of rounding, you find that 18,000,000,000,000,000,000 ÷ 30,000,000 = 600,000,000,000 years. The

level of accuracy of your answer is dependent upon the sophistication of your students and available technology. Long before calculators were readily available in the classroom, I let fifth graders do enough calculations to realize that they were dealing with a very large number. I told them the actual number is 18,446,744,073,709,551,615, and have them use rounding to estimate the number of years. If your students know how to use a scientific calculator, this is a good problem for them to solve:

$2^{64} \div (60 \times 60 \times 24 \times 365) = 5.8494 \times 10^{11}$.

**References**

Burton; Gardner: *The Scientific American Book of Mathematical Puzzles & Diversions*; Kasner; *Tower Puzzle*

## Mersenne Primes and Perfect Numbers, pages 157–158

**Notes**

This is a good activity to do after students have looked at factors of numbers and have developed the idea that to find the factors of a large number they need to check only those numbers less than or equal to the square root of that number. For example, in Problem 1, $n = 11$ gives $2^n - 1 = 2{,}047$. The square root of 2,047 is 45.243 . . .; so we know that we need to check only the numbers less than or equal to 45. A quick check of the divisibility rules eliminates all the even numbers and multiples of 3 or 5. Checking the other possible factors is a good calculator activity. If students ask what we call numbers that are *not perfect*, tell them that the ancient Greeks called them *abundant* and *deficient*, and then ask which were the abundant ones.

After students have completed *Mersenne Primes and Perfect Numbers*, you might tell them the story of $M_{67}$. As they should realize from the activity, the fact that 67 is a prime number does not guarantee that $M_{67}$ is a prime. In 1876, Edouard Lucas figured out that $M_{67}$ was a composite number, but he could not find the actual factors. In October, 1903, Frank Nelson Cole was to present a paper titled "On the Factorization of Large Numbers" at the American Mathematical Society meeting. When Cole was introduced to speak, he went to the blackboard and calculated $2^{67} - 1$. On the other part of the blackboard, he calculated longhand 193,707,721 × 761,838,257,287. The two answers agreed. The audience gave him a standing ovation and he sat down without saying one word during his "speech." Later, Cole told a friend that it took him "three years of Sundays" to find the factors of $M_{67}$. (Burton) On January 27, 1998, $2^{3{,}021{,}377} - 1$ was discovered to be a Mersenne prime.

There is an organized computer search to find Mersenne primes. If you have students who want to participate or to find out what the current greatest known Mersenne prime is, check the following web site:

http:\\www.mersenne.org\prime.htm

**Answers**

1.

| $n$ | Is $n$ a Prime? | $2^n - 1$ | Is $2^n - 1$ a Prime? List Its Factors. |
|---|---|---|---|
| 1 | No | 1 | No; 1 |
| 2 | Yes | 3 | Yes; 1, 3 |
| 3 | Yes | 7 | Yes; 1, 7 |
| 4 | No | 15 | No; 1, 3, 5, 15 |
| 5 | Yes | 31 | Yes; 1, 31 |
| 6 | No | 63 | No; 1, 3, 7, 9, 21, 63 |
| 7 | Yes | 127 | Yes; 1, 127 |
| 8 | No | 255 | No; 1, 3, 5, 15, 17, 51, 85, 255 |
| 9 | No | 511 | No; 1, 7, 73, 511 |
| 10 | No | 1,023 | No; 3, 11, 31, 33, 93, 341, 1,023 |
| 11 | Yes | 2,047 | No; 1, 23, 89, 2,047 |

2. 11; $2^{11} - 1 = 2{,}047 = 23 \times 89$

Fermat's claim was that if $2^n - 1$ is a prime then $n$ is a prime. Students often assume that the converse of a true statement is also true, namely that if $n$ is a prime then $2^n - 1$ is a prime.

**3.** 6 is a perfect number; 1 + 2 + 3 = 6.

**4.**

| $n$ | $(2^{n-1})(2^n - 1)$ | List of Factors | Sum of Proper Factors |
|---|---|---|---|
| 2 | 2 × 3 = 6 | 6 1, 2, 3, 6 | 1 + 2 + 3 = 6 |
| 3 | 4 × 7 = 28 | 1, 2, 4, 7, 14, 28 | 1 + 2 + 4 + 7 + 14 = 28 |
| 5 | 16 × 31 = 496 | 1, 2, 4, 8, 16, 31, 62, 124, 248, 496 | 1 + 2 + 4 + 8 + 16 + 31 + 62 + 124 + 248 = 496 |
| 7 | 64 × 127 = 8,128 | 1, 2, 4, 8, 16, 32, 64, 127, 254, 508, 1,016, 2,032, 4,064, 8,128 | 1 + 2 + 4 + 8 + 16 + 32 + 64 + 127 + 254 + 508 + 1,016 + 2,032 + 4,064 = 8,128 |

**References**

Burton; Gardner: *The Scientific American Book of Mathematical Puzzles & Diversions*; Kasner

## Chess; Chess Epilogue, pages 159–160

**Notes**

This is a good activity to use when students are working on exponents and scientific notation. Now that students have access to scientific calculators, they can quickly calculate using exponents what took a great deal of time and effort in the past. Sometimes students do not fully understand the real size of such large numbers, so calculating the number of years it would take to count out that many grains of wheat gives some meaning to the enormity of the quantity.

Historically, writing and computing with large numbers has been a challenge. People have not always had the luxury of exponential notation. You can tell the class about early attempts to compute with large numbers, as well as about the origins of exponents and our terms *squared* and *cubed*. See notes on *Oh, for the Good Old Days when Things Were Simpler*, page 20.

The concept of squaring a number has been around for a long time. The Egyptian papyrus in Moscow (1650 B.C.E.) includes a calculation of the volume of the frustum of a pyramid which uses a pair of walking legs ⩘ to indicate squaring a number. Not quite that long ago, but still in ancient times, Greek and Sanskrit mathematicians both approached squaring a number geometrically. The Greeks had figurate numbers (triangular, square, pentagonal, hexagonal, and so on). Their square numbers

```
                              • • • • •
                    • • • •   • • • • •
           • • •    • • • •   • • • • •
     • •   • • •    • • • •   • • • • •
•    • •   • • •    • • • •   • • • • •
```

are what we call square numbers, and you can see how the shape relates to the area. When thinking about volume, we can see why numbers to the third power are called "cubed."

The Sanskrit term for square is *varga*. Âryabhata (c. 499) said: "A square figure of four equal sides and the (number representing its area) are called varga. The product of two equal quantities is also varga." There are references to powers of 2, 3, 4, and 6 in the *Utt arâ-dhyayana-sûtra* which dates to 300 B.C.E. (Datta). For an activity on figurate numbers, see *The Shapes of Numbers*, pages 124–125.

Many different mathematicians over the years have used the concepts of exponents, but it was René Descartes's suggestion of the notation $x^3$ for $xxx$ that eventually gave us today's notation.

**Answers**

*Chess*

**1.** Answers will vary.

**2.** 512 grains; 524,288 grains

**3.** $2^9$ and $2^{19}$, or $2^n - 1$

**4.** 1,023 grains; 1,048,575 grains

**5.** $2^{10} - 1$ grains

**6.** $2^{63}$ grains

**7.** $2^{64} - 1$ grains

**8. and 9.** Answers will vary.

*Chess Epilogue*

1. Eighteen quintillion, four hundred forty-six quadrillion, seven hundred forty-four trillion, seventy-three billion, seven hundred nine million, five hundred fifty-one thousand, six hundred fifteen
2. $2 \times 10^{19}$
3. $(2 \times 10^{19}) \div (5 \times 10^{6}) = 4 \times 10^{12}$ bushels
4. $(4 \times 10^{12}$ bushels$) \div (2 \times 10^{10}$ bushels/year$)$ = 200 years
5. Answers will vary.
6. $60 \times 60 \times 24 \times 365 \times 60 = 1{,}892{,}160{,}000$ grains
7. $2{,}000{,}000{,}000 = 2 \times 10^{9}$; $(2 \times 10^{9}) \div (2 \times 10^{19}) = \frac{1}{10{,}000{,}000{,}000}$

**References**

Cajori: *A History of Mathematical Notations*; Datta

## Exploring the Perpetual Calendar; Time Travel Historical News Service, Parts 1 and 2; Friday the 13th, Birthday Parties; Birthday Parties, the Sequel, pages 161–170

**Notes**

Imagine you lived a few thousand years ago. How would you measure the passage of time? Probably the most obvious natural occurrence would be sunrise or sunset. However, as we know, the length of daylight varies over the year; and, as a result, the time of sunrise or sunset is not consistent from day to day to the average person, even if you do not consider that the amount of daylight on the same day is different for people in different locations in the world. See *Egyptian Hours*, page 89. In grade school, we were taught that there are 365 days in a year except in a leap year, 12 months in a year, and 52 weeks in a year—all very cut and dried and simple. However, if you were able to measure the mean solar day, you would find that it is 24 hours 3 minutes 56.55 seconds long.

Another possible natural occurrence to "watch for" in order to measure the passage of time would be the phases of the moon. The moon takes 29.53059 days, a synodic month, to complete a cycle. What about using the solar year? If you could measure the solar year, you would find it lasts 365.242199 mean solar days. Twelve lunar months is 354.36706 days, about 11 days short of the solar year. Unfortunately, the year is not a multiple of either the day or the month, so people have tried to intercalate in such a way as to have a calendar year that does not get too far out of sync with the actual year and existing seasons. Measuring the passage of time is necessary for a variety of reasons; for example, in an agricultural culture, planting is seasonal. In addition, religious celebrations are important within various groups. It is not surprising than the calendar has been a religious concern. Today, our most widely used calendar, the Gregorian calendar, grew out of Christianity. Measuring the passage of time is a little more complicated than we were taught in grade school, and different peoples in different times and cultures have come up with different solutions to this problem. See notes on *The Egyptian Year*, page 24. Hidden in the solutions are some interesting patterns that students will investigate in these activities.

The solution the students investigate here uses what we call the Gregorian calendar. This was developed in order to keep the seasons in sync with the solar calendar and the Christian religious holidays. This calendar was developed to correct the problems with the Julian calendar. The Julian calendar is based on a year of 365.25 days. The solar year is quite close at 365.242199 days. This is off by only 11 minutes and 14 seconds per year. This does not sound like much time, but it amounts to about 7 days every 1,000 years. Over time, the Julian calendar year became out of sync with the seasons. The Gregorian calendar was really an adjustment of the Julian calendar, taking 365.2422 days instead of 365.25 days as the length of the solar year. This value differs from the Julian calendar by 0.78 day per century. Again, 0.78 does not seem like much time, but it amounts to 3.12 days every 400 years. This resulted in the decree that every centennial year not divisible by 400 should *not* be a leap year, so 3 out of 4 centennial years are not leap years. The year 2000, which is divisible by 400, is a leap year; while the year 1900, which is not divisible by 400, was not a leap year.

The Gregorian calendar was commissioned by Pope Gregory XIII in 1572 and was slowly accepted around the world over the next 300 years. This adjusted calendar was not universally accepted at the same time; so when reading historical accounts of events, you will sometimes find that the dates do not coordinate because one country used the Gregorian calendar and another used the Julian calendar. In 1752 when the Gregorian calendar was adopted in England, it was necessary to drop 11 days from the year so that the days of the year would correspond to the dates in other countries already using the Gregorian calendar. People rioted, demanding that the 11 days be given back.

Most students today do not have any better understanding of the calendar than I did when I was in elementary school. They may have looked at some of the patterns on a calendar that derive from the 7-day week, such as choosing a number and averaging the surrounding numbers. So, when students study the *Perpetual Calendar*, pages 162–164, they are fascinated that they can find the day of the week for any date in any year.

In the activity *Exploring the Perpetual Calendar*, students learn how to use the calendar and to look for patterns.

The *Perpetual Calendar* is not the one that Gauss developed, as his was developed in order to determine the date of Easter, not to determine the day of the week for any date. If students ask for the formal definition for Easter, you can tell them, "Easter is the first Sunday after the first full moon occurring on or after the vernal equinox. Easter is thus delayed one week if the full moon is on Sunday to lessen the likelihood of its being on the same day as the Jewish Passover." (Dershowitz)

*Time Travel Historical News Service, Part 1,* should be given as homework to be used in class with *Time Travel Historical News Service, Part 2.* Students need to work in groups on Problems 1–4 of *Part 2.* Give each student 10 small sticky notes. Within their groups, students should make a sticky note for each event they listed in *Part 1.* However, they need to eliminate any duplicates within the group. Prior to class, you need to make a table with columns labeled with the days of the week, so that students can make a bar graph with their sticky notes. If you are doing this with more than one class, collect all of the data from each of the classes before you have students complete the assignment. A long piece of chart or craft paper works nicely for this activity. As each group finishes a few notes, one member should go up to the graph and post the pieces of data, checking to see that no one else has already recorded that event; if so, the note is not added to the graph.

This is an interesting activity to use to look at what happens as one gathers more data. Just because the first event someone looks up is the explosion of the *Challenger* on January 28, 1986, we cannot assume that most events will occur on Monday. When a student starts out with a few events, there may be more things happening on Tuesday; but within that person's group, Friday might have the most. Whole-class data might show another day as having the most events.

In the class discussion following this activity, it is good to talk about the number of events that occurred per day on weekdays and per day on weekend days. Sometimes students will say, "There are more weekdays so we need more reporters on weekdays," rather than thinking about whether those two weekend days can generate as much significant news per day as the other 5 days of the week can.

Students are always fascinated by Friday the 13th. You can introduce *Friday the 13th* by asking what *triskaidekaphobia* means. Any year will have from 1 to 3 Friday the 13ths. The question of the probability is a bit more complicated. It is not a question of rolling a "7-sided die" and checking to see how often Friday comes up. The probability that Friday will come up is $\frac{1}{7}$, but this probability is based on the patterns inherent in the calendar. If some students find the pattern, be sure to have them share their results with the class. If none of the students find the pattern, this is a nice one to develop as a class discussion and to look at the patterns involved.

As you know from the initial investigations, the years occur in a 28-year cycle. A cursory look at what happens in a 28-year cycle does not seem to yield any pattern in how many Friday the 13ths occur each year.

| Year | Year Type | Number of Friday the 13ths |
|---|---|---|
| 1801 | 5 | 3 |
| 1802 | 6 | 1 |
| 1803 | 7 | 1 |
| 1804 | 8 | 3 |
| 1805 | 3 | 2 |
| 1806 | 4 | 1 |
| 1807 | 5 | 3 |
| 1808 | 13 | 1 |
| 1809 | 1 | 2 |
| 1810 | 2 | 2 |
| 1811 | 3 | 2 |
| 1812 | 11 | 2 |
| 1813 | 6 | 1 |
| 1814 | 7 | 1 |
| 1815 | 1 | 2 |
| 1816 | 9 | 2 |
| 1817 | 4 | 1 |
| 1818 | 5 | 3 |
| 1819 | 6 | 1 |
| 1820 | 14 | 1 |
| 1821 | 2 | 2 |
| 1822 | 3 | 2 |
| 1823 | 4 | 1 |
| 1824 | 12 | 2 |
| 1825 | 7 | 1 |
| 1826 | 1 | 2 |
| 1827 | 2 | 2 |
| 1828 | 10 | 1 |

If instead, you look at the year type in numerical order and how many 13ths there are on each day of the week, you will find some interesting patterns. The break in the pattern comes when the year type switches to leap years.

| Year Type | S | M | T | W | T | F | S |
|---|---|---|---|---|---|---|---|
| 1 | 1 | 3 | 1 | 2 | 2 | 2 | 1 |
| 2 | 1 | 1 | 3 | 1 | 2 | 2 | 2 |
| 3 | 2 | 1 | 1 | 3 | 1 | 2 | 2 |
| 4 | 2 | 2 | 1 | 1 | 3 | 1 | 2 |
| 5 | 2 | 2 | 2 | 1 | 1 | 3 | 1 |
| 6 | 1 | 2 | 2 | 2 | 1 | 1 | 3 |
| 7 | 3 | 1 | 2 | 2 | 2 | 1 | 1 |
| 8 | 1 | 2 | 2 | 1 | 2 | 3 | 1 |
| 9 | 1 | 1 | 2 | 2 | 1 | 2 | 3 |
| 10 | 3 | 1 | 1 | 2 | 2 | 1 | 2 |
| 11 | 2 | 3 | 1 | 1 | 2 | 2 | 1 |
| 12 | 1 | 2 | 3 | 1 | 1 | 2 | 2 |
| 13 | 2 | 1 | 2 | 3 | 1 | 1 | 2 |
| 14 | 2 | 2 | 1 | 2 | 3 | 1 | 1 |
| Totals | 24 | 26 | 22 | 24 | 24 | 24 | 24 |

From this table, it would appear that Monday the 13th would be most likely to occur. The following table takes into account how many times in a 28-year cycle each of the year types occur.

| Year Type | Number of Occurrences in 28-Year Cycle | S | M | T | W | T | F | S |
|---|---|---|---|---|---|---|---|---|
| 1 | 3 | 1 | 3 | 1 | 2 | 2 | 2 | 1 |
| 2 | 3 | 1 | 1 | 3 | 1 | 2 | 2 | 2 |
| 3 | 3 | 2 | 1 | 1 | 3 | 1 | 2 | 2 |
| 4 | 3 | 2 | 2 | 1 | 1 | 3 | 1 | 2 |
| 5 | 3 | 2 | 2 | 2 | 1 | 1 | 3 | 1 |
| 6 | 3 | 1 | 2 | 2 | 2 | 1 | 1 | 3 |
| 7 | 3 | 3 | 1 | 2 | 2 | 2 | 1 | 1 |
| 8 | 1 | 1 | 2 | 2 | 1 | 2 | 3 | 1 |
| 9 | 1 | 1 | 1 | 2 | 2 | 1 | 2 | 3 |
| 10 | 1 | 3 | 1 | 1 | 2 | 2 | 1 | 2 |
| 11 | 1 | 2 | 3 | 1 | 1 | 2 | 2 | 1 |
| 12 | 1 | 1 | 2 | 3 | 1 | 1 | 2 | 2 |
| 13 | 1 | 2 | 1 | 2 | 3 | 1 | 1 | 2 |
| 14 | 1 | 2 | 2 | 1 | 2 | 3 | 1 | 1 |
| Totals in 28-Year Cycle | | 48 | 48 | 48 | 48 | 48 | 48 | 48 |

Now the chances for the 13th to occur on any particular day of the week are equally likely.

*Birthday Parties* and *Birthday Parties, the Sequel* offer an opportunity to discuss the difference between experimental and theoretical probability. They will need to use the *Perpetual Calendar.* When students bring in their data, you can summarize the class data. Based on these numbers, you can ask students to predict what they think is the probability that someone's day of birth and 50th birthday will occur on the same day of the week. (Problem 2, *Birthday Parties, the Sequel*) This is an example of experimental probability. Since most students in the same class will have been born in the same year or in a 2-year time period, the data can be skewed. So, it is wise to eliminate those dates from the survey. If you give this assignment to more than one class, it is good to pool the data for the discussion. Do not have students complete Problems 3–7 until after they have completed the table on page 170, as they will need to refer to the data in the table.

For the theoretical data, have each group of students do just a fraction of the data calculating. You can pass out copies of the table to everyone, or just display it on the overhead and record the data as each group figures out their results. You will find that the 29th of February plays a role in this investigation, and that is why the table is made the way it is. As students give you data, record it; do not question it even if you know there is an error. Then ask students for any patterns that they notice and where things do not seem to fit. Then ask for volunteers to check those pieces of data.

The finished table should look like this:

| **Birth** | **Fifty Years Later** | | **Totals** | |
|---|---|---|---|---|
| **Year** | **Days Before Feb. 29** (Yes or No) | **Days After Feb. 28** (Yes or No) | **Yes** | **No** |
| 1901 | No | No | 0 | 365 |
| 1902 | No | Yes | 306 | 59 |
| 1903 | Yes | Yes | 365 | 0 |
| 1904 | Yes | No | 59 | 307 |
| 1905 | No | No | 0 | 365 |
| 1906 | No | Yes | 306 | 59 |
| 1907 | Yes | Yes | 365 | 0 |
| 1908 | Yes | No | 59 | 307 |
| 1909 | No | No | 0 | 365 |
| 1910 | No | Yes | 306 | 59 |
| 1911 | Yes | Yes | 365 | 0 |
| 1912 | Yes | No | 59 | 307 |
| 1913 | No | No | 0 | 365 |
| 1914 | No | Yes | 306 | 59 |
| 1915 | Yes | Yes | 365 | 0 |
| 1916 | Yes | No | 59 | 307 |
| 1917 | No | No | 0 | 365 |
| 1918 | No | Yes | 306 | 59 |
| 1919 | Yes | Yes | 365 | 0 |
| 1920 | Yes | No | 59 | 307 |
| 1921 | No | No | 0 | 365 |
| 1922 | No | Yes | 306 | 59 |
| 1923 | Yes | Yes | 365 | 0 |
| 1924 | Yes | No | 59 | 307 |
| 1925 | No | No | 0 | 365 |
| 1926 | No | Yes | 306 | 59 |
| 1927 | Yes | Yes | 365 | 0 |
| 1928 | Yes | No | 59 | 307 |

This gives a total of 5,110 "yes" days and 5,117 "no" days. So, the theoretical probability that someone's 50th birthday and birth day will be on the same day of the week is ≈50% (49.96%). From the preceding table, you can see that you really do not need to look at a 28-year cycle; the probability that someone's 50th birthday and birth day will be on the same day of the week is based on a 4-year cycle in relation to the leap year, as shown in the following table.

| Birth | Fifty Years Later | | Totals | |
|---|---|---|---|---|
| Year | Days Before Feb. 29 | Days After Feb. 28 | Yes | No |
| 3 Years Before | No | No | 0 | 365 |
| 2 Years Before | No | Yes | 306 | 59 |
| 1 Year Before | Yes | Yes | 365 | 0 |
| Leap Year | Yes | No | 59 | 307 |
| | | Totals | 730 | 731 |

What you will notice is that there is a 4-year cycle, and once you know whether the year is a leap year or how many years before a leap year, you can tell whether it will match or not. Starting on March 1 two years before a leap year and continuing through February 28 of that leap year, everyone will match; everyone else will not match until the 4-cycle repeats again.

**Extensions**

- Ask the students to think about when their day starts and why they might choose a different starting point than midnight if they were developing a calendar and unaware of what others in the world have done. The choice of midnight as the beginning of the day feels almost artificial, whereas sundown or sunrise is an observable phenomenon. With the Jewish, Baha'i, Coptic, and Islamic calendars, the day begins at sunset; the Hindu day begins at sunrise; and the Julian day begins at noon.
- Other calendars besides the Gregorian have been developed, and many are still in use today. Some are lunar, some solar, some a combination of both lunar and solar, and some astronomical. Some that students might research are the Islamic, Hebrew, Baha'i, Coptic, Persian, Mayan (actually 3 different ones), and Chinese.
- Calendars were not always structured the way we find them today. Calendars measure the passage of time. Show the students the video *The Sun Dagger* (Bullfrog Films, Oley, PA). This video shows the Anasazi Indians' tracking of the 19-year moon and sun cycles. These natives from what is now New Mexico lived 1,000 years ago. These are not the only people to use a 19-year cycle, as, for example, the Hebrew calendar is also based on a 19-year cycle.

**Answers**

***Exploring the Perpetual Calendar***

1. Answers will vary.
2. The patterns students notice will vary in sophistication. Some patterns my students noticed are the following:
   - Every time a month starts on a Sunday, there is a Friday the 13th.
   - There are only 14 ways for years to be formed; calendars 1 through 7 are not leap years, but years 8 through 14 are.
   - There is a cycle of the calendar year numbers: 5, 6, 7, 8, 3, 4, 5, 13, 1, 2, 3, 11, 6, 7, 1, 9, 4, 5, 6, 14, 2, 3, 4, 12, 7, 1, 2, 10; then the cycle starts all over again.
   - Whenever there is a 7 in the list of calendar numbers, it is in a pattern. It goes 6, 7; 6, 7; 12, 7; 6, 7; 6, 7; 12, 7; and so on. It messes up at the turn of the twentieth century, but picks itself up again afterward.
   - There is a pattern in the year number and the next year with the same number.

| Year | Next Year for Same Calendar | Years Between | Leap Year |
|---|---|---|---|
| 1801 | 1807 | 6 | No |
| 1802 | 1813 | 11 | No |
| 1803 | 1814 | 11 | No |
| 1804 | 1832 | 28 | Yes |
| 1805 | 1811 | 6 | No |
| 1806 | 1817 | 11 | No |
| 1807 | 1818 | 11 | No |
| 1808 | 1836 | 28 | Yes |
| 1809 | 1815 | 6 | No |
| 1810 | 1821 | 11 | No |
| 1811 | 1822 | 11 | No |
| 1812 | 1840 | 28 | Yes |

- Pattern using the table I made:

  1 2 3 4 5 6 7 1 2 3 4 5 6
  7 1 2 3 8 9 10 11 12 13 14
  8 9 10 11 12 13 14 8 9 10

  Knowing the calendar number for a certain year on the chart, starting with the first calendar number move this way:

  normal year to normal year →

  normal year to leap year → ↓

  leap year to normal year → → ↑

  You can have student groups share their patterns and check to see if they agree on the validity of what their peers have noticed about the calendar. Any patterns with which they disagree should be rewritten so the description is accurate.

3. Answers will vary.

*Time Travel Historical News Service, Parts 1 and 2*

Answers will vary.

*Friday the 13th*

1. Answers will vary.
2. There may be 1, 2, or 3 Friday the 13ths.
3. $\frac{1}{7}$; answers will vary.
4. There is no day that is more likely than any other; explanations will vary.

*Birthday Parties*

**1.–4.** Answers will vary.

*Birthday Parties, the Sequel*

**1., 2., and 4.** Answers will vary.

3. About 50%
5. Because there were so many people born in the same 2-year period; students born in a year 3 years before a leap year will not have a match, whereas those born 1 year before a leap year will all have a match.
6. Because the cycle repeats every 28 years
7. Anyone born after February 28 of a leap year through February two years before a leap year will not match. Anyone born from March 1 two years before a leap year through February 29 of a leap year will match.

**References**

Bear; Brinkworth; Dershowitz; *Information Please Almanac*; *The New Encyclopaedia Britannica*, 15th ed., s.v. "calendar."

# Bibliography

al-Daffá, Ali Abdullah. *The Muslim Contribution to Mathematics.* Atlantic Highlands, NJ: Humanities Press, 1977.

*Ancient China's Technology and Science.* Compiled by Institute of the History of Natural Sciences, Chinese Academy of Sciences. Beijing: Foreign Languages Press.

Andrew, W.S. *Magic Squares and Cubes.* New York: Dover Publications, 1960 (1917).

Armstrong, Karen. *Jerusalem: One City, Three Faiths.* New York: Alfred A. Knopf, 1996.

Augarten, Stan. *Bit by Bit: An Illustrated History of Computers.* New York: Ticknor and Fields, 1984.

Babbage, Charles. *On the Principles and Development of the Calculator.* Edited by Philip and Emily Morrison. New York: Dover Publications, 1961.

Bag, A.K. *Mathematics in Ancient and Medieval India.* Delhi: Chaukhambha Orientalia, 1979.

Bear, Magdalen. *Days, Months, and Years.* Norfolk, England: Tarquin Publications, 1989.

Beckmann, Petr. *A History of π.* New York: St. Martin's Press, 1971.

Benson, William H., and Oswald Jacoby. *New Recreations with Magic Squares.* New York: Dover Publications, 1976.

Berggren, Lennart, Jonathan Borwein, and Peter Borwein. *Pi: A Source Book.* New York: Springer-Verlag, 1997.

Bezuszka, Stanley, Margaret Kenney, and Linda Silvey. *Tessellations: The Geometry of Patterns.* Palo Alto, CA: Creative Publications, 1977.

Blatner, David. *The Joy of π.* New York: Walker and Company, 1997.

Boyer, Carl B., and Uta C. Merzbach. *A History of Mathematics,* 2nd ed. New York: John Wiley & Sons, 1989.

Brinkworth, Peter, and Paul Scott. *The Making of Mathematics: A Friendly History.* Adelaide: The Australian Association of Mathematics Teachers, 1994.

Britton, Jill, and Walter Britton. *Teaching Tessellating Art.* Parsippany, NJ: Dale Seymour Publications, 1992.

Bunt, Lucas N.H., Phillip S. Jones, and Jack D. Bedient. *The Historical Roots of Elementary Mathematics.* New York: Dover Publications, reprinted in 1988.

Burton, David M. *The History of Mathematics, an Introduction,* 2nd ed. Dubuque, IA: Wm. C. Brown, 1991.

Cajori, Florian. *A History of Mathematical Notations: Two Volumes Bound as One.* New York: Dover Publications, 1928, reprinted in 1993.

Cajori, Florian. *A History of Mathematics.* New York: Chelsea, 1919, reprinted in 1985.

Chase, Arnold Buffum. *The Rhind Mathematical Papyrus.* Reston, VA: NCTM, 1979.

Chinese Academy of Science Institute of the History of Natural Sciences, *Ancient China's Technology and Science.* Beijing: Foreign Languages Press (no date).

Colledge, Tony. *Pascal's Triangle.* Norfolk, England: Tarquin Publications, 1992.

Datta, Bibhutibhusan, and Avadhesh Narayan Singh. *History of Hindu Mathematics: A Sourcebook, Parts 1 and 2.* Lahore: Notilal Banarsi Das, 1935, 1938.

Dedron, P., and J. Itard. *Mathematics and Mathematicians,* vols. 1 and 2. Translated by J.V. Field. London: Transworld, 1973.

Dershowitz, Nachum, and Edward M. Reingold. *Calendrical Calculations.* Cambridge, England: Cambridge University Press, 1997.

Dolan, Daniel T., and James Williamson. *Teaching Problem-Solving Strategies.* Menlo Park, CA: Addison-Wesley, 1983.

Dunham, William. *The Mathematical Universe.* New York: John Wiley & Sons, 1994.

Eves, Howard, W. *Mathematical Circles Revisited.* Boston: Prindle, Weber & Schmidt, 1971.

Fults, John Lee. *Magic Squares.* LaSalle, IL: Open Court, 1974.

# Bibliography


Gaines, Judith. "Preserving a Prank: Who'll Save the Smoot?" *The Boston Globe*, Saturday, January 14, 1989.

Gardner, Martin. *The Scientific American Book of Mathematical Puzzles & Diversions*. New York: Simon & Schuster, 1967.

Gardner, Martin. *The 2nd Scientific American Book of Mathematical Puzzles & Diversions*. New York: Simon & Schuster, 1961.

Gillings, Richard J. *Mathematics in the Time of the Pharaohs*. New York: Dover Publications, 1972.

Gullberg, Jan. *Mathematics from the Birth of Numbers*. New York: W.W. Norton, 1997.

Ifrah, Georges. *From One to Zero: A Universal History of Numbers*. New York: Viking, 1985.

*Information Please Almanac*, 1993, s.v. "perpetual calendar."

Karpinski, Louis Charles. *The History of Arithmetic*. Chicago: Rand McNally, 1925.

Kasner, Edward, and James R. Newman. "Pastimes of Past and Present Times" in James R. Newman. *The World of Mathematics,* vol. 4. New York: Simon & Schuster, 1966.

Katz, Victor J. *A History of Mathematics: An Introduction*. New York: HarperCollins, 1993.

Kenny, Margaret J. *The Incredible Pascal Triangle*. Chestnut Hill, MA: Boston College Press, 1976.

Knorr, Wilbur. "Techniques of Fractions in Ancient Egypt and Greece." *Historia Mathematica*, vol. 9, no. 2, May, 1982.

Martzloff, Jean-Claude. *A History of Chinese Mathematics*. New York: Springer-Verlag, 1997.

Martzloff, Jean-Claude. "π in the Sky" in *From Five Fingers to Infinity*. Edited by Frank Swetz. Chicago: Open Court, 1994.

Menninger, Karl. *Number Words and Number Symbols: A Cultural History of Numbers*. Translated by Paul Broneer. Cambridge, MA: MIT Press, 1969.

Meyer, C.D., and N.J. Rose. "A Pandect of Pi," *1985 Mathematical Calendar*. Raleigh, WV: Rome Press, 1984.

Moore, David S. "Probability: The Mathematics of Choice," *For All Practical Purposes: An Introduction to Contemporary Mathematics*. New York: W.H. Freeman, 1988.

Moran, Jim. *The Wonders of Magic Squares*. New York: Vintage Books, 1981.

Moseley, Maboth. *Irascible Genius: The Life of Charles Babbage*. Chicago: Henry Regnery, 1970.

Needham, Joseph, *Science and Civilisation in China*, vol. 3. Cambridge, England: Cambridge University Press, 1959.

Neugebauer, O. *The Exact Sciences in Antiquity*, 2nd ed. New York: Dover Publications, 1969.

Newman, Daisy. *A Procession of Friends*. Richmond, VA: Friends United Press, 1972

*Notable Mathematicians: From Ancient Times to the Present*. Edited by Robyn V. Young. Detroit: Gale Research, 1998.

Olivastro, Dominic. *Ancient Puzzles: Classic Brainteasers and Other Timeles Mathematical Games of the Last 10 Centuries*. New York: Bantam Books, 1993.

Pappas, Theoni. *The Joy of Mathematics*. San Carlos, CA: Wide World Publishing/Tetra, 1989.

Pappas, Theoni. *More Joy of Mathematics*. San Carlos, CA: Wide World Publishing/Tetra, 1991.

Pearcy, J.F.F., and K. Lewis. *Experiments in Mathematics Stage 2*. New York: Houghton Mifflin, 1966.

Perl, Teri. *Math Equals*. Menlo Park, CA: Addison-Wesley, 1978.

Perl, Teri. *Women and Numbers*. San Carlos, CA: Wide World Publishing/Tetra, 1993.

Peterson, Ivars. "Games Mathematicians Play," *Science News*, vol. 130, no. 12, September 20, 1986.

Peterson, Ivars. *Islands of Truth: A Mathematical Mystery Cruise*. New York: W.H. Freeman and Company, 1990.

Popp, Walter, translated by Maxim Bruckheimer. *History of mathematics: Topics for Schools*. London: Transworld Publishers Ltd., 1975.

Ranucci, E.R., and J.L. Teeters. *Creating Escher-Type Drawings.* Parsippnay, NJ: Creative Publications, 1977.

Ray, Joseph. *The Principles of Arithmetic, Analyzed and Practically Applied.* Cincinnati: Winthrop B. Smith, 1856.

Reimer, Luetta, and Wilbert Reimer. *Mathematicians are People, Too.* Parsippany, NJ: Dale Seymour Publications, 1990.

Reimer, Luetta, and Wilbert Reimer. *Mathematicians Are People, Too,* vol. two. Parsippany, NJ: Dale Seymour Publications, 1995.

Reimer, Wilbert, and Luetta Reimer. *Historical Connections in Mathematics.* Fresno, CA: AIMS Educational Foundation, 1992.

Saidan, A.S. "The Earliest Extant Arabic Arithmetic." *ISIS*, vol. 57, no. 190, 1966.

Seymour, Dale, and Jill Britton. *Introduction to Tessellations.* Parsippany, NJ: Dale Seymour Publications, 1989.

Seymour, Dale. *Visual Patterns in Pascal's Triangle.* Parsippany, NJ: Dale Seymour Publications, 1986.

Smith, David Eugene, and Yoshio Mikami. *A History of Japanese Mathematics.* LaSalle, IL: Open Court, 1914.

Smith, David Eugene. *A Sourcebook in Mathematics*, vol I. New York: Dover Publications, 1959.

Smith, David Eugene. *A History of Mathematics*, vols. I and II. New York: Dover Publications, 1958.

Straffin, Philip D., Jr. "Liu Hui and the First Golden Age of Chinese Mathematics," *Mathematics Magazine*, June, 1998.

Swetz, Frank J. *Capitalism & Arithmetic: The New Math of the 15th Century.* LaSalle, IL: Open Court, 1987.

Swetz, Frank J. *From Five Fingers to Infinity.* Chicago: Open Court, 1994.

Swetz, Frank J. "The Evolution of Mathematics in Ancient China," in *Mathematics Magazine*, vol. 52, no. 1, January, 1979.

Temple, Robert. *The Genius of China: 3,000 Years of Science, Discovery, and Invention.* New York: Simon & Schuster, 1986.

*The Catch Club or Merry Companions Being a Choice Collection of the Most Diverting Catches for Three and Four Voices.* Introduced by Joel Newman. New York: Da Capo Press, 1965.

*The New Encyclopaedia Britannica*, 15th ed., 1987, s.v. "calendar."

*The New Encyclopaedia Britannica*, 15th ed., 1987, s.v. "coins."

*The New Encyclopaedia Britannica*, 15th ed., 1987, s.v. "systems of weights and measures, in measurement and observation."

*Tower Puzzle.* Madison Project, Independent Exploration Material. Math Media Division, H&M Associates.

van der Waerden, B.L. *Geometry and Algebra in Ancient Civilizations.* Berlin: Springer-Verlag, 1983.

van der Waerden, B.L. *Science Awakening I: Egyptian, Babylonian, and Greek Mathematics.* Princeton, NJ: Scholar's Bookshelf, 1988.

van der Waerden, B.L. *Science Awakening I.* Translated by Arnold Dresden. New York: Oxford University Press, 1971.

Williams, Michael R. *A History of Computing Technology.* Englewood Cliffs, NJ: Prentice Hall, 1985.

Yan, Li, and Du Shiran: *Chinese Mathematics: A Concise History.* Translated by John N. Crossley and Anthony W. C. Lun. Oxford, England: Clarendon Press, 1987.

Zaslavsky, Claudia. *Africa Counts.* Boston: Prindle, Weber & Schmidt, 1973.

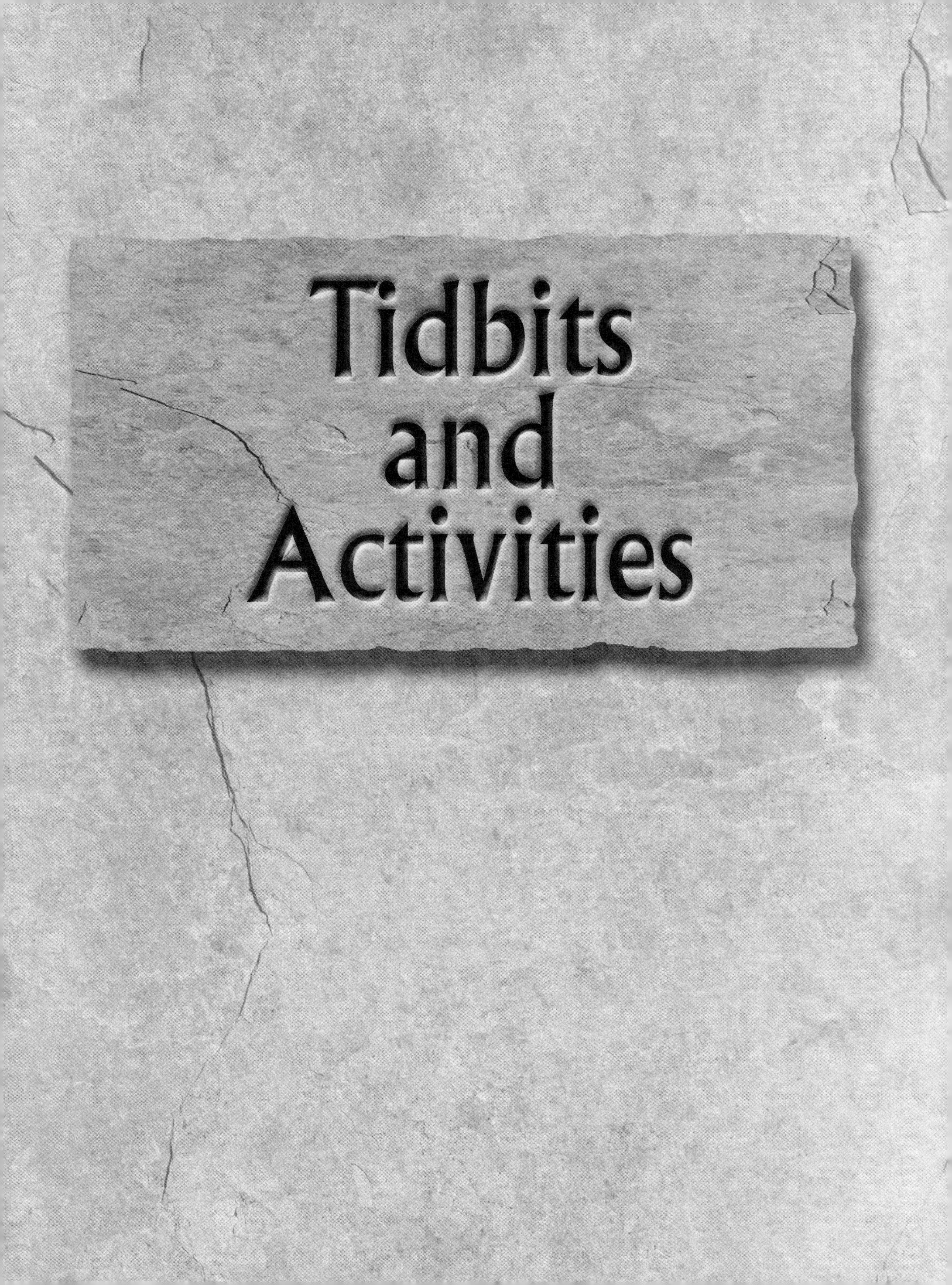
Tidbits
and
Activities

Name ______________________ Date ______________________

# Mathematical Signs

Just because someone makes up a symbol and uses it does not mean that it will be accepted immediately or accepted at all. You may have wondered when some of the math signs we use were invented. To find out, determine each number described in the years column. Then put the years in numerical order in the blanks in the facts column on page 79. All dates are after the year 1000.

**YEARS**

A. __ __ __ __

- The year is divisible by 9 but not by 2.
- The hundreds and tens digits are the same prime number.
- The number formed by the thousands and hundreds digits is not prime.

B. __ __ __ __

- The tens and ones digits form a prime number less than $6^2$ and greater than the fifth multiple of 6.
- The thousands and hundreds digits form a square number.

C. __ __ __ __

- The hundreds digit is half the tens digit.
- The sum of the hundreds and tens digits is 12.
- The ones digit is an odd square number not equal to the thousands digit.

D. __ __ __ __

- The year is divisible by 25, but is not a multiple of 10.
- The hundreds and ones digits are the same.
- The thousands and tens digits are consecutive.

E. __ __ __ __

- The number formed by the thousands and hundreds digits is prime.
- The hundreds digit is greater than $2^2$ and less than $3^2$.
- The ones digit has exactly 4 factors and is not a cube.
- The tens digit is neither positive nor negative.

F. __ __ __ __

- The hundreds and ones digits are each the third prime.
- The thousands and tens digits are unequal cubes.

Name ________________________ Date ________________________

Mathematical Signs (cont.)

G. __ __ __ __
- The year is the product of the third and fifth primes added to the square of 40.

H. __ __ __ __
- The year is 4 years after Wallis used the ∞ symbol.

**FACTS**

1. In __________, Johannes Widman invented the addition (+) and subtraction (–) signs to indicate surplus or deficits in business. It was 400 years before people started using them for addition and subtraction.

2. In __________, Christoff Rudolff invented the $\sqrt{\ }$ symbol for square root.

3. In __________ Robert Recorde chose = for the equal symbol because "no two things could be more equal." However, it was not adopted until the 18th century.

4. In __________, Simon Stevin wrote a book explaining the use of decimals to simplify computation with fractions. But he did not use the decimal point; it did not come into general use until the 17th century.

5. In __________, William Oughtred invented the × symbol for multiplication. Sixty-seven years later, Gottfried Leibniz recommended the raised dot for multiplication because the × symbol was confusing.

6. In __________, John Wallis proposed using the ∞ symbol for infinity. This had been the Roman symbol for 1,000 and the Greek symbol for 10,000.

7. In __________, Johann Heinrich Rahn published an algebra book in which he introduced the ÷ symbol for division. Nine years later, John Pell translated his book into English, so some people think Pell invented the ÷ symbol.

8. In __________, William Jones chose the Greek letter π to stand for the ratio of the circumference to the diameter of a circle. Often this was attributed to Euler.

Name ______________________ Date ______________________

Tidbit

# Oh, for the Good Old Days when Things Were Simpler

Marco Polo, the Venetian trader who traveled with his father and his uncle to China, brought back many extraordinary tales of life in China after his 24-year journey. Many of his tales were so fantastic that people had trouble believing him. He told and wrote of living and working in the court of the Mongolian ruler Kublai Khan. He told of a message system that could deliver messages all over the empire with a series of runners and riders who went from station to station. This was similar to the pony express that was used in the United States 600 years later. He told of paper currency when Europeans had only silver, gold, and lead coins. For a piece of paper to acquire the value of gold just by having printing on it seemed like an alchemist's dream. Even printing was unknown to the Europeans at that time. The Chinese had been printing since the ninth century, but the Europeans did not learn the printing process until the fifteenth century. He told of black stones that burned all night to produce heat. (We call them coal.)

Marco Polo used *millione* to describe the many people and the incredible wealth he saw in China. His fantastic tales were often thought of as tall tales, and he became known as "Marco of the Millions." He used the term *millione* to mean *many thousand*. During the fourteenth century, the Italian merchants started using millione for a thousand thousand. This was the first use of this term.

Just because the word *million* had been invented, it did not mean that everyone used it. In 1536, Adam Riese wrote a well-known arithmetic book in which he told how to read very large numbers. After writing one rather long number, he explained to his readers that it was:

> "six and eighty thousand thousand times a thousand / seven hundred thousand times a thousand / nine and eighty thousand times a thousand / three hundred thousand / five and twenty thousand / one hundred eight and seventy."

1. What was this one large number that Riese wrote? ______________________

2. How would we write that number in words today?

______________________

______________________

______________________

______________________

Name ______________________________ Date ______________________________

Oh, for the Good Old Days when Things Were Simpler (cont.)

Dividing the number into periods using commas, as we do today, was not done then. Riese advised dividing the number into "triads" by putting dots over the thousands place, millions place, billions place, and so on.

So when we write 2,345,678,002, Riese would have written $\dot{2}34\dot{5}67\dot{8}002$.

3. Write Riese's large number using his triad notation. ____________________

4. Which system do you think makes a number easier to read, our system of commas dividing periods or Riese's system of triads? Why?

______________________________________________________________

______________________________________________________________

Look at *The Period Names in the USA* closely. The numerical value of the Latin root does not correspond to the number of zeros; for example, a trillion has 12 zeros and "tri-" means 3; similarly, octillion has 27 zeros and "octo-" means 8. Look for the pattern.

5. If $n$ is the value of the Latin root, complete the rule to show how many zeros will be in the number. Try your rule. Does it always work?

   The number of zeros = ______________________________

**Bonus**

The name $10^{100}$ does not follow the pattern with the Latin roots. Why is it called a *googol?*

______________________________________________________________

______________________________________________________________

# PERIOD NAMES IN THE USA

| Name | Number of Zeros | Latin Root and Value |
|---|---|---|
| million | 6 | |
| billion | 9 | bi- (2) |
| trillion | 12 | tri- (3) |
| quadrillion | 15 | quater (4) |
| quintillion | 18 | quintus (5) |
| sextillion | 21 | sex (6) |
| septillion | 24 | septem (7) |
| octillion | 27 | octo (8) |
| nonillion | 30 | novem (9) |
| decillion | 33 | decem (10) |
| undecillion | 36 | undecim (11) |
| duodecillion | 39 | duodecim (12) |
| tredecillion | 42 | tredecim (13) |
| quattuordecillion | 45 | quattuordecim (14) |
| quindecillion | 48 | quindecim (15) |
| sexdecillion | 51 | sexdecim (16) |
| septendecillion | 54 | septendecim (17) |
| octodecillion | 57 | octodecim (18) |
| novemdecillion | 60 | novemdecim (19) |
| vigintillion | 63 | viginti (20) |
| trigintillion | 93 | triginta (30) |
| googol | 100 | |
| quadragintillion | 123 | quadrageni (40) |
| quinquagintillion | 153 | quinquaginta (50) |
| sexagintillion | 183 | sexaginta (60) |
| septuagintillion | 213 | septuaginta (70) |
| octogintillion | 243 | octoginta (80) |
| nonagintillion | 273 | nonaginta (90) |
| centillion | 303 | centum (100) |
| googolplex | googol | |

Name ______________________ Date ______________________

# Roman-Numeral Riddle

When Roman numerals were written the same way as letters in the Latin alphabet were written, people might hide a date in a sentence.

Here is a Roman-numeral riddle:

My cat Max likes vans.

1. What year is hidden in this sentence? ______________________

2. Choose a year that is important for you. Why did you choose this year?

   ______________________________________________

3. Write your special year in Roman numerals. ______________________

4. Write a Roman numeral riddle hiding your special year. Be sure that your riddle sentence includes all of the letters of your year in the order that they appear in your year. Be sure that no other letters that could be used when writing a number in Roman numerals is included in your sentence. Have another student try to solve your riddle.

   ______________________________________________

   ______________________________________________

# A Catch

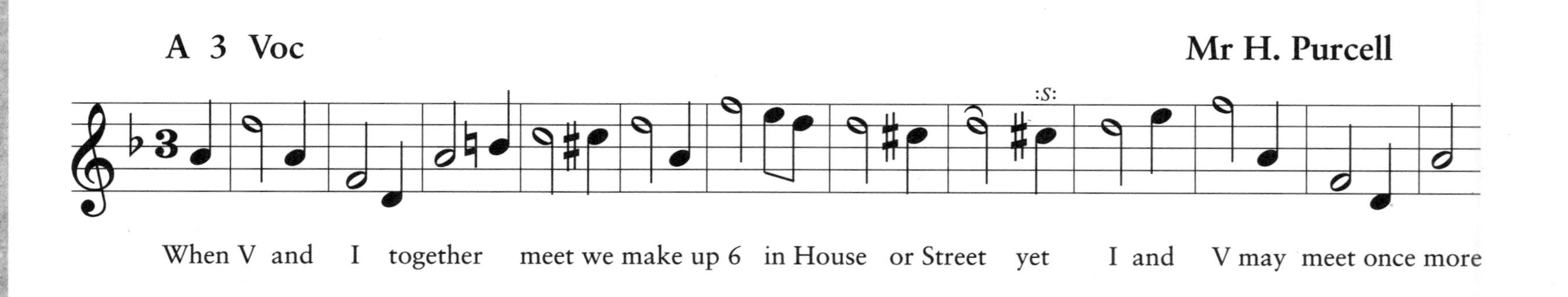
A 3 Voc
Mr H. Purcell
:S:
When V and I together meet we make up 6 in House or Street yet I and V may meet once more

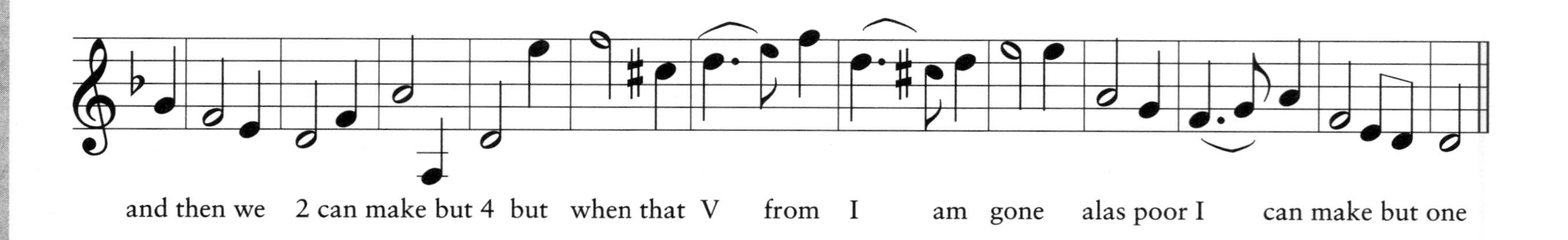
and then we 2 can make but 4 but when that V from I am gone alas poor I can make but one

Name ______________________ Date ______________________

# Say What You Mean and Mean What You Say

Have you ever said, "You KNOW what I meant!"?

How can you tell how much something costs if you are told that "it costs two fifty"? Does it cost \$2.50, \$250, or \$250,000?

About 2,000 years ago, Livia did not say exactly what she meant. As a result, her relative Galba did not receive most of her inheritance. The ancient Romans did not have symbols for numbers greater than 100,000. One way that they wrote large numbers was to put a $\overline{\ \ }$ over the number. This symbol meant to multiply by 1,000. A $\sqcap$ around a number meant to multiply by 100,000.

Give the value of each number.

**1.** $\overline{\text{X}}$ __________ **2.** $\overline{|\text{X}|}$ __________ **3.** $\overline{\text{D}}$ __________ **4.** $\overline{|\text{D}|}$ __________

**5.** $\overline{\text{C}}$ __________ **6.** $\overline{|\text{C}|}$ __________ **7.** $\overline{\text{XX}}$ __________ **8.** $\overline{|\text{XX}|}$ __________

**9.** $\overline{|\text{CXXX}|}$ MMLV ______________ **10.** $\overline{|\text{MMM}|}\,\overline{\text{CCC}}$ ______________

Livia was the mother of Emperor Tiberius. Livia and Tiberius were not on the best of terms both when she wrote her will and when she died. She left sestertium quingenties to Galba. After Galba was paid, whatever else was left was to go to Tiberius. *Sestertium quingenties* means "of sesterces 500 times." A sesterce was a silver or bronze coin worth $\frac{1}{4}$ denarius. Two thousand years ago, the Romans did not have the words or the symbols for numbers like 100,000, so they would say "times" and mean "times 100,000." So Livia meant $\overline{|\text{D}|}$ when she left money to Galba. However, Tiberius gave Galba only $\overline{\text{D}}$ sesterces, because Livia did not say exactly what she meant!

**11.** Out of how many sesterces did Tiberius cheat Galba? ______________

**12.** If a denarius was worth 10 asses, how many asses was one sesterce worth? ______________

**13.** Originally an as was worth 1 pound of copper, but it was devalued over the years until it was worth only $\frac{1}{2}$ ounce of copper. How many pounds of copper did Galba lose? (Use the lesser value for an as.) ______________

**14.** Today, copper sells for \$0.92 per pound. How much did Livia's not saying exactly what she meant cost Galba at today's prices? ______________

Name ______________________ Date ______________________

# Olden-Days Math from India

Here is a problem from the Hindu mathematician Sridara. It is in his book *Trisatika*, written about 1,250 years ago in India.

"What is the result when half, one-fourth of one-fourth, one divided by one-third, half plus half of itself, and one-third diminished by half of itself, are added together?"

When this problem is written in the Hindu notation of 750 for fractions using our symbols for numbers, it looks something like this:

| 1<br>2 | 1<br>4 | 1<br>4 | 1<br>1<br>3 | 1<br>2 | 1<br>3 |
|---|---|---|---|---|---|
| | | | | 1<br>2 | •1<br>2 |

The Hindus wrote fractions without a dividing bar. For $\frac{3}{4}$, they wrote $\boxed{\begin{matrix}3\\4\end{matrix}}$ or $\begin{matrix}3\\4\end{matrix}$.

1. Carefully examine the wording in the problem and then look at the way the Hindus wrote it. What do you think the dot in front of a number means?

   ______________________________________________

2. In this problem, what do you think $\boxed{\begin{matrix}1\\1\\3\end{matrix}}$ means?

   ______________________________________________

3. Carefully reread Sridara's problem and write it in our notation.

   ______________________________________________

   ______________________________________________

4. Solve the problem. ______________

Name ______________________ Date ______________________

Tidbit

# The Egyptian Year

Legend says that the ancient Egyptians initially had a 360-day year with 12 months of 30 days each. When the sky goddess Nut secretly married the earth god Geb, the sun god Re was furious. In a rage, Re cast a spell on Nut preventing her from giving birth during any month of the year. Nut was extremely sad and went to her magician friend Thoth, who was the protector of the moon and ruler of time and the calendar. To find out how he helped her by playing dice with the moon, solve the following problems and use the solutions to decode the answer on the next page.

| Letter | No. | Problem | Answer | Letter | No. | Problem | Answer |
|---|---|---|---|---|---|---|---|
| T | 1. | $\frac{3}{4} \div 8$ | $\frac{3}{32}$ | ___ | 14. | $8 - \frac{3}{4}$ | ___ |
| ___ | 2. | $\frac{2}{3} \div \frac{8}{9}$ | ___ | ___ | 15. | $\frac{24}{25} \times \frac{5}{9}$ | ___ |
| ___ | 3. | $\frac{8}{9} \div \frac{2}{3}$ | ___ | ___ | 16. | $\frac{36}{99} \times \frac{22}{39}$ | ___ |
| ___ | 4. | $\frac{3}{8} \times \frac{5}{9}$ | ___ | ___ | 17. | $5 \div 8$ | ___ |
| ___ | 5. | $\frac{3}{8} \div \frac{5}{9}$ | ___ | ___ | 18. | $6 \times 1\frac{2}{3}$ | ___ |
| ___ | 6. | $\frac{5}{9} \div \frac{3}{8}$ | ___ | ___ | 19. | $6 \div 1\frac{2}{3}$ | ___ |
| ___ | 7. | $1\frac{2}{3} \times 4$ | ___ | ___ | 20. | $1\frac{2}{3} \div 6$ | ___ |
| ___ | 8. | $1\frac{2}{3} \div 4$ | ___ | ___ | 21. | $\frac{2}{3} - \frac{5}{8}$ | ___ |
| ___ | 9. | $4 \div 1\frac{2}{3}$ | ___ | ___ | 22. | $\frac{2}{3} \div \frac{5}{8}$ | ___ |
| ___ | 10. | $4 + 1\frac{2}{3}$ | ___ | ___ | 23. | $\frac{5}{8} \div \frac{2}{3}$ | ___ |
| ___ | 11. | $8 \times \frac{3}{4}$ | ___ | ___ | 24. | $\frac{5}{8} + \frac{2}{3}$ | ___ |
| ___ | 12. | $8 \div \frac{3}{4}$ | ___ | ___ | 25. | $1\frac{1}{2} \div 3$ | ___ |
| ___ | 13. | $\frac{2}{3} \times \frac{8}{9}$ | ___ | ___ | 26. | $3 \div 1\frac{1}{2}$ | ___ |

A. $3\frac{3}{5}$
B. $\frac{5}{12}$
C. $\frac{5}{24}$
D. $1\frac{1}{15}$
E. 6
F. $1\frac{7}{24}$
G. $2\frac{2}{5}$
H. $\frac{5}{18}$
I. $\frac{3}{4}$
J. $7\frac{1}{4}$
K. $\frac{16}{27}$
L. $\frac{5}{8}$
M. $\frac{1}{2}$
N. $10\frac{2}{3}$
O. $\frac{8}{15}$
P. 10
Q. $6\frac{2}{3}$
R. $\frac{15}{16}$
S. $1\frac{1}{3}$
T. $\frac{3}{32}$
U. $\frac{27}{40}$
V. 2
W. $1\frac{13}{27}$
X. $5\frac{2}{3}$
Y. $\frac{8}{39}$
Z. $\frac{1}{24}$

Name ______________________ Date ______________________

The Egyptian Year (cont.)

1(T) 20 15 1(T) 20 / 6 15 12 / 1(T) 20 11 / 22 2 4 11 / 9 19 25 11

19 12 22 / 19 3 / 20 2 3 / 18 23 2 21 11 / 25 19 22 11 / 1(T) 20 11

25 15 15 12 / 9 2 26 11 / 20 2 25 $\frac{1}{72}$ 15 24 / 20 11 23 / 17 2 9 20 1(T).

6 2 1(T) 20 / 1(T) 20 2 3 / 17 2 9 20 1(T) / 1(T) 20 15 1(T) 20 / 25 19 22 11 5

22 19 16 3. 1(T) 20 11 3 11 / 22 19 16 3 / 22 2 22 / 12 15 1(T)

19 18 18 11 19 23 / 15 12 / 1(T) 20 11 / 4 19 17 11 12 22 19 23, 8 5 1(T)

6 11 23 11 / 19 22 22 11 22 / 15 12 / 19 1(T) / 1(T) 20 11 / 11 12 22

15 24 / 1(T) 20 11 / 16 11 19 23. 12 5 1(T) / 5 3 11 22 / 1(T) 20 11 3 11

22 19 16 3 / 6 20 2 4 20 / 6 11 23 11 / 5 12 13 12 15 6 12 1(T) 15

23 11 / 1(T) 15 / 9 2 26 11 / 8 2 23 1(T) 20 / 1(T) 15 / 24 2 26 11

9 15 22 3 / 19 12 22 / 9 15 22 22 11 3 3 11 3. 1(T) 20 2 3 / 2 3

6 20 16 / 1(T) 20 11 / 11 9 16 18 1(T) 2 19 12 / 4 19 17 11 12 22 19 23

20 19 22 12 / 25 15 12 1(T) 20 3 / 15 24 / 1(T) 20 2 23 1(T) 16 / 22 19 16 3

6 2 1(T) 20 / 19 12 / 11 10 1(T) 23 19 5 / 20 15 17 2 22 19 16 3

19 22 22 11 22 / 15 12 / 19 1(T) / 1(T) 20 11 / 11 12 22.

27. How many days is $\frac{1}{72}$ of the initial Egyptian year? __________

28. How long was the Egyptian year after the help of Thoth? __________

29. Look up how long one solar year is. Is the Egyptian year close enough to being the "right" length? __________

30. What would happen to the seasons and holidays after 100 Egyptian years?

______________________________________________

Name ______________________ Date ______________________

# Egyptian Hours

Around 1300 B.C.E., the ancient Egyptians made the contribution of dividing the day into 24 hours beginning at midnight. But their 24 hours were not exactly the same as our 24 hours. They decided that the day was 12 hours long and the night was 12 hours long. So the length of the individual hours varied with the season and the time of day. Our use of hours of equal length is a Hellenistic variation on an Egyptian idea.

1. Check yesterday's and today's newspapers for the time of sunrise and sunset.

   Sunset yesterday ______ Sunrise today ______ Sunset today ______

2. How long was the night last night? ______

   How long will the day be today? ______

3. In "Egyptian hours," how many minutes long was each hour last night? Round to the nearest minute. ______

   How many minutes long will each hour be today? Round to the nearest minute. ______

4. What happens to the length of the day and night on the vernal equinox or autumnal equinox?

   ______________________________

   ______________________________

5. What would predict to be the length of each hour during the day on the equinox that you looked up? ______

6. What would you predict to happen with the Egyptian hours on the winter solstice?

   ______________________________

   ______________________________

Name ______________________ Date ______________________

Tidbit

# The Perfect Bride

In some Jewish, Moslem, and Greek writings of the Middle Ages, individual letters of the alphabet were assigned numerical values. The value of a word or phrase could be calculated by adding these numerical values. These values are called *chronograms*. Sometimes chronograms were used for religious interpretations; for example, in Greek the words *God, Holy,* and *Good* all have the value 284. Sometimes people would attribute religious significance to this.

| GOD | HOLY | GOOD |
|---|---|---|
| Θ Ε Ο Σ | Α Γ Ι Ο Σ | Α Γ Α Θ Ο Σ |
| 9 5 70 200 | 1 3 10 70 200 | 1 3 1 9 70 200 |
| 284 | 284 | 284 |

In Morocco, poets, historians, and biographers used chronograms to commemorate special occasions. To have the numerical value of the sentence equal the date required great imagination.

عام "حل بيت السعد بدر جمالي"

YEAR: "THE FULL MOON OF MY BEAUTY CAME INTO THE CHAMBER OF HAPPINESS."

ح ل ب ي ت ال س ع د ب د ر ج م ا ل ي

10 30 1 40 3 200 4 2 4 70 300 30 1 400 10 2 30 8

1145

Three dots over a Hebrew word indicates that the word is a chronogram. These examples were found on a Jewish gravestone in Toledo, Spain, dating from the year 5144 on the Jewish calendar.

שנת הײנה אין אב

2 1 50 10 1 5 50 10 10 5 YEAR

YEAR: "WE ARE LEFT FATHERLESS"

144

Pretend that the letters in our alphabet have the numerical values given below.

| | | | | | | |
|---|---|---|---|---|---|---|
| a 1 | e 5 | i 9 | m 40 | q 80 | u 300 | y 700 |
| b 2 | f 6 | j 10 | n 50 | r 90 | v 400 | z 800 |
| c 3 | g 7 | k 20 | o 60 | s 100 | w 500 | |
| d 4 | h 8 | l 30 | p 70 | t 200 | x 600 | |

1. What is your full given name? ______________
2. What is the numerical value of your full name? ______________
3. What 5-letter word can you find that has the greatest possible value? ______________
4. What 5-letter word can you find that has the least possible value? ______________
5. What word can you find that has a value close to 1,000? ______________

Name ______________________ Date ______________________

The Perfect Bride (cont.)

A number is said to be ***perfect*** if it equals the sum of its proper factors. The proper factors are all the factors of the number except the number itself. For example, 6 is perfect because its proper factors are 1, 2, and 3, and 1 + 2 + 3 = 6.

**6.** What is the perfect number between 25 and 35? ______________

A number is said to be ***deficient*** if the sum of its proper factors is less than it and ***abundant*** if the sum of its proper factors is greater than it. For example:

- 20 is abundant because its proper factors are 1, 2, 4, 5, and 10; and 1 + 2 + 4 + 5 + 10 = 22 and 22 > 20.
- 21 is deficient because its proper factors are 1, 3, and 7; and 1 + 3 + 7 = 11 and 11 < 21.

**7.** Classify each number as abundant (A) or deficient (D).

**a.** 30 ______ **b.** 31 ______ **c.** 32 ______ **d.** 33 ______

**e.** 34 ______ **f.** 35 ______ **g.** 36 ______ **h.** 37 ______

**8.** Can a prime number be abundant? Explain your answer.

______________________________________________

**9.** Do you think most numbers are perfect, deficient, or abundant? Why?

______________________________________________

**10.** What is the numerical value of your first name? Is it perfect, deficient, or abundant? ______________

**11.** What does *amicable* mean? ______________________________

Two numbers are said to ***amicable*** if each is equal to the sum of the proper factors of the other. For example: 1,184 = 1 + 2 + 5 + 10 + 11 + 22 + 55 + 110 + 121 + 242 + 605 = the sum of the proper factors of 1,210, and 1,210 = 1 + 2 + 4 + 8 + 16 + 32 + 37 + 74 + 48 + 296 + 592 = the sum of the proper factors of 1,184. This pair of amicable numbers was discovered by a 16-year-old schoolboy, Nicolò Paganini, in 1866.

**12.** There is a legend about a medieval prince whose name had a numerical value of 284. It just so happens that 284 is half of a pair of amicable numbers. The prince wanted a bride whose name would have the numerical value of the other half of this pair. He felt this would guarantee him Heaven's blessing of a happy marriage. What is the numerical value of his bride's name? ______________

Name ______________________________ Date ______________________________

# Prime-Formula Search

Ever since Euclid proved more than 2,300 years ago that the list of primes is infinitely long, mathematicians have looked for ways to find the prime numbers. One idea was to find a formula that would generate all of the prime numbers.

1. Try the formula: $2^n - 1$ to see if it will generate primes. Let $n = 1, 2, 3, 4, 5, 6, 7$. Decide whether your answer is prime in each case. For example, for $n = 1$: $2^1 - 1 = 2 - 1 = 1$; 1 is not prime.

   **a.** $n = 2$ ________ **b.** $n = 3$ ________ c. $n = 4$ ________ **d.** $n = 5$ ________
   e. $n = 6$ ________ **f.** $n = 7$ ________

   **g.** Which values of $n$ gave answers for $2^n - 1$ that were prime numbers? ________________

   **h.** Now try $n = 11$. Is your answer prime? If not, what are the factors of your answer? ________________

Any primes that $2^n - 1$ generates are called *Mersenne numbers* after the seventeenth-century monk Marin Mersenne, who studied number theory and met with and wrote to all the famous mathematicians in Europe when he was alive. You should have discovered that his formula does not always give prime numbers.

2. Try the formula $n^2 + n + 17$.

   **a.** $n = 1$ ________ **b.** $n = 2$ ________ c. $n = 3$ ________ **d.** $n = 4$ ________
   e. $n = 5$ ________ **f.** $n = 6$ ________ **g.** $n = 7$ ________
   **h.** Which values of $n$ gave answers for $n^2 + n + 17$ that were prime numbers? ________________
   **i.** Now try $n = 16$. Is your answer prime? If not, what are the factors of your answer? ________________

3. Try the formula $n^2 + n + 41$.

   **a.** $n = 1$ ________ **b.** $n = 2$ ________ c. $n = 3$ ________ **d.** $n = 4$ ________
   e. $n = 5$ ________ **f.** $n = 6$ ________ **g.** $n = 7$ ________
   **h.** Which values of $n$ gave answers for $n^2 + n + 41$ that were prime numbers?

4. When you investigated $n^2 + n + 17$, you should have found that $n = 16$ did not give you a prime answer. In fact, all values of $n$ less than 16 will give you prime answers. Predict what value of $n$ will *not* give you a prime for $n^2 + n + 41$. Check your prediction. ________________

Mathematicians have searched unsuccessfully for one formula that would generate primes. Leonhard Euler (1707–1783) investigated $n^2 + n + 41$. If you substitute all of the numbers from 1 to 100, you will get primes 86 times.

Name ______________________ Date ______________________

# Women in the History of Mathematics

Solve the following puzzles. Insert your answers in the appropriate places to complete the ministories about some female mathematicians.

A. _ _ _ _

- The hundreds digit is a cube but not a square and 1 greater than the tens digit.
- The ones digit is an even square.
- The thousands digit is neither prime nor composite.

B. _ _ _ _

- The hundreds, tens, and ones digits are decreasing consecutive numbers.
- The thousands digit is a cube.
- The hundreds digit is a different cube.

C. _

- The number is the odd prime between the two least square numbers.

D. _ _

- The number is 3 less than the square of the third prime.

E. _ _ _ _

- The number is 45 more than the square of the greatest prime number less than 45.

F. _ _ _ _

- This year has no digit that is a prime.
- The tens digit equals the hundreds digit, and their sum is a square number.
- The sum of the tens and thousands digits is a square number.
- The sum of the tens and ones digits equals the hundreds digit.

G. _ _

- The sum of the digits is the third prime.
- The ones digit is 1 less than an odd square.

H. _

- The number is the least even cube.

Name ______________________ Date ______________________



I. __ __ __ __

- The sum of the thousands and ones digits is 1 less than the hundreds digit.
- No digit is prime.
- The tens digit equals the hundreds digit, and their sum is a square number.

J. __ __ __ __

- This year is divisible by 9 and 6, but not by 4.
- The hundreds digit is odd and has exactly 3 factors.
- The tens digit is less than the ones digit.

K. __ __

- The digits are consecutive, and their sum is 15.
- The tens digit is prime.

L. __ __

- This number is the product of the least even square number and the least prime greater than 10.

M. __ __ __ __

- The hundreds digit of this year is a square number.
- The fourth prime squared equals the number formed by the tens and ones digits.
- The number formed by the thousands and hundreds digits is a prime greater than 11.

In (A) __ __ __ __, Gottingen University in Germany awarded Sonya Kovalevskaya the first Ph.D. in mathematics given to a woman. As a young woman, Sonya wanted to study higher math but there were no universities open to women in Russia. In fact, there were very few universities anywhere that she could attend. She had to marry to leave Russia because the Russian law at that time would not allow a female to leave the country without the written permission of her husband or father. After earning her degree, she returned to Russia but could not get a job. Ten years later, she was hired to teach at the University of Stockholm in Sweden as the first woman professor. She did research in algebra and differential equations.

In (B) __ __ __ __, Charlotte Angas Scott started attending Girton College, the only college in England open to women. Girton was (C) __ miles from Cambridge University and (D) __ __ of the Cambridge professors would allow women to listen to their lectures from behind a screen. However, women attending lectures had to be chaperoned until (E) __ __ __ __. If women were unaccompanied, they could be arrested and sent to a special prison for prostitutes and "suspected prostitutes." In (F) __ __ __ __, Scott took the (G) __ __ -hour math exam at Cambridge and did as well as the (H) __th man; but women could not receive degrees nor could they be present or have their names mentioned in the awards ceremony. During the ceremony, when the (H) __th man's name was to be read, the male undergraduates shouted "Scott of Girton." For many years, Scott was the math department chair at Bryn Mawr College. Her textbook on analytic geometry was used for more than 30 years.

In (I) __ __ __ __, when Winifred Edgerton received her degree from Columbia University, she became the first woman to earn a Ph.D. in mathematics from an American university.

In (J) __ __ __ __ at the age of (K) __ __, Christine Ladd-Franklin received her Ph.D. in mathematics from Johns Hopkins University. This was (L) __ __ years after completing her dissertation. She had to wait all those years because at the time she earned her degree, Johns Hopkins did not give them to women. Ironically, the university had not only allowed her to attend classes but had given her a fellowship to help pay the tuition. She was known for her work on symbolic logic and the optics of color vision.

Before (M) __ __ __ __, no black woman had earned a Ph.D. in mathematics. That year, Marjorie Lee Browne was awarded her Ph.D. from the University of Michigan and Evelyn Boyd Granville was awarded hers from Yale. Granville taught college courses and worked in the space industry. Browne was a college professor.

Name ______________________ Date ______________________

# "Calculators"

Solve the following equations to find the value of each variable. Then use your answers to fill in the lettered blanks below to complete the story. For example, the value of the variable *a* matches the blank (*a*). Do your work on a separate piece of paper.

| | | | |
|---|---|---|---|
| $m^3 = j$ | $e = q^2 + 9j$ | $r - 1906 = h$ | $gy = w$ |
| $32y = 160$ | $s + 1 = t$ | $g + l + m + z = j$ | $x + y = d$ |
| $u + 1 = v$ | $10j = k$ | $b - n = g$ | $t + u = 3655$ |
| $c = x = w = \sqrt{100}$ | $a - 150 = 1492$ | $v + g = o$ | $3c = f$ |
| $h - 1776 = c + j$ | $\frac{v}{3} = 611$ | $g + d = n$ | $j - m = i$ |
| $cx + q = p$ | $4c = q$ | $l = z$ | $2a + 416 = r$ |

| | | | |
|---|---|---|---|
| *a* = _____ | *b* = _____ | *c* = _____ | *d* = _____ |
| *e* = _____ | *f* = _____ | *g* = _____ | *h* = _____ |
| *i* = _____ | *j* = _____ | *k* = _____ | *l* = _____ |
| *m* = _____ | *n* = _____ | *o* = _____ | *p* = _____ |
| *q* = _____ | *r* = _____ | *s* = _____ | *t* = _____ |
| *u* = _____ | *v* = _____ | *w* = _____ | *x* = _____ |
| *y* = _____ | *z* = _____ | | |

What would you do if you saw your father staying up until 2 or 3 A.M. night after night doing paper-and-pencil calculations for his next day's work? You would probably suggest that he buy a calculator; or you might even buy him one as a present. Unfortunately, in (*a*) __ __ __ __, Blaise Pascal could not suggest that because there were no calculators. At the age of (*b*) __ __, Blaise solved the problem by building one! Blaise had trouble marketing his calculators because the average person could not afford them. The wealthy people did not need them because they had their servants to do the work. Pascal probably sold only (*c*) __ __ or (*d*) __ __.

In (*e*) __ __ __ __, only (*f*) __ __ years after Pascal built his "Pascaline," Gottfried Leibniz invented the "Stepped Reckoner." Leibniz was the first western mathematician to study binary numbers and to think of building a calculator that used base (*g*) __; but he never did actually build a binary calculator.

Name ________________________ Date ________________________

"Calculators" (cont.)

Until recently, a *computer* was a person who computed answers. During World War II, people needed to calculate the thousands of possible trajectories for weapons. Computers were developed during World War II to create these trajectory tables more quickly and with greater accuracy.

Human computers have been around for centuries. Any banker, navigator, astronomer, engineer, or scientist who worked with numbers relied upon tables that had been hand-calculated. In (*h*) __ __ __ __, as part of the development of the metric system, the new French government wanted new tables drawn up. They hired G. Riche de Prony who employed (*i*) __ mathematicians who developed the formulas for the (*j*) __ foremen who supervised (*k*) __ __ human computers. Many of these computers were hairdressers, unemployed because powdered wigs had gone out of fashion during the French Revolution. After (*l*) __ years, they produced (*m*) __ handwritten copies of the *Tables du Cadastre* that filled (*n*) __ __ volumes.

The accuracy of mathematical tables was important. For example, the errors in the tables in the British *Nautical Almanac* were said to be the cause of ships lost at sea or run aground. In (*o*) __ __ __ __, a survey of one scientist's library listed (*p*) __ __ __ books of tables. When (*q*) __ __ these books were checked, (*r*) __ __ __ __ errors were found.

After talking with the astronomer John Herschel about the calculating of tables, Charles Babbage thought of building a steam-powered calculating machine. He had been impressed by the division of labor used by de Prony and was farsighted in his ideas about manufacturing. By (*s*) __ __ __ __, Babbage had a working model of his calculating machine, the "Difference Engine." In (*t*) __ __ __ __, he started building the full-sized model. He could not go to the hardware store and pick up parts, nor could he order the parts to be specially made at a factory as someone might do today. So, he hired someone to make the parts. However, the available tools were inadequate, so he had to first design new tools to make the parts. This greatly increased his cost and time. In (*u*) __ __ __ __, he had enough parts completed to have the Difference Engine partially assembled and working. He then realized that he could build an "Analytical Engine" which could do everything that the Difference Engine could do and more. He stopped work on his original project and began his new one. In (*v*) __ __ __ __, Ada Augusta Lovelace met Babbage. She worked with him and wrote an explanation of how the Analytical Engine worked and a description of programming techniques using punch cards similar to the ones used by the Jacquard looms. The first computer programmer signed her work A.A.L. to hide the fact that she was a woman. Babbage never finished either machine. If he had finished the Difference Engine , it would have been (*w*) __ __ feet by (*x*) __ __ feet by (*y*) __ feet and would have weighed (*z*) __ tons!

Name ______________________ Date ______________________

Tidbit

# Coins

The Egyptian King Croesus, who reigned from 560 to 546 B.C.E., issued pieces of metal marked with their value to be used for exchange—namely coins. The Chinese started using coins at about the same time and for 2,500 years did not make many changes in the design. In Europe, coins varied by the country and over time. Over the years, there were problems with coins; some less-than-honest people would chip off pieces, for example. As a result, it was not unusual for coins to be weighed by various money changers. In the Venetian Republic in 1321, laws were passed to inspect the money changers, and someone could lose a right hand for debasing coins.

Early coins did not have dates on them. Europeans were slow to use what we call Hindu-Arabic numerals for official business; so it is not surprising that dates on coins written in Hindu-Arabic numerals did not appear until 51 years after the first coin using Roman numerals appeared in Aachen, Germany.

Use the clues below to figure out when England, France, Germany, Italy, Scotland, Sweden, and Switzerland first put dates on their coins using Hindu-Arabic numerals.

- England's, Italy's, and Scotland's years were in the sixteenth century.
- England's, France's, and Scotland's years were odd numbers.
- England's year is divisible by 3.
- Neither Sweden's nor Germany's year was the first.
- Germany's year is divisible by 8.

| | Year | Country | | Year | Country |
|---|---|---|---|---|---|
| 1. | 1424 | ______________ | 5. | 1534 | ______________ |
| 2. | 1448 | ______________ | 6. | 1549 | ______________ |
| 3. | 1478 | ______________ | 7. | 1551 | ______________ |
| 4. | 1485 | ______________ | | | |

8. You are at a flea market and a dealer offers you an old Roman coin at a bargain price. The coin looks really old and used, but you're not sure whether it really is as old as the dealer claims. He explains that you can tell it is a really an old Roman coin because it has the date XLIX B.C.E. on it. Do you buy the coin? Explain your decision.

______________________________________________________________

______________________________________________________________

Name ______________________ Date ______________________

# Firsts in Math Books

For each of the following "firsts," use the clues on page 100 to figure out the name of the book, the author, and the date.

**First place goes to. . . .**

1. Published in Mexico, this was the first book with math content published in the Western Hemisphere.

   Author: ______________________ Date: ____________

   Title: ______________________________________

2. Published in Belgium, this book was the first to give a complete explanation of how to compute with decimals.

   Author: ______________________ Date: ____________

   Title: ______________________________________

3. This book receives two first-place prizes; it was the first book on algebra written in English and the first book to use "=" for an equal sign.

   Author: ______________________ Date: ____________

   Title: ______________________________________

4. The Chinese Emperor Gaozong made this the first required math textbook; after studying it for seven years, if you passed the test on it, you qualified to be a low-ranking official.

   Author: ______________________ Date: ____________

5. Written more than 1,000 years before it was mass-printed, this book became the first printed textbook in recorded Chinese history. This is the first book in the world to show how to systematically compute with fractions.

   Date mass-printed: ________ Title: ______________________

6. This book had been written almost 2,000 years earlier than when it was brought to China and it is still in use today (in updated versions). It was the first western book translated into Chinese by the first Jesuit missionary to China, Matteo Ricci, and recorded by Xú Guangqi.

   Author: ______________________ Date: ____________

   Title: ______________________________________

Name ______________________ Date ______________________

Firsts in Math Books (cont.)

These are the dates, not necessarily in the same order as they occur in the answers: 656, 1084, 1556, 1557, 1585, and 1607

These are the authors and their books, not necessarily in the same order as they occur in the answers:

Euclid, *Elements*

Juan Diez Freyle, *Summario de las Quentas de Plata y Ore*

*Nine Chapters on the Mathematical Art*

Simon Stevin, *La Thiende*

*Ten Mathematical Manuals*

Robert Recorde, *The Whetstone of Witte*

**Clues**

- The earliest and the latest books on this list were printed in China.
- Recorde, Stevin, and Freyle all authored books in the sixteenth century.
- 428 years before the first printed textbook, which had nine chapters, this book (really a collection of manuals) was required to be studied by anyone who wanted to become a government official.
- Recorde wrote an algebra book while Stevin wrote about decimals.
- Recorde's book was written before Stevin's and after Freyle's.
- The most recent book on this list is actually a translation of a book that was written 1900 years earlier by a Greek in Alexandria, Egypt.

| | Euclid | Freyle | Nine Chapters | Stevin | 10 Math Manuals | Recorde | 656 | 1084 | 1556 | 1557 | 1585 | 1607 |
|---|---|---|---|---|---|---|---|---|---|---|---|---|
| **1.** Mexico | | | | | | | | | | | | |
| **2.** Decimals, Belgium | | | | | | | | | | | | |
| **3.** Algebra, = | | | | | | | | | | | | |
| **4.** Required math textbook | | | | | | | | | | | | |
| **5.** First printed textbook | | | | | | | | | | | | |
| **6.** First book translated into Chinese | | | | | | | | | | | | |
| 656 | | | | | | | | | | | | |
| 1084 | | | | | | | | | | | | |
| 1556 | | | | | | | | | | | | |
| 1557 | | | | | | | | | | | | |
| 1585 | | | | | | | | | | | | |
| 1607 | | | | | | | | | | | | |

Name ______________________ Date ______________________

# The More Things Change, the More They Stay the Same

If you lived in the eighth or ninth century in Europe and wanted to be a member of the clergy or a government worker, you would study from the book *Propositions for Sharpening Youthful Minds*, by Alcuin of York. Some of the problems in that book sound similar to problems students are asked to solve today.

1. *789 version* A man must ferry across a river a wolf, a goat, and a head of cabbage. The available boat, however, can carry only the man and one other thing. The goat cannot be left alone with the cabbage, nor the wolf with the goat. How should the man ferry his three items across the river?

   ______________________

   ______________________

2. *1983 version* A family of four wants to cross a river. Their raft can hold at most 100 kilograms. The father weighs 85 kg, the mother weighs 54 kg, the son weighs 45 kg, and the daughter weighs 40 kg. How can they cross the river?

   ______________________

   ______________________

3. *1983 version* Three girls received a quarter each to spend for candy. The candy store contained lollipops at 3 for a nickel, licorice sticks at 4 for a nickel, and cinnamon bears at 1 cent each. Each girl ended up with a different selection of candy, but each spent her entire quarter. Each girl received exactly 20 pieces of candy. What were their selections?

   ______________________

   ______________________

4. *789 version* A certain master of a household has 100 people in his service to whom he proposes to distribute 100 bushels of corn: 3 bushels per man, 2 bushels per woman, and $\frac{1}{2}$ bushel per child. Can anyone say how many men, women, and children there were?

   ______________________

   ______________________

Name ________________________ Date ________________________

# Noah's Descendants

If you were a student in school 175 years ago instead of today, you might have used *The Scholar's Arithmetic*, by Jacob Willets (Poughkeepsie, New York, 1817), as your math book while you sat on your hard bench in the local one-room schoolhouse. You probably would have been assigned this problem. You have a calculator to help you, while the students who first worked on this problem did not.

1. If the posterity of Noah, which consisted of 6 persons at the flood, increased so as to double their number in 20 years, how many inhabitants were in the world 2 years before the death of Shem, who lived 502 years after the flood?

   ________________________

2. Problem 1 is one that might have been solved using a table. Write your own problem that could be solved using a table. Solve your problem. Be sure that your problem also has to do with families—past, present, or future.

   ________________________

   ________________________

   ________________________

   ________________________

   ________________________

Name ______________________________ Date ______________________________

# Greenleaf's National Arithmetic

If you lived 130 years ago and went to school in New York City or Philadelphia, your textbook would have been *The National Arithmetic*, by Benjamin Greenleaf (1869). Some problems in this book are not at all like those in today's textbooks. For example, some questions require you to figure out the tonnage of a ship. Here is your chance to solve the problems of yesteryear.

1. A father gave his 3 sons 4,698 dollars, of which James received 250 dollars more than George, and Edwin 410 dollars more than George. What sum did each receive?

   ______________________________

2. George Adams bought an equal number of cows and oxen for 3,952 dollars. For the cows he paid 31 dollars each, and for the oxen 45 dollars each. How many of each kind did he buy?

   ______________________________

3. A farmer has 12 bushels of oats, 18 bushels of rye, 24 bushels of corn, and 30 bushels of wheat. [You are] required [to find] the largest bin, of uniform size, and containing an exact number of bushels, into which the whole can be put, each kind by itself, and all the bins be full.

   ______________________________

4. S. Walker has engaged to work at yearly wages of $200 and a suit of clothes. At the end of 9 months, falling sick, and being unable to labor longer, he receives the suit of clothes and $144 as the amount justly due. What was the cost of the clothes?

   ______________________________

5. A gentleman gave $\frac{1}{4}$ of his property to his son James; $\frac{1}{3}$ of it to his son William; $\frac{1}{5}$ of the remainder to his daughter Mary; and the balance to his wife. It appeared that Mary received $2243.26 less than James. What was the amount divided and how much did each receive?

   ______________________________

Name ______________________ Date ______________________

# Greenleaf's National Arithmetic, the Sequel

1. James Cooper has manufactured in 4 years 5,608 pairs of shoes, making each successive year 100 pairs more than the year before; how many pairs did he manufacture each year?

______________________

2. If a man can dig a small square cellar, which will measure 6 feet each way, in one day, how long would it take him to dig a similar one that measured 10 feet each way?

______________________

3. A gentleman has two horses, and a saddle worth $50. Now if the saddle be put on the first horse, it will make his value double that of the second horse; but if it be put on the second, it will make his value triple that of the first. What was the value of each horse?

______________________

4. A gentleman hired a laborer for 90 days on these conditions: that for every day he wrought (worked) he should receive 60 cents; and for every day he was absent he should forfeit 80 cents. At the expiration of the term he received $33. How many days did he work, and how many days was he idle?

______________________

5. A schoolmaster, being asked how many scholars he had, replied that if he had as many more as he now has, and half as many more, he should have 200. Of how many scholars did his school consist?

______________________

6. John Lee gave $\frac{1}{2}$ of his estate to his wife, $\frac{1}{5}$ of the remainder to his oldest son, and $\frac{1}{4}$ of the residue to his oldest daughter, and $\frac{1}{2}$ of what then remained, which was $1,500, was to be equally distributed among his other children, who received $150 each; required, the number of his children and the value of his estate.

______________________

Name ______________________ Date ______________________

# How Large Is Your Yard?

Before units of measure were standardized, they were based on body parts. You are going to find out how large your family's measurements are. Measure yourself and each *adult* in your home. For this activity, anyone who has finished growing is an adult. Take each measurement to the nearest $\frac{1}{8}$ inch.

| Name | Yard | Cubit | Hand | Foot | Digit | Span | Palm | Fathom | Inch |
|---|---|---|---|---|---|---|---|---|---|
| Myself | | | | | | | | | |
| | | | | | | | | | |
| **Adult Average** | | | | | | | | | |

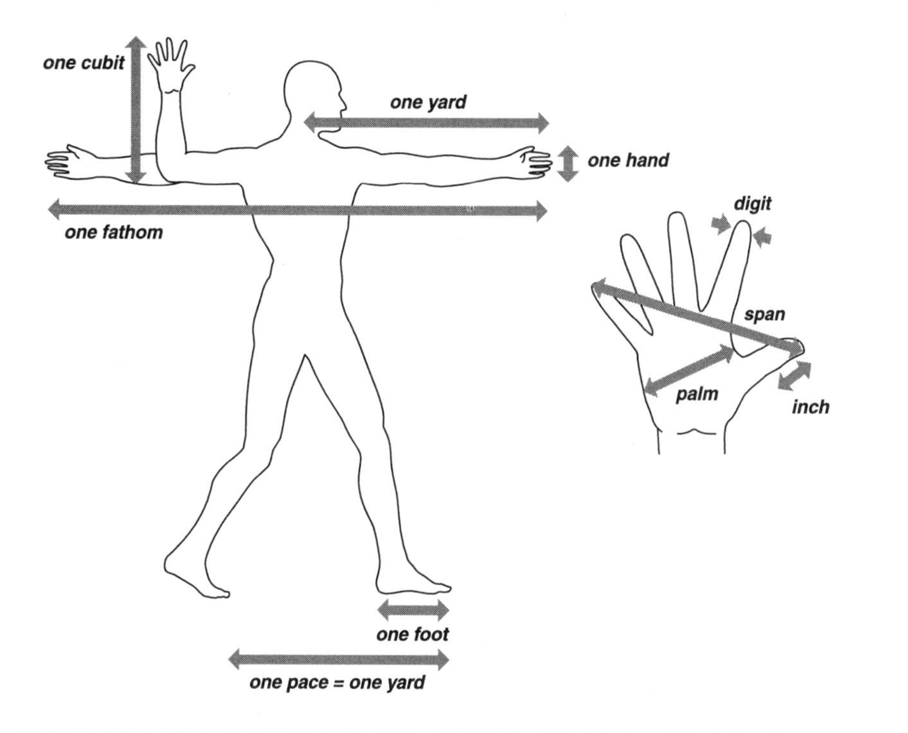

Name ______________________ Date ______________________

Activity

# Picky Little Details

What would life be like if we did not have standardized units of measure?

- What if Noah had decided to take some time off from ark building and had asked his eldest son to finish measuring and cutting some boards for him? Would it matter that one part of the ark was measured in Noah-cubits and another part in Shem-cubits?
- What if the foot had been declared to be the length of the foot of the king and he died? What should the community do? Was the new foot the size of the new king's foot? What if the new king had been only a teenager and was still growing?

You can imagine that in either of these situations, one could have an "interesting" problem and an interesting story could follow. Imagine what would happen if we did not have standardized units of measure today. Think of your own interesting situation involving units of measure, and write a short story describing what happens.

______________________________________________

______________________________________________

______________________________________________

______________________________________________

______________________________________________

______________________________________________

______________________________________________

______________________________________________

______________________________________________

______________________________________________

______________________________________________

______________________________________________

______________________________________________

______________________________________________

______________________________________________

Name ______________________ Date ______________________

# "For All People, for All Time"

The metric system is a result of the French Revolution. One hundred twenty years before the Revolution, Gabriel Mouton suggested a decimal system of measurement. In 1790, after the Revolution, the French Academy of Sciences was directed to develop a measurement system. The meter was defined as $\frac{1}{10,000}$ the length of the meridian from the North Pole to the equator passing through Paris. King Louis XVI approved the metric system the day before he was imprisoned; and in 1792, from his prison cell, he directed the engineers to start to determine the necessary measurements of the meridian. The metric system was formally adopted in France in June, 1799. The motto for the system was "For all people, for all time."

1. Complete these lists of units of measure.

   **Customary Units**

   _____ inches = 1 foot    _____ feet = 1 yard    _____ yards = 1 mile

   **Metric Units**

   _____ millimeters = 1 centimeter    _____ meters = 1 dekameter

   _____ centimeters = 1 decimeter    _____ dekameters = 1 hectometer

   _____ decimeters = 1 meter    _____ hectometers = 1 kilometer

2. In which system is it easier to convert between units? ______________

Today the International System of Units (S.I.) is the system of measurement used all over the world outside of the United States. It was adopted in 1960 at an international convention. The base units were more precisely defined than in 1790. For example, a meter is 1,650,763.73 wavelengths of krypton-86 in a vacuum. The base units are *meter* (length), *gram* (mass), *second* (time), *ampere* (electric current), *kelvin* (temperature), and *candela* (light intensity). Converting between units is only a matter of multiplying or dividing by a power of 10.

**Prefixes and Their Meanings in the S.I. System of Measurement**

| Prefix | Meaning | Language of Origin |
|---|---|---|
| tera- | trillion | Greek (*teras*, monster) |
| giga- | billion | Greek (*gigas*, giant) |
| mega- | million | Greek (*megas*, great) |
| kilo- | thousand | Greek (*khiliol*, thousand) |
| hecto- | hundred | Greek (*hekaton*, hundred) |
| deka- | ten | Greek (*deca*, ten) |
| deci- | tenth | Latin (*decimus*, tenth) |
| centi- | hundredth | Latin (*centum*, hundred) |
| milli- | thousandth | Latin (*mille*, thousand) |

Name ______________________________ Date ______________________________



| | | |
|---|---|---|
| micro- | millionth | Greek (*mikros*, small) |
| nano- | billionth | Greek (*nanos*, dwarf) |
| pico- | trillionth | Spanish (*pico*, small quantity) |
| femto- | quadrdillionth | Danish or Norwegian (*femten*, fifteen) |
| atto- | quintillionth | Danish or Norwegian (*atten*, eighteen) |
| myria- | ten thousand | Greek (*murios*, countless; *murioi*, ten thousand) [not official but sometimes used] |

| | | | | | | | | |
|---|---|---|---|---|---|---|---|---|
| | | | | gram | | | | |
| kilo- | hecto- | deka- | ← ÷ 10 | liter | × 10 → | deci- | centi- | milli- |
| | | | | meter | | | | |

3. Complete each set of measurements.

   a. 23 centimeters (cm) = _______ millimeters (mm) = _______ kilometers (km)

   b. 3.5 liters (L) = _______ milliliter (mL) = _______ hectoliters (hL)

   c. 0.002 kilogram (kg) = _______ grams (g) = _______ megagrams (Mg)

   d. 42.5 meters (m) = _______ nanometers (nm) = _______ dekameters (dkm)

4. Customary units of measure are ingrained in our society's sayings, songs, and poems. If we convert to metric, some of them will need to be adjusted. Translate these customary units of measure into metric units.
   Recall that 1 inch = 2.54 cm, 1 mile = 1.609 km, 1 quart = 0.946 L,
   1 pound = 0.4536 kg, 1 peck = 8.810 L, and 1 bushel = 4 pecks.

**Sayings**

a. Before you criticize someone, walk a mile in his shoes.
   Before you criticize someone, walk _______ kilometers in his shoes.

b. A pint's a pound the whole world round. [This is true only for water.]
   _______ liters is _______ kilograms the whole world round.

c. Give him an inch and he'll take a mile.
   Give him _______ centimeters and he'll take _______ kilometers.

**Songs**

d. *Five Hundred Miles*: _______ *Kilometers*

e. *Sixteen Tons*: _______ *Kilograms*

f. *I Love You a Bushel and a Peck: I Love You* _______ *Liters*

**Miscellaneous**

g. 10-gallon hat: _______-liter hat

h. Inch worm: _______-centimeter worm

i. Mile-long hot dog: _______-kilometer-long hot dog

Name ______________________ Date ______________________

# Circumference of Circles

For a very long time, people have noticed that there is a special relationship between the circumference and the diameter of any circle. It is mentioned in the Bible (1 Kings 7:23 and 2 Chronicles 4:2). This relationship was known even by the Babylonians and Egyptians 1,500 years before the Bible was written. You will have a chance to discover that relationship yourself.

Find 5 circles of different sizes. Use a centimeter measuring tape to measure the circumference and the diameter of each circle to the nearest tenth of a centimeter. Record your results in the table below. Then complete the last four columns.

| | Circumference ($C$) in Centimeters | Diameter ($d$) in Centimeters | $C + d$ | $C - d$ | $C \times d$ | $C \div d$ |
|---|---|---|---|---|---|---|
| **1.** | | | | | | |
| **2.** | | | | | | |
| **3.** | | | | | | |
| **4.** | | | | | | |
| **5.** | | | | | | |

**6.** Study the table above. Which expression gives approximately the same number for each circle? ______________

Name ______________________________ Date ______________________________

Pi = 3.14159265358979323846264338327950288419716939937510582097494459230781640628620899862803482

Activity

# Pi

Pi has fascinated people for many centuries. By 2000 B.C.E., some people realized that the ratio of the circumference to the diameter of a circle was a constant that we now call *pi* ($\pi$). The ancient Babylonians thought pi was about $3\frac{1}{8}$.

Archimedes (c. 287–212 B.C.E.) and Luí Hui (264) calculated pi by inscribing a many-sided polygon in a circle. The more sides the polygon had, the closer it was to being a circle. In fact, today, the way a "circle" is drawn using LOGO is to draw a polygon with many very short sides. Luí Hui used a 192-sided polygon to find pi = 3.14159. In the sixteenth century, François Viète used a 393,216-sided polygon to calculate pi to 10 decimal places.

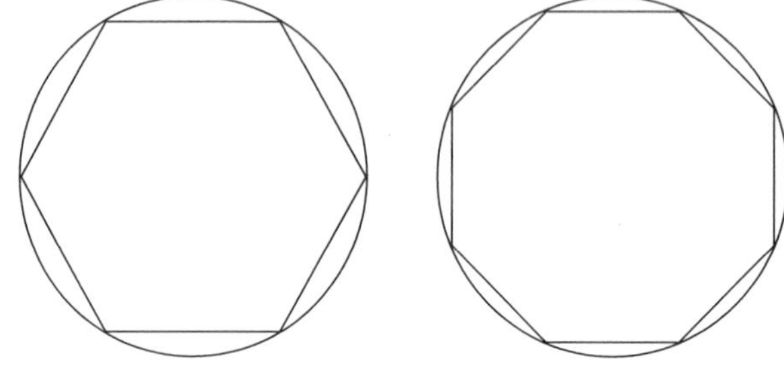

1. Here are some of the ratios people have used for pi over the years. Use your calculator to compute each ratio to 9 decimal places.

   a. the Egyptians (2000 B.C.E.) $\frac{256}{81}$ ______________

   b. Tsu Chhung (fifth century B.C.E.) $\frac{355}{113}$ ______________

   c. Archimedes (third century B.C.E.) between $3\frac{1}{7}$ ______________

   and $3\frac{10}{71}$ ______________

   d. Ptolemy (139–161) $3\frac{17}{120}$ ______________

   e. Wang Fan (255) $\frac{142}{45}$ ______________

   f. Luí Hui (264) $\frac{157}{50}$ ______________

   g. Aryabhata (530) $\frac{62{,}832}{20{,}000}$ ______________

   h. Brahmagupta (seventh century) $\sqrt{10}$ ______________

   i. Fibonacci (thirteenth century) $\frac{864}{275}$ ______________

2. Whose ratio above is the most accurate? ______________

In 1761, Johann Lambert proved that pi is an irrational number; the decimal part of the number never ends and it never repeats. Before then, some people tried to calculate pi to many places to see if it was a rational number.

2534211706798214808651328230664709384460955058223172535940812848111745028410270193852110555964462294895493038196442881097566593344612847564823378678316527120190914564856692346034861045432664821339360726024914127372458700660631558817488152092096282925409171536436789259036001133053054882046652138414695194151160943305727036575959195309218611738193261179310511854807446237996274956735188575 . . .

Name ____________________ Date ____________________

**Pi (cont.)**

By 1998, pi had been calculated to 51.5 billion decimal places. In 1986 it took a computer 28 hours and 2 trillion arithmetic operations to compute pi to 29,360,000 decimal places. When it had been computed to only 16 million places in 1984, *The Boston Globe* reported the news story saying that if pi were printed it "would take roughly two full Sunday editions of *The Washington Post*, and every page would contain nothing but numbers." We really do not need to know the value of pi to 51.5 billion places; for example, to calculate the circumference of the earth accurately to a fraction of an inch, you need only 10 decimal places. However, calculation of pi is one way to check out the accuracy of a computer.

For the past 300 years, people have developed formulas to compute pi rather than try to inscribe polygons in circles. Here are some of the formulas that people have used:

François Viète (1540–1603) $\frac{2}{\pi} = \sqrt{\frac{1}{2}} \times \sqrt{\frac{1}{2} + \frac{1}{2}\sqrt{\frac{1}{2}}} \times \sqrt{\frac{1}{2} + \frac{1}{2}\sqrt{\frac{1}{2} + \frac{1}{2}\sqrt{\frac{1}{2}}}} \times \ldots$

Isaac Newton (1642–1727) $\frac{\pi}{6} = \frac{1}{2} + \left(\frac{1}{2}\right)\left(\frac{1}{2 \cdot 2^3}\right) + \left(\frac{1 \cdot 3}{2 \cdot 4}\right)\left(\frac{1}{5 \cdot 2^5}\right) + \left(\frac{1 \cdot 3 \cdot 5}{2 \cdot 4 \cdot 6}\right)\left(\frac{1}{7 \cdot 2^7}\right) \ldots$

Gottfried Wilhelm Leibniz (1646–1716) $\pi = 4(1 - \frac{1}{3} + \frac{1}{5} - \frac{1}{7} + \ldots)$

Leonhard Euler (1707–1783) $\frac{\pi^2}{6} = \frac{1}{1^2} + \frac{1}{2^2} + \frac{1}{3^2} + \ldots$

Aida Ammei (1747–1817) $\frac{\pi}{2} = 1 + \frac{1!}{3} + \frac{2!}{3 \cdot 5} + \frac{3!}{3 \cdot 5 \cdot 7} + \frac{4!}{3 \cdot 5 \cdot 7 \cdot 9} + \ldots$

Sakabe Kohan (1759–1834) $\frac{\pi}{4} = 1 - \frac{1}{5} - \frac{1 \cdot 4}{5 \cdot 7 \cdot 9} - \frac{(1 \cdot 3)(4 \cdot 6)}{5 \cdot 7 \cdot 9 \cdot 11 \cdot 13} - \frac{(1 \cdot 3 \cdot 5)(4 \cdot 6 \cdot 8)}{5 \cdot 7 \cdot 9 \cdot 11 \cdot 13 \cdot 15 \cdot 17} - \ldots$

Wada Yenzo Nei (1787–1840) $\frac{\pi}{2} = 1 + \frac{1}{3 \cdot 2} + \frac{3}{5 \cdot 8} + \frac{15}{7 \cdot 48} + \frac{105}{9 \cdot 384} + \frac{945}{11 \cdot 3{,}840} + \ldots$

Srinivasa Ramanujan (1887–1920) $\pi = \left(9^2 + \frac{19^2}{22}\right)^{\frac{1}{4}}$

Srinivasa Ramanujan (1887–1920) $\frac{\pi}{4} = \cfrac{1}{1 + \cfrac{1^2}{2 + \cfrac{3^2}{2 + \cfrac{5^2}{2 + \cfrac{7^2}{2 + \cfrac{9^2}{2 + \ldots}}}}}}$

There is a pattern to each of the formulas above. They continue infinitely, but only the first few terms are listed. Write the next two terms for each formula below.

3. $\pi = 4\left(1 - \frac{1}{3} + \frac{1}{5} - \frac{1}{7} + \_\_\_\_ - \_\_\_\_ + \ldots\right)$

4. $\pi = 3\left(1 + \frac{1^2}{4 \cdot 6} + \frac{1^2 \cdot 3^2}{4 \cdot 6 \cdot 8 \cdot 10} + \frac{1^2 \cdot 3^2 \cdot 5^2}{4 \cdot 6 \cdot 8 \cdot 10 \cdot 12 \cdot 14} + \_\_\_\_\_\_ + \_\_\_\_\_\_ \ldots\right)$

5. $\frac{\pi}{2} = 1 + \frac{1!}{3} + \frac{2!}{3 \cdot 5} + \frac{3!}{3 \cdot 5 \cdot 7} + \frac{4!}{3 \cdot 5 \cdot 7 \cdot 9} + \_\_\_\_\_\_ + \_\_\_\_\_\_ \ldots$

6. $\frac{\pi}{4} = 1 - \frac{1}{5} - \frac{1 \cdot 4}{5 \cdot 7 \cdot 9} - \frac{(1 \cdot 3)(4 \cdot 6)}{5 \cdot 7 \cdot 9 \cdot 11 \cdot 13} - \frac{(1 \cdot 3 \cdot 5)(4 \cdot 6 \cdot 8)}{5 \cdot 7 \cdot 9 \cdot 11 \cdot 13 \cdot 15 \cdot 17} - \_\_\_\_\_\_ - \_\_\_\_\_\_ \ldots$

7. $\frac{\pi}{2} = 1 + \frac{1}{3 \cdot 2} + \frac{3}{5 \cdot 8} + \frac{15}{7 \cdot 48} + \frac{105}{9 \cdot 384} + \frac{945}{11 \cdot 3{,}840} + \_\_\_\_\_\_ + \_\_\_\_\_\_ \ldots$

Name ______________________ Date ______________________

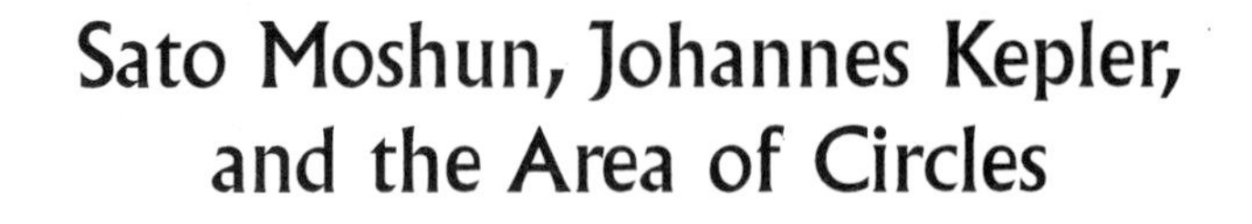

# Sato Moshun, Johannes Kepler, and the Area of Circles

A method attributed to Johannes Kepler (1571–1630) and used by Sato Moshun in Japan (1698) demonstrates how to find the area of a circle.

1. Start with a circle and divide it into many very small equal sections. In this example, we used 24 congruent sections. Rearrange the 24 sections as shown here.

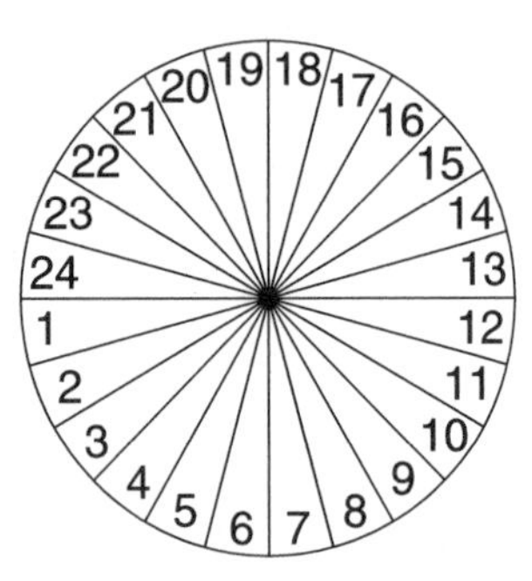


   a. Look at the rearrangement. What polygon does it resemble? ______________

   b. What are its base ($b$) and height ($h$)? ______________

   c. What is its area ($A$)? ______________

Here is another one of Kepler's methods for finding the area of a circle. You need to remember one important fact: two triangles with the same base and height have the same area even if they look quite different.

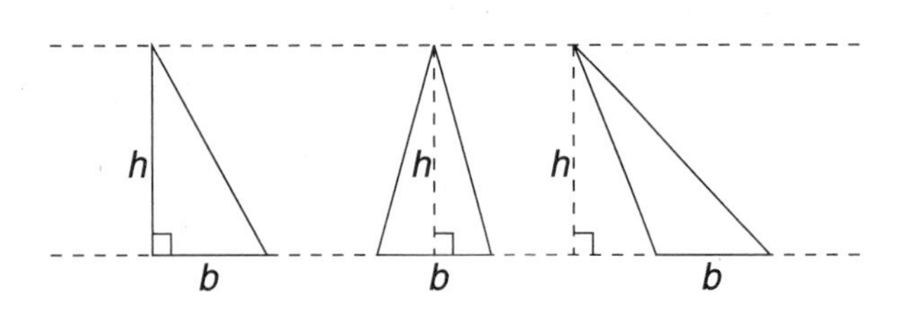

Name ______________________________ Date ______________________________

**Sato Moshun, Johannes Kepler, and the Area of Circles (cont.)**

2. Start with a circle and divide it into infinitely small congruent sections. In this example, we used 24 congruent sections, so imagine that this was done with many more very small pieces. Stretch out the circumference and arrange the triangle sections as shown below.

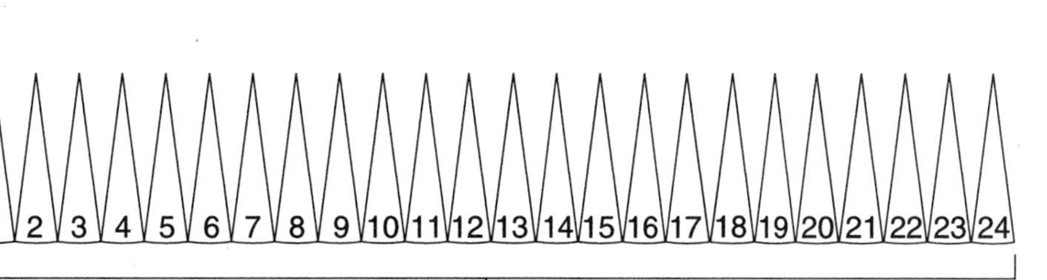


circumference

Remember that triangles with the same base and height have the same area. Study the drawing below and explain why the large triangle has the same area as the circle.

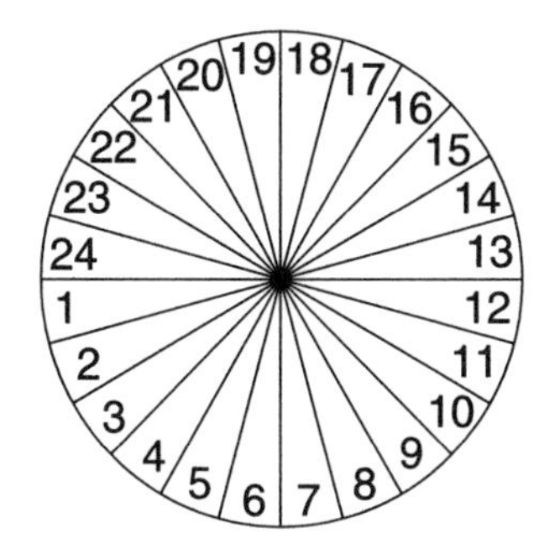


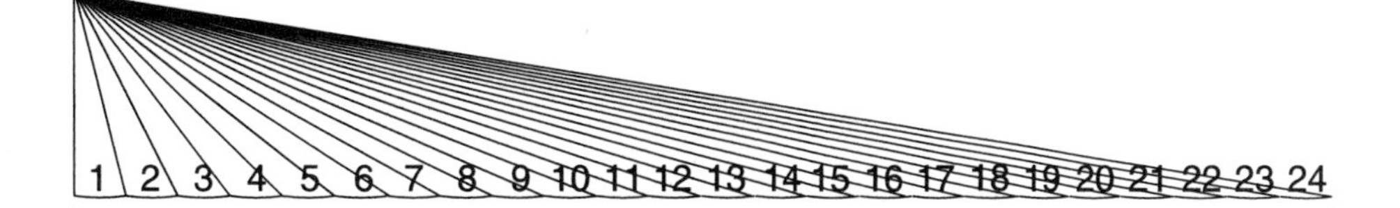


circumference

______________________________________________________________

______________________________________________________________

______________________________________________________________

Name ______________________ Date ______________________

# Thales, Triangles, Playing Column, and Playing Ship

When studying similar and congruent triangles, you should become familiar with Thales of Miletus (c. 640–c. 546 B.C.E.), considered to be one of the Seven Wise Men of Ancient Greece. None of his works have survived, so what we know about Thales is from others' writings and legend. He traveled to Egypt where he learned about Egyptian science and philosophy and to Babylonia where he learned about geometry and astronomy. In 585 B.C.E., Thales surprised his contemporaries by accurately predicting a solar eclipse. He was also a successful entrepreneur. Having accurately predicted a large olive crop, he bought all the olive-oil presses in advance and became wealthy by monopolizing the local olive-oil business. Thales is credited with introducing geometry to Greece. He was the first person to formalize geometry as this set of theorems that he possibly proved.

1. Any circle is bisected by its diameter.
2. The angles at the base of an isosceles triangle are equal.
3. When two lines intersect, the vertical angles are equal.
4. An angle in a semicircle is a right angle.
5. The sides of similar triangles are proportional.
6. Triangles are congruent if they have two angles and a side respectively equal.

Do any of these sound familiar to you?

**Playing Column**

Legend tells us that when Thales was traveling in Egypt, he was asked by the Pharaoh to calculate the height of the Great Pyramid. Your teacher can help you can act this out with your classmates when studying similar triangles. One student should pretend to be a Greek column rather than a pyramid, standing straight with hands at the side on a spot marked on the floor with masking tape. A second student stands on the other side of the room, and using the thumb and index finger "sight" the height of the student-column by holding the finger and thumb vertically the same distance apart as the height of the student across the room "appears" to be. Be sure the student does not bend his or her elbow. The second student rotates the hand 90° without changing the distance between the fingers, lines up the thumb with the feet of the student-column, and directs a third student to move into position with the sighting finger. Now the original student-column lies down on the floor, feet touching where the third student stood and head where the original tape is on the floor.

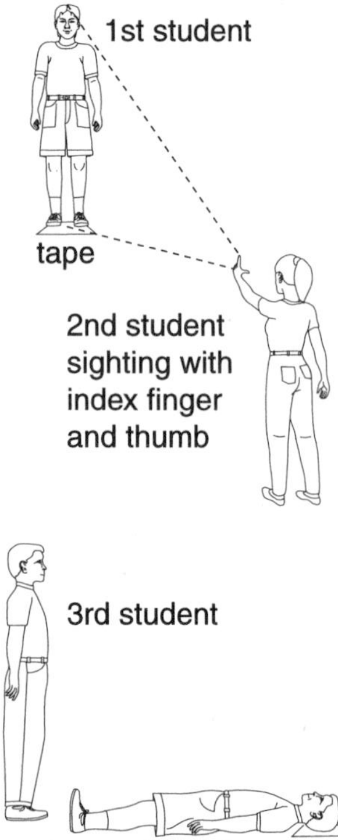

Name ______________________________ Date ______________________________



The height of the "column" is the distance on the floor. While measuring the actual height of a column would be difficult, the distance is measurable. When Thales was asked to measure the height of the pyramid, he put a stick in the ground and waited until the shadow cast by the stick was equal to the height of the stick. At that time, he measured the length of the pyramid's shadow. The triangle formed by the shadow and the pyramid is a right isosceles triangle, so the height of the pyramid is the same as the length of the shadow.

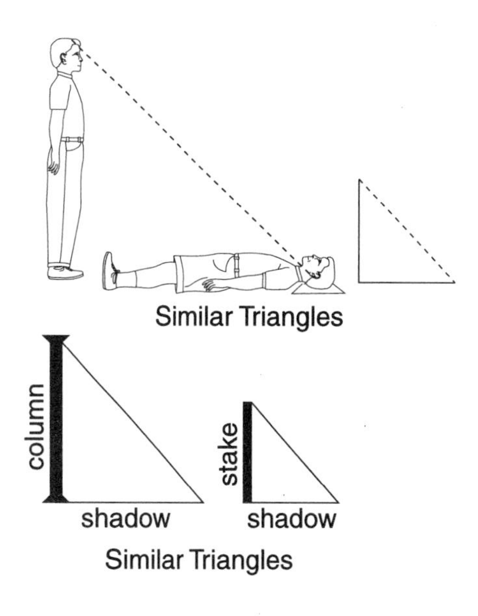

Similar Triangles

**Playing Ship**

Thales used his knowledge of congruent triangles to measure the distance of a ship from the shore. There are various theories as to how he did it, but you and your classmates can also act out this method, which works if the ship is relatively close to the shore. Imagine the ship is at *S* and point *A* is on the shoreline so that looking out at *S*, your line of vision is perpendicular to the shoreline.

Have one student pretend to be a ship and put down a rope on the floor and call it the shoreline. Make sure that the student-ship does not move from the designated anchored location (you might want to mark it with tape on the floor). Mark this point with a piece of tape labeled *A*, and have a second student stand there, on the shoreline. What you want to know is the distance from *S* to *A*, but since that is the ocean, you cannot just walk out and measure it. Have the second student turn and walk along the shoreline, heel-to-toe, a given number of paces, 10, for example. Mark that spot with a piece of tape labeled *B*. Have the second student continue along the shoreline, heel-to-toe, another 10 paces and mark that spot with a piece of tape labeled *C*. Have a third student stand on point *B*. Have the second student carefully walk backward, perpendicular to the shore while looking at the student-ship and at the student at *B*. As soon as the ship and *B* appear lined up in the second student's line of sight, the student should stop and mark the spot with a piece of tape labeled *D*. The distance from *C* to *D*, which is equal to the distance from *S* to *A*, is on land, so it can be measured.

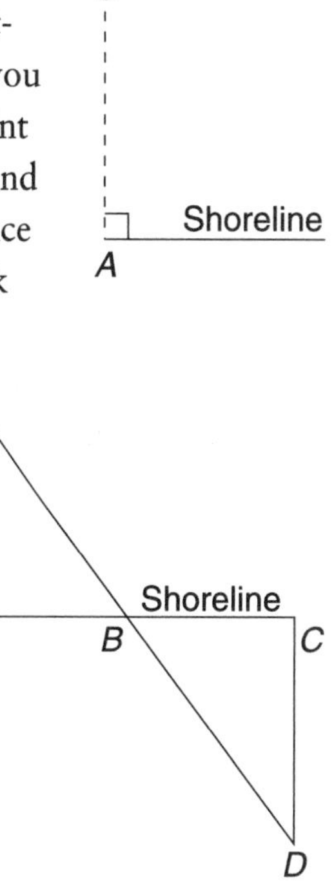

Name ______________________ Date ______________________

Activity

# The Tile Detectives

Jerusalem was captured by the Romans in the year 70. After destroying the Temple, the soldiers went through the city and burned, smashed, and leveled the mansions that were there. Until 130, when the Roman emperor Hadrian arrived in the city, much of what had been destroyed remained as rubble. Hadrian decided to build a new city on top of the remains of Jerusalem, much to the dismay of the descendants of the Jews who had lived in Jerusalem. In the 1970s, excavation began for a building to be constructed on the same site and the remains of one of the mansions that had been destroyed and buried was unearthed. The archaeologists discovered mosaic-tiled baths as well as the pieces of plastered walls that had tessellating patterns drawn into the wet plaster.

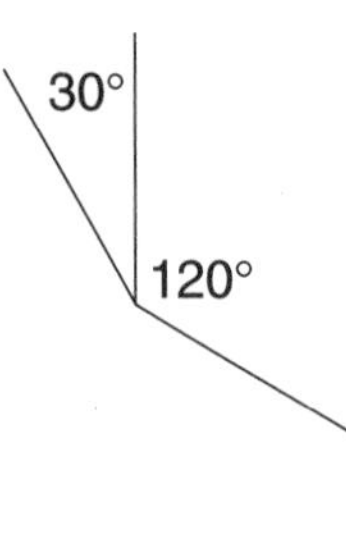


One piece of the plaster looked like the diagram at the left. The archaeologists tried to reconstruct what the original wall looked like from that small piece. They had to consider what geometric shapes could have angles of that size and how they would fit together. They decided it must have looked something like the pattern on the right and recreated the plaster wall for tourists who now visit the house-museum.

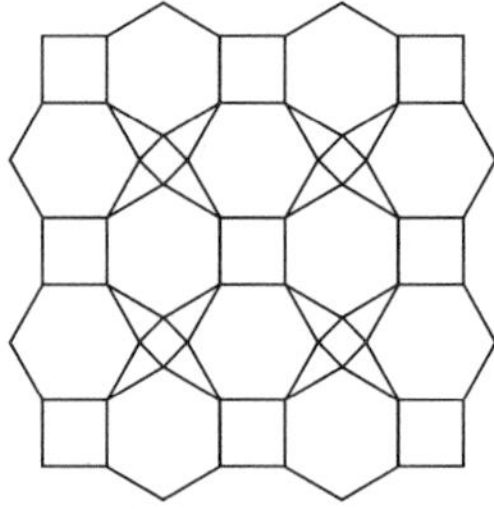

Now you can be archaeologists and try to decide what tessellating patterns the following "remains" come from. Use pattern blocks to reconstruct the original patterns. Keep in mind that for a pattern to tessellate, it must repeat the same pattern over the surface with no gaps and no overlaps. Trace your solutions on a separate sheet of paper. Problems 1–5 are separate designs, each with one allover pattern. In the Bonus, two different corners are given, each of which can be found in the completed pattern, but there are two solutions!

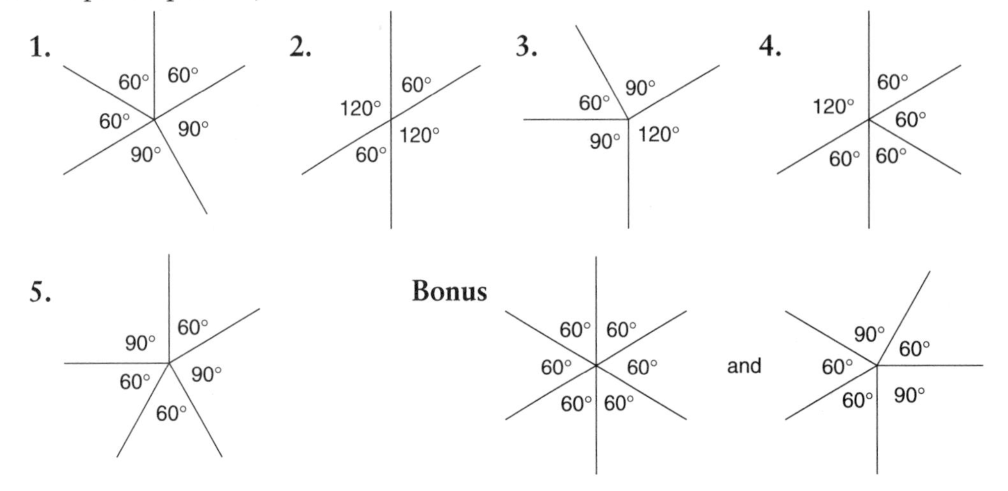

Name ______________________________ Date ______________________________

# A Pythagorean Puzzle

Your teacher will give you a right triangle and a strip of paper containing two rectangles made up of squares and triangles. The sides of the right triangle have lengths *a*, *b*, and *c*. Glue the triangle to the middle of a piece of paper. Save this paper for later use.

1. Compare the areas of the rectangle made up of a pieces and b pieces with the rectangle made up of c pieces. Are they equal? ________

Cut out the a piece. Next cut out all the b pieces and put them together to make a square. Then cut out all the c pieces and put them together to make a square.

2. Describe in terms of the three squares the relationship you found in Problem 1.

   ______________________________________________

Finally, take out the paper with the triangle in the middle. Remember that the triangle has side lengths *a*, *b*, and *c*. Glue the a square on the *a* side of the triangle, the b square on the *b* side, and the c square on the *c* side.

3. What is the area of each square?

   a square ____________ b square ____________ c square ____________

4. Summarize in your own words what the triangle and the squares demonstrate.

   ______________________________________________

   ______________________________________________

What you have just written is called the Pythagorean Theorem. This relationship works for all right triangles with *a* and *b*, the sides next to the right angle, or the *legs*, and *c* the longest side, or the *hypotenuse*. This theorem is named after Pythagoras, the leader of a mystical religious sect about 2,500 years ago. The members felt that whole numbers or their ratios could explain everything. Any mathematical discovery made by someone within the Pythagorean society was attributed to their leader, Pythagoras. Other ancient scholars also noticed this relationship in right triangles. For example, the Babylonians wrote a cuneiform table listing 15 sets of Pythagorean triples, now known as *Plimpton 322,* 3,700 years ago during the dynasty of Hammurabi. The Chinese used the relationship to solve problems and demonstrated a proof of it 2,200 years ago, about the same time that it appeared in manuscripts in India. Western mathematicians did not know until the twentieth century about these cultures' work, so only the Greeks received credit for the origin of these ideas.

# A Pythagorean Puzzle Pieces A

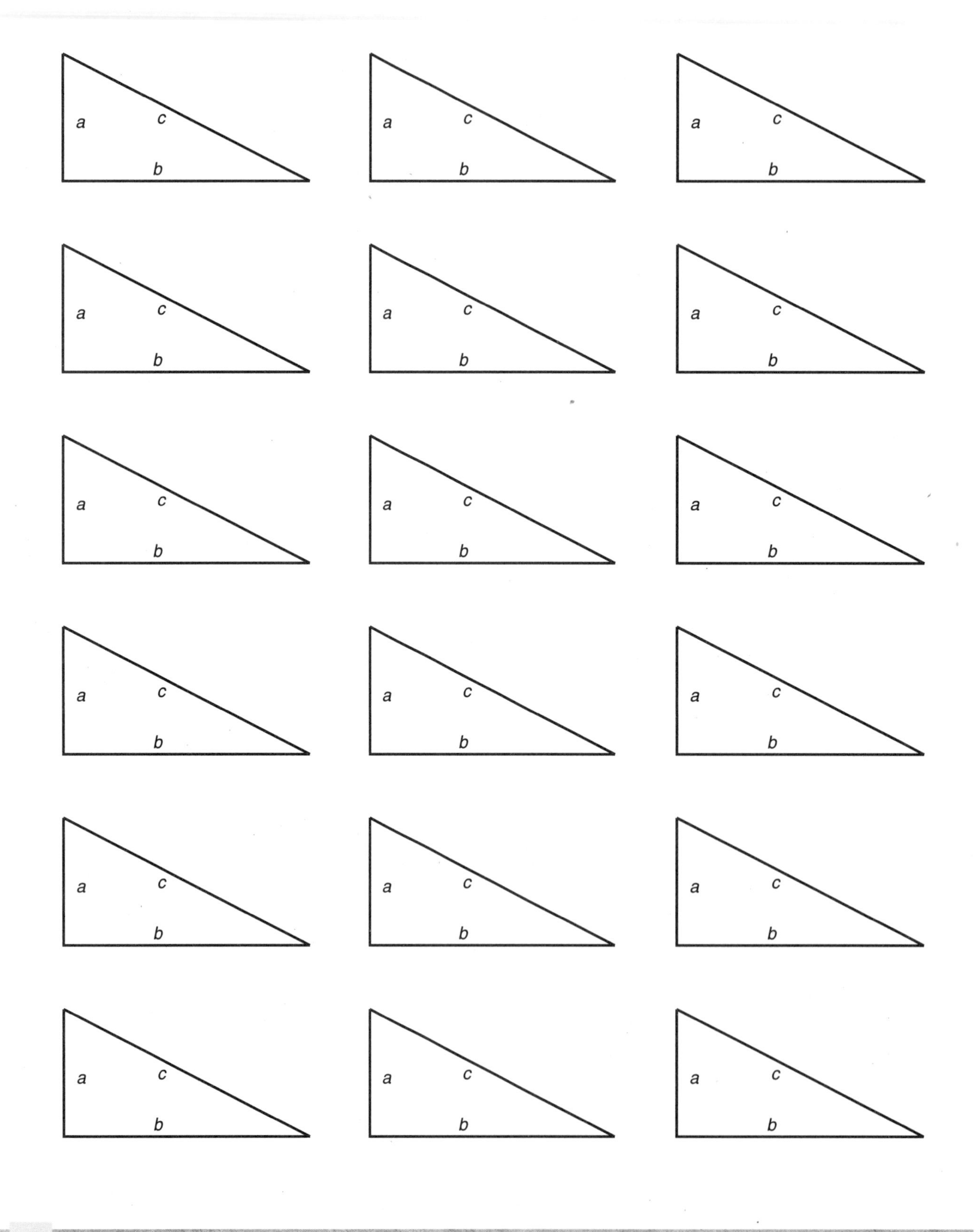

# A Pythagorean Puzzle Pieces B

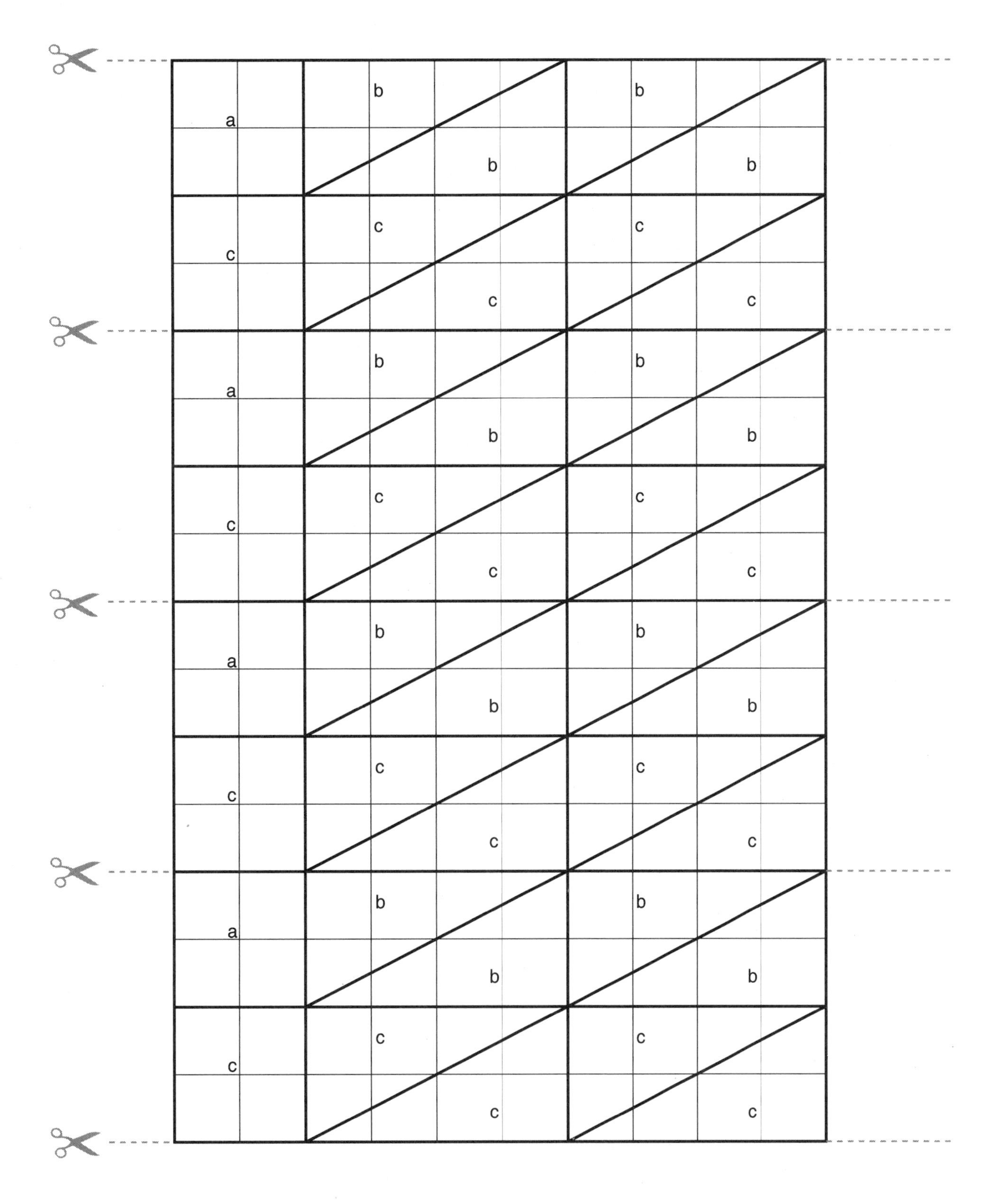

Name ______________________ Date ______________________

# Legendary City Land Acquisition

About 2,000 years ago, Virgil wrote about the Greek legend of the founding of the ancient city of Carthage near what is now Tunis. After Princess Dido's husband was murdered by her brother Pygmalion, she fled to the northern coast of Africa and bought land from Iarbas. They agreed that the amount of land would be what she could enclose with the hide of one bull. Dido took the hide, cut it into strips, and sewed the strips together in order to enclose an area larger than the area of the hide would cover. Then she used the coastline as one side of her shape.

Today you are Dido's assistants. Cut the sheet labeled *Hide of Bull* into thin strips, tape them together, and investigate various geometric shapes to use to enclose the land to build Carthage.

1. How long is your piece of hide after reconstruction? ______________

2. Choose three different geometric shapes to form with the hide and compute the area of each one.

   ______________ ______________ ______________

3. Draw diagrams of how these shapes are placed in relationship to the shore. Be sure to clearly label all of the dimensions.

4. Dido actually chose the shape that would enclose the most land. Which shape was it? ______________

5. Your new shape is how many times as large as your original piece of hide? ______________

# Hide of Bull

MEASUREMENT GRADE·U.S. PRIME·PMTAR APPROVED
CERTIFIED HIDE OF BULL

Name ______________________________ Date ______________________________

Activity

# The Sieve of Eratosthenes

Eratosthenes (276–194 B.C.E.) was a famous scholar who worked in Alexandria, Egypt. He figured out a way to measure the circumference of the earth, and his was the most accurate measurement in ancient times. Eratosthenes also figured out a method to find prime numbers up to any chosen number. You can use his method to find all the primes up to 100, or even 1,000,000. Today you will use the 100 chart below to find the primes up to 100 using the sieve of Eratosthenes. A sieve is like a strainer or a colander. This is called the *sieve method* because it catches all the primes and lets the other numbers go. Remember that a *prime* has exactly two distinct factors, itself and 1.

- The number 1 has only one distinct factor, so it is not prime. Cross it out.
- Two is a prime, so circle it.
- Any multiple of 2, besides 2, has 2 as a factor, as well as itself and 1. So all other multiples of 2 are *composite*, not prime. Cross them out.
- The next number not crossed out is 3. It is prime, so circle it. Now all other multiples of 3 are composite because they have 3 as a factor, so cross them out.
- The next number not crossed out is _____.
  It is prime, so circle it. Now cross out all other multiples of _____.
- The next number not crossed out is _____.
  It is prime, so circle it. Now cross out all other multiples of _____.
- The next number not crossed out is _____.
  It is prime, so circle it. Now cross out all other multiples of _____.
- Circle all numbers that are neither crossed out nor circled. All circled numbers are the primes less than 100. List them on the back of this sheet.

| | | | | | | | | | |
|---|---|---|---|---|---|---|---|---|---|
| 1 | 2 | 3 | 4 | 5 | 6 | 7 | 8 | 9 | 10 |
| 11 | 12 | 13 | 14 | 15 | 16 | 17 | 18 | 19 | 20 |
| 21 | 22 | 23 | 24 | 25 | 26 | 27 | 28 | 29 | 30 |
| 31 | 32 | 33 | 34 | 35 | 36 | 37 | 38 | 39 | 40 |
| 41 | 42 | 43 | 44 | 45 | 46 | 47 | 48 | 49 | 50 |
| 51 | 52 | 53 | 54 | 55 | 56 | 57 | 58 | 59 | 60 |
| 61 | 62 | 63 | 64 | 65 | 66 | 67 | 68 | 69 | 70 |
| 71 | 72 | 73 | 74 | 75 | 76 | 77 | 78 | 79 | 80 |
| 81 | 82 | 83 | 84 | 85 | 86 | 87 | 88 | 89 | 90 |
| 91 | 92 | 93 | 94 | 95 | 96 | 97 | 98 | 99 | 100 |

Name ______________________ Date ______________________

# Primes, Multiples, and Squares

**Multiples of 4**

| | | | | |
|---|---|---|---|---|
| 1 | 2 | 3 | 4 | 5 |
| | 6 | 7 | 8 | 9 |
| | 10 | 11 | 12 | 13 |
| | 14 | 15 | 16 | 17 |
| | 18 | 19 | 20 | 21 |
| | 22 | 23 | 24 | 25 |
| | 26 | 27 | 28 | 29 |
| | 30 | 31 | 32 | 33 |
| | 34 | 35 | 36 | 37 |
| | 38 | 39 | 40 | 41 |
| | 42 | 43 | 44 | 45 |
| | 46 | 47 | 48 | 49 |
| | 50 | 51 | 52 | 53 |
| | 54 | 55 | 56 | 57 |
| | 58 | 59 | 60 | 61 |
| | 62 | 63 | 64 | 65 |
| | 66 | 67 | 68 | 69 |
| | 70 | 71 | 72 | 73 |
| | 74 | 75 | 76 | 77 |
| | 78 | 79 | 80 | 81 |
| | 82 | 83 | 84 | 85 |
| | 86 | 87 | 88 | 89 |
| | 90 | 91 | 92 | 93 |
| | 94 | 95 | 96 | 97 |
| | 98 | 99 | 100 | |

**Multiples of 6**

| | | | | | | |
|---|---|---|---|---|---|---|
| 1 | 2 | 3 | 4 | 5 | 6 | 7 |
| | 8 | 9 | 10 | 11 | 12 | 13 |
| | 14 | 15 | 16 | 17 | 18 | 19 |
| | 20 | 21 | 22 | 23 | 24 | 25 |
| | 26 | 27 | 28 | 29 | 30 | 31 |
| | 32 | 33 | 34 | 35 | 36 | 37 |
| | 38 | 39 | 40 | 41 | 42 | 43 |
| | 44 | 45 | 46 | 47 | 48 | 49 |
| | 50 | 51 | 52 | 53 | 54 | 55 |
| | 56 | 57 | 58 | 59 | 60 | 61 |
| | 62 | 63 | 64 | 65 | 66 | 67 |
| | 68 | 69 | 70 | 71 | 72 | 73 |
| | 74 | 75 | 76 | 77 | 78 | 79 |
| | 80 | 81 | 82 | 83 | 84 | 85 |
| | 86 | 87 | 88 | 89 | 90 | 91 |
| | 92 | 93 | 94 | 95 | 96 | 97 |
| | 98 | 99 | 100 | | | |

You will have a chance to look at a prime-number pattern explored by Pierre de Fermat and proved by Leonhard Euler back in the 1600s and 1700s. In each of the 100 charts, circle all of the prime numbers less than 100.

1. Look at the multiples-of-4 chart; what do you notice about each of the prime numbers? ______________________

2. Look at the multiples-of-6 chart; what do you notice about each of the prime numbers? ______________________

3. Some prime numbers can be written as the sum of two square numbers. For example, $7^2 + 2^2 = 49 + 4 = 53$. Check each of the prime numbers less than 100 to find those that can be written as the sum of two squares.

______________________________________________

4. In the charts, use a colored pencil or highlighter to color in all of the primes that can be written as the sum of two squares. What do you notice about these special primes?

______________________________________________

Name ______________________ Date ______________________

# The Shapes of Numbers

You can build number patterns using cubes, tiles, or disks. Draw the next three pictures in each pattern and complete the accompanying tables.

1.

| Number of Picture | 1 | 2 | 3 | 4 | 5 | 6 |
|---|---|---|---|---|---|---|
| Number of Blocks | 1 | 3 | | | | |

1 2 3

2.

| Number of Picture | 1 | 2 | 3 | 4 | 5 | 6 |
|---|---|---|---|---|---|---|
| Number of Blocks | 1 | 4 | | | | |

1 2 3

In each table above, the pattern continues following a rule that could be described in words. For example, in Problem 1 the rule could be: "Add a new row to the bottom of the last picture with one more square than the last bottom row."

3. Draw a sequence of pictures to illustrate the pattern in the following table. What is your rule to go from one picture to the next?

______________________________________________

| Number of Picture | 1 | 2 | 3 | 4 |
|---|---|---|---|---|
| Number of Blocks | 1 | 5 | 12 | 22 |

4. How many blocks would be in the fifth and sixth pictures of Problem 3? ______________

5. Create your own building rule.

______________________________________________

Draw pictures of your first 4 terms here. Complete this table for your rule.

| Number of Picture | 1 | 2 | 3 | 4 |
|---|---|---|---|---|
| Number of Blocks | | | | |

Name ______________________________ Date ______________________________

The Shapes of Numbers (cont.)

6. One way to look at number patterns is to look at the differences between terms. Complete this table by finding the indicated differences.

| Number of Picture | 1 | 2 | 3 | 4 | 5 | 6 |
|---|---|---|---|---|---|---|
| Number of Blocks | 1 | 3 | 6 | | | |

Differences: 2 3 __ __ __

Complete these difference tables for Problems 2 and 3.

7.

| Number of Picture | 1 | 2 | 3 | 4 | 5 | 6 |
|---|---|---|---|---|---|---|
| Number of Blocks | 1 | 4 | 9 | 16 | | |

Differences: __ __ __ __ __

8.

| Number of Picture | 1 | 2 | 3 | 4 | 5 | 6 |
|---|---|---|---|---|---|---|
| Number of Blocks | 1 | 5 | 12 | 22 | | |

Differences: __ __ __ __ __

Second differences: __ __ __ __

Sometimes it helps to take a second difference to see the ← number pattern.

9. The Ancient Greeks called the pattern in Problem 1 *triangular numbers*. Try to tell why.

______________________________________________

10. They called the pattern in Problem 2 *square numbers*. Show how to rearrange the patterns for 4 and 9 to look like squares.

We still call numbers that make squares *square numbers* and numbers that make cubes *cubic numbers*.

11. They called the pattern in Problem 3 *pentagonal numbers*. Did your design look anything like a pentagon? ____________

12. The Greeks were also interested in how number patterns related to each other. For example, take two consecutive triangular numbers and add them. What kind of number do you get? Try it again. Try to figure out a way to show that this will always happen.

______________________________________________

Name ________________________ Date ________________________

Activity

# The Shapes of Numbers, the Puzzle

The triangular number our group is assigned is _________.

Use linking cubes or $\frac{1}{2}$-inch graph paper to make 8 copies of the triangular number that your group is assigned. When using cubes to make your triangular numbers, make each one a different solid color. Take an additional cube and put away all the others.

Use all 8 copies of your triangular number and your additional cube to build a square. You may not take the triangular numbers apart.

Record your solution on the grid below.

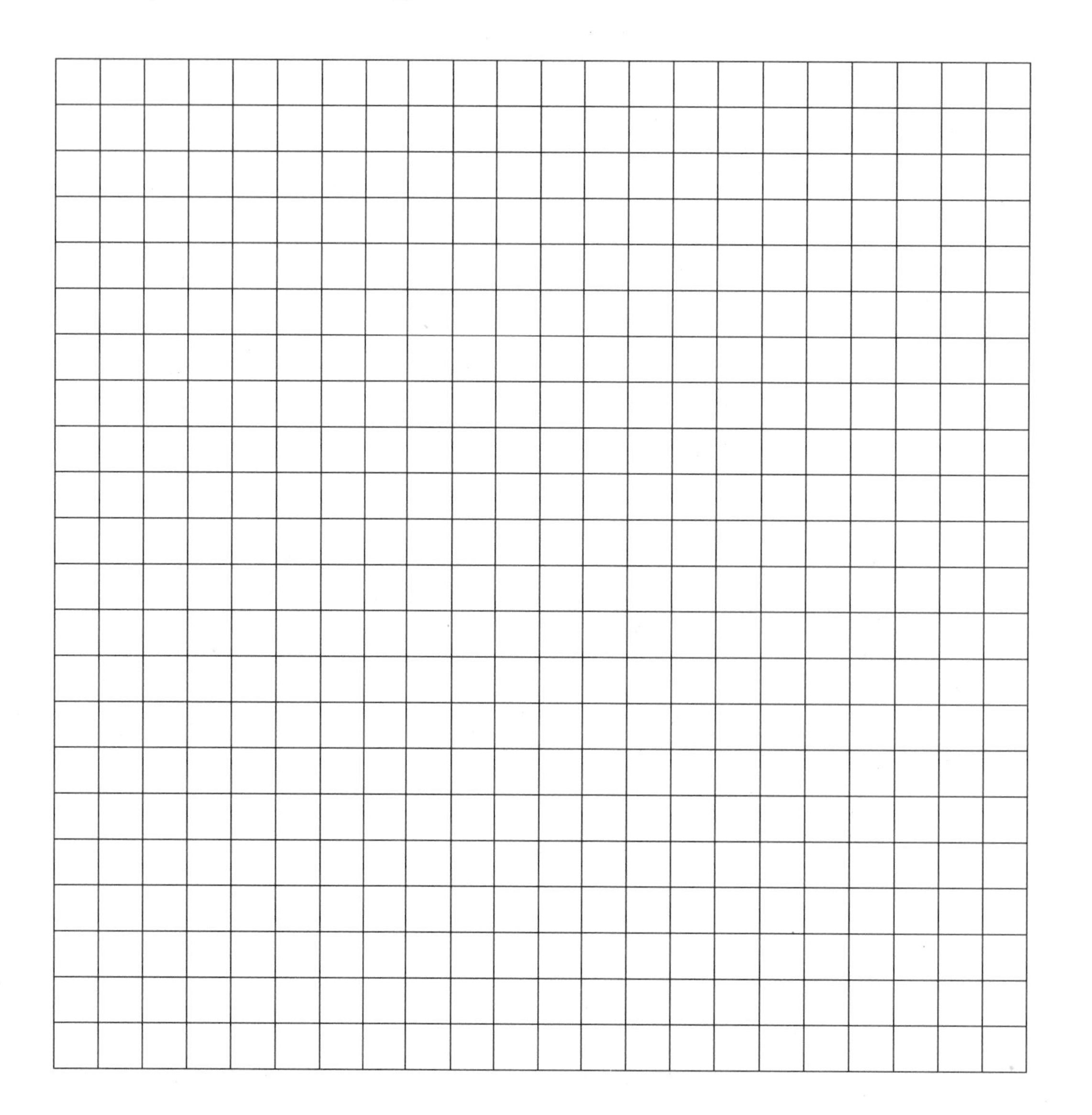

Name ______________________ Date ______________________

# The Shapes of Numbers, the Sums

The sums of consecutive natural numbers display an interesting pattern, which was found by Carl Gauss.

1. a. Complete each sum.

   1 = _____  1 + 2 = _____  1 + 2 + 3 = _____  1 + 2 + 3 + 4 = _____

   1 + 2 + 3 + 4 + 5 = _____  1 + 2 + 3 + 4 + 5 + 6 = _____

   b. The sum of each set of consecutive natural numbers is a __________ number.

When Gauss was 10 years old, his teacher decided that his class was too rowdy and told the students to take out their slates (small chalkboards) and to add all of the numbers from 1 to 100. In the late 1700s, students would do their work on their slates, and then stack the slates facedown on the teacher's desk when finished. Young Carl quickly wrote down the answer and then waited a long time while everyone else finished. Much to his teacher's surprise, Carl's answer was correct. Carl figured out a pattern that helped him add the numbers quickly.

2. When Carl considered the sum 1 + 2 + 3 + 4 + . . . + 97 + 98 + 99 + 100, he noticed that 100 + 1 = _____, 99 + 2 = _____, and 98 + 3 = _____. He decided that the sum of each pair was _____. Then he also noticed that if there were 100 numbers that there must be _____ pairs of numbers each with a sum of _____. What do you think Carl did to solve this problem?

   ______________________________________________

3. What is the sum of all the numbers from 1 through 100? ______________

4. Write a rule for finding the sum of consecutive numbers starting with 1 that you could use whenever you are given the greatest number in the sequence.

   ______________________________________________

5. a. Complete each sum of consecutive odd natural numbers. 1 = _____

   1 + 3 = _____  1 + 3 + 5 = _____  1 + 3 + 5 + 7 = _____

   1 + 3 + 5 + 7 + 9 = _____

   b. The sum of consecutive odd natural numbers is a __________ number.

6. Predict the sum of the first 50 odd natural numbers. Explain how you got your answer.

   ______________________________________________

Name ______________________ Date ______________________

Activity

# The 15 Game

Play this game several times with a partner.

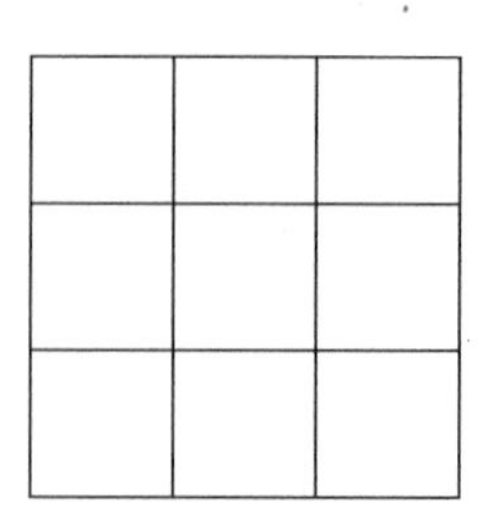

Draw a 3-by-3 square like one on the right on a piece of paper. The first person uses the odd digits. The second person uses the even digits. Take turns writing a digit in a square. You may use each digit only once. The winner is the person who writes the last number in a row, column, or diagonal so that the sum of the three numbers is 15.

Now think about the game. Write answers to the questions assigned to your group after you have discussed them with your group members. If you have time, take a look at the other groups' questions.

**Group A**

1. What are all the different winning number combinations?
2. In how many different positions can the winning numbers be placed?
3. How many different ways can someone win this game?

**Group B**

1. Is this a fair game? What makes a game fair?
2. Would you rather go first or second in this game? Why?
3. Is there a "best place" to write the first number? Why?

**Group C**

1. Is this a fair game? What makes a game fair?
2. Would the game be fair if the first person used the even digits instead of the odd ones? Why?

**Group D**

1. What would happen if both players used only odd digits? Only even digits?
2. What would happen if digits could be used more than once?

**Group E**

1. What is the least number of moves required for someone to win?
2. What is the greatest number of moves that can be made without having a winner?

**Group F**

Change the rules of this game. Play your new game with your partner. Is it fair? Why or why not?

Name ______________________ Date ______________________

# Magic Squares

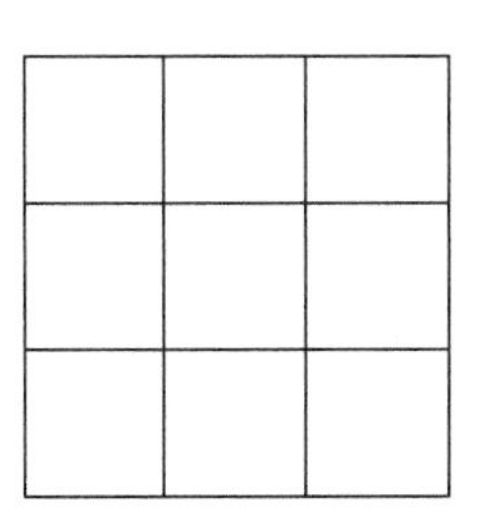

1. Write the numbers 1 through 9 in the square at the right so that the sum of each row, each column, and each diagonal is the same number. Use each number exactly once.

2. What patterns do you notice in the magic square?

______________________________________________

______________________________________________

______________________________________________

At the right is shown the Lo Shu Magic Square. Chinese legend tells us that this magic square was a gift from a turtle from the River Lo to the engineer-Emperor Yu, probably around 4,000 years ago. The *yin* numbers, which are the numbers of the earth, are black. The *yang* numbers, which are the numbers of the heavens, are white.

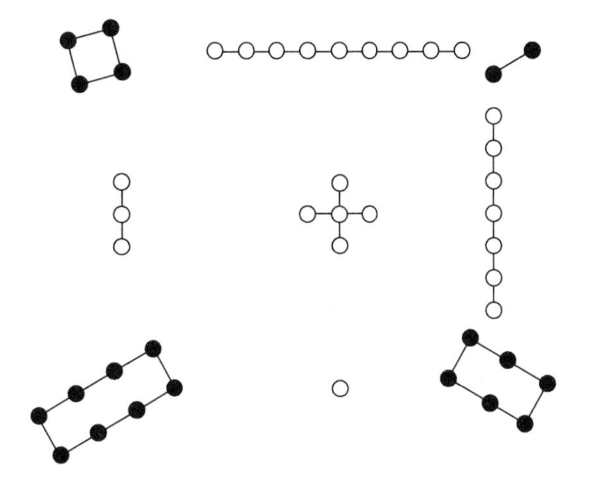

3. What do we call the yin numbers? ______________________

   The yang numbers? ______________________

Name ______________________ Date ______________________

# Constructing Odd Magic Squares

An *odd* magic square has an odd number of cells. Complete each odd magic square.

1. 3-by-3 magic square

2. 5-by-5 magic square

3. 7-by-7 magic square

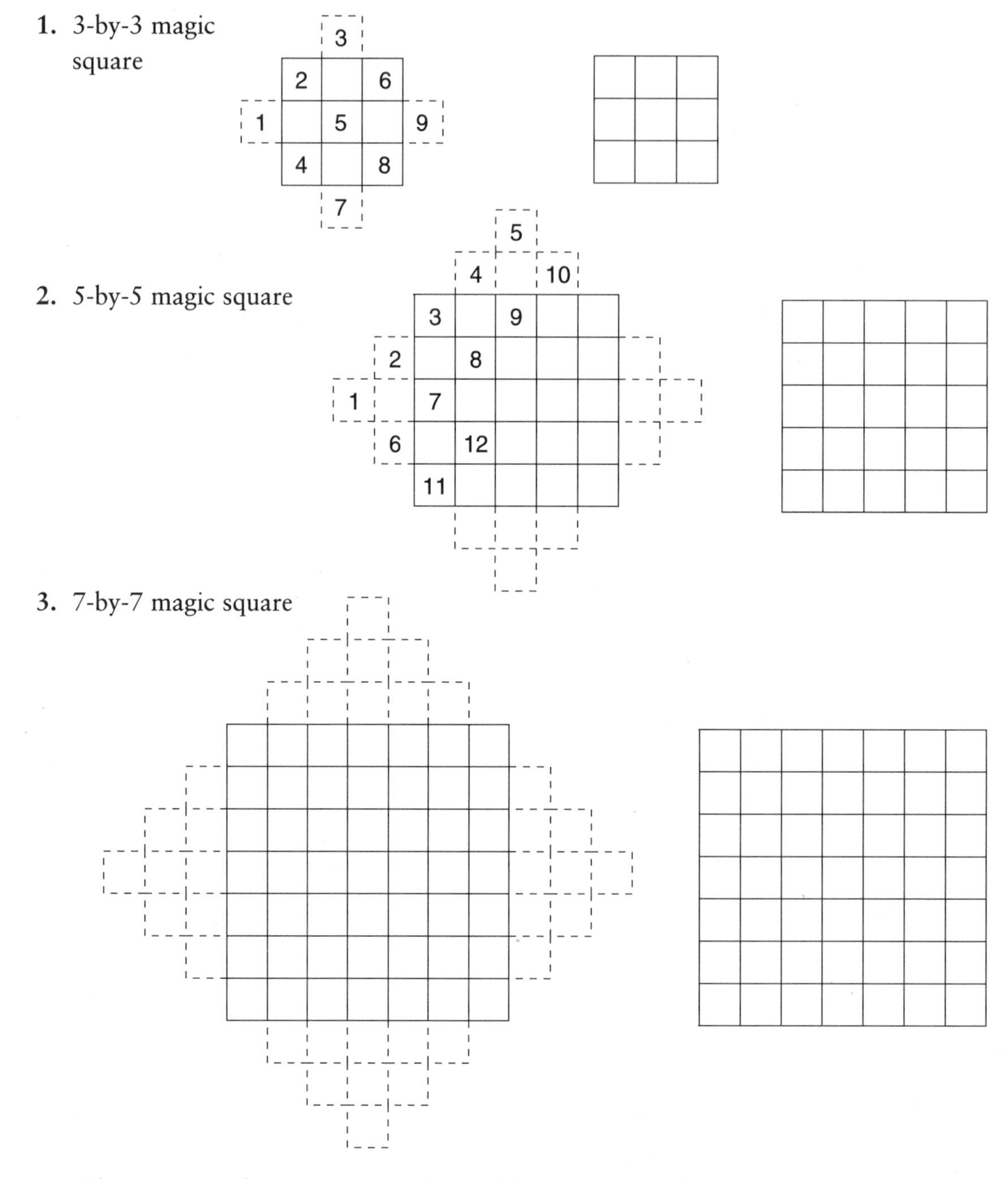


4. What patterns do you notice in these odd magic squares?

______________________________________________

______________________________________________

# C. A. Browne Jr.'s Fabulous 27 × 27 Composite Magic Square

| | | | | | | | | | | | | | | | | | | | | | | | | | | |
|---|---|---|---|---|---|---|---|---|---|---|---|---|---|---|---|---|---|---|---|---|---|---|---|---|---|---|
| 352 | 381 | 326 | 439 | 468 | 413 | 274 | 303 | 248 | 613 | 642 | 587 | 700 | 729 | 674 | 535 | 564 | 509 | 118 | 147 | 92 | 205 | 234 | 179 | 40 | 69 | 14 |
| 327 | 353 | 379 | 414 | 440 | 466 | 249 | 275 | 301 | 588 | 614 | 640 | 675 | 701 | 727 | 510 | 536 | 562 | 93 | 119 | 145 | 180 | 206 | 232 | 15 | 41 | 67 |
| 380 | 325 | 354 | 467 | 412 | 441 | 302 | 247 | 276 | 641 | 586 | 615 | 728 | 673 | 702 | 563 | 508 | 537 | 146 | 91 | 120 | 233 | 178 | 207 | 68 | 13 | 42 |
| 277 | 306 | 251 | 355 | 384 | 329 | 433 | 462 | 407 | 538 | 567 | 512 | 616 | 645 | 590 | 694 | 723 | 668 | 43 | 72 | 17 | 121 | 150 | 95 | 199 | 228 | 173 |
| 252 | 278 | 304 | 330 | 356 | 382 | 408 | 434 | 460 | 513 | 539 | 565 | 591 | 617 | 643 | 669 | 695 | 721 | 18 | 44 | 70 | 96 | 122 | 148 | 174 | 200 | 226 |
| 305 | 250 | 279 | 383 | 328 | 357 | 461 | 406 | 435 | 566 | 511 | 540 | 644 | 589 | 618 | 722 | 667 | 696 | 71 | 16 | 45 | 149 | 94 | 123 | 227 | 172 | 201 |
| 436 | 465 | 410 | 271 | 300 | 245 | 358 | 387 | 332 | 697 | 726 | 671 | 532 | 561 | 506 | 619 | 648 | 593 | 202 | 231 | 176 | 37 | 66 | 11 | 124 | 153 | 98 |
| 411 | 437 | 463 | 246 | 272 | 298 | 333 | 359 | 385 | 672 | 698 | 724 | 507 | 533 | 559 | 594 | 620 | 646 | 177 | 203 | 229 | 12 | 38 | 64 | 99 | 125 | 151 |
| 464 | 409 | 438 | 299 | 244 | 273 | 386 | 331 | 360 | 725 | 670 | 699 | 560 | 505 | 534 | 647 | 592 | 621 | 230 | 175 | 204 | 65 | 10 | 39 | 152 | 97 | 126 |
| 127 | 156 | 101 | 214 | 243 | 188 | 49 | 78 | 23 | 361 | 390 | 335 | 448 | 477 | 422 | 283 | 312 | 257 | 595 | 624 | 569 | 682 | 711 | 656 | 517 | 546 | 491 |
| 102 | 128 | 154 | 189 | 215 | 241 | 24 | 50 | 76 | 336 | 362 | 388 | 423 | 449 | 475 | 258 | 284 | 310 | 570 | 596 | 622 | 657 | 683 | 709 | 492 | 518 | 544 |
| 155 | 100 | 129 | 242 | 187 | 216 | 77 | 22 | 51 | 389 | 334 | 363 | 476 | 421 | 450 | 311 | 256 | 285 | 623 | 568 | 597 | 710 | 655 | 684 | 545 | 490 | 519 |
| 52 | 81 | 26 | 130 | 159 | 104 | 208 | 237 | 182 | 286 | 315 | 260 | 364 | 393 | 338 | 442 | 471 | 416 | 520 | 549 | 494 | 598 | 627 | 572 | 676 | 705 | 650 |
| 27 | 53 | 79 | 105 | 131 | 157 | 183 | 209 | 235 | 261 | 287 | 313 | 339 | 365 | 391 | 417 | 443 | 469 | 495 | 521 | 547 | 573 | 599 | 625 | 651 | 677 | 703 |
| 80 | 25 | 54 | 158 | 103 | 132 | 236 | 181 | 210 | 314 | 259 | 288 | 392 | 337 | 366 | 470 | 415 | 444 | 548 | 493 | 522 | 626 | 571 | 600 | 704 | 649 | 678 |
| 211 | 240 | 185 | 46 | 75 | 20 | 133 | 162 | 107 | 445 | 474 | 419 | 280 | 309 | 254 | 367 | 396 | 341 | 679 | 708 | 653 | 514 | 543 | 488 | 601 | 630 | 575 |
| 186 | 212 | 238 | 21 | 47 | 73 | 108 | 134 | 160 | 420 | 446 | 472 | 255 | 281 | 307 | 342 | 368 | 394 | 654 | 680 | 706 | 489 | 515 | 541 | 576 | 602 | 628 |
| 239 | 184 | 213 | 74 | 19 | 48 | 161 | 106 | 135 | 473 | 418 | 447 | 308 | 253 | 282 | 395 | 340 | 369 | 707 | 652 | 681 | 542 | 487 | 516 | 629 | 574 | 603 |
| 604 | 633 | 578 | 691 | 720 | 665 | 526 | 555 | 500 | 109 | 138 | 83 | 196 | 225 | 170 | 31 | 60 | 5 | 370 | 399 | 344 | 457 | 486 | 431 | 292 | 321 | 266 |
| 579 | 605 | 631 | 666 | 692 | 718 | 501 | 527 | 553 | 84 | 110 | 136 | 171 | 197 | 223 | 6 | 32 | 58 | 345 | 371 | 397 | 432 | 458 | 484 | 267 | 293 | 319 |
| 632 | 577 | 606 | 719 | 664 | 693 | 554 | 499 | 528 | 137 | 82 | 111 | 224 | 169 | 198 | 59 | 4 | 33 | 398 | 343 | 372 | 485 | 430 | 459 | 320 | 265 | 294 |
| 529 | 558 | 503 | 607 | 636 | 581 | 685 | 714 | 659 | 34 | 63 | 8 | 112 | 141 | 86 | 190 | 219 | 164 | 295 | 324 | 269 | 373 | 402 | 347 | 451 | 480 | 425 |
| 504 | 530 | 556 | 582 | 608 | 634 | 660 | 686 | 712 | 9 | 35 | 61 | 87 | 113 | 139 | 165 | 191 | 217 | 270 | 296 | 322 | 348 | 374 | 400 | 426 | 452 | 478 |
| 557 | 502 | 531 | 635 | 580 | 609 | 713 | 658 | 687 | 62 | 7 | 36 | 140 | 85 | 114 | 218 | 163 | 192 | 323 | 268 | 297 | 401 | 346 | 375 | 479 | 424 | 453 |
| 688 | 717 | 662 | 523 | 552 | 497 | 610 | 639 | 584 | 193 | 222 | 167 | 28 | 57 | 2 | 115 | 144 | 89 | 454 | 483 | 428 | 289 | 318 | 263 | 376 | 405 | 350 |
| 663 | 689 | 715 | 498 | 524 | 550 | 585 | 611 | 637 | 168 | 194 | 220 | 3 | 29 | 55 | 90 | 116 | 142 | 429 | 455 | 481 | 264 | 290 | 316 | 351 | 377 | 403 |
| 716 | 661 | 690 | 551 | 496 | 525 | 638 | 583 | 612 | 221 | 166 | 195 | 56 | 1 | 30 | 143 | 88 | 117 | 482 | 427 | 456 | 317 | 262 | 291 | 404 | 349 | 378 |

| | | |
|---|---|---|
| 4 | 9 | 2 |
| 3 | 5 | 7 |
| 8 | 1 | 6 |

Cornerstone 3 × 3

Name ______________________ Date ______________________

# Altering Magic Squares

Your have made magic squares of various sizes. In each case, the numbers in the square were consecutive natural numbers starting with 1. Do you think if we add, subtract, multiply, or divide each number of a magic square by the same number that you will still have a magic square?

1. Try adding 6 to each term of this 3-by-3 magic square.

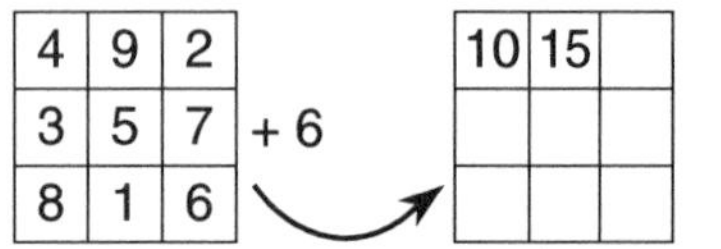


Is this also a magic square? ________

If so, what is the magic sum? ________

2. Choose four numbers greater than 1.

$A$ = _____ $B$ = _____ $C$ = _____ $D$ = _____

a. Take the number you chose for $A$ and add it to each term of the magic square.

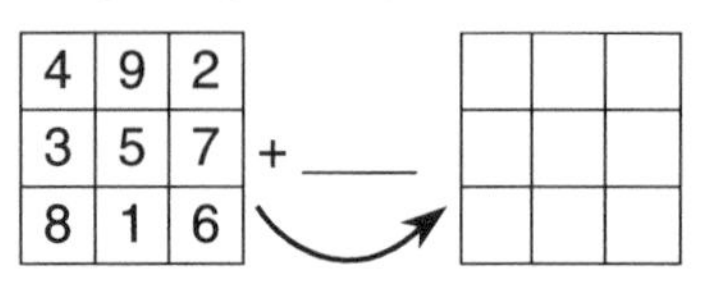


Is this also a magic square? ________

If so, what is the magic sum? ________

b. Take the number you chose for $B$ and subtract it from each term of the magic square.

| 4 | 9 | 2 |
|---|---|---|
| 3 | 5 | 7 |
| 8 | 1 | 6 |

+ ____

| | | |
|---|---|---|
| | | |
| | | |

Is this also a magic square? ________

If so, what is the magic sum? ________

c. Take the number you chose for $C$ and multiply it times each term of the magic square.

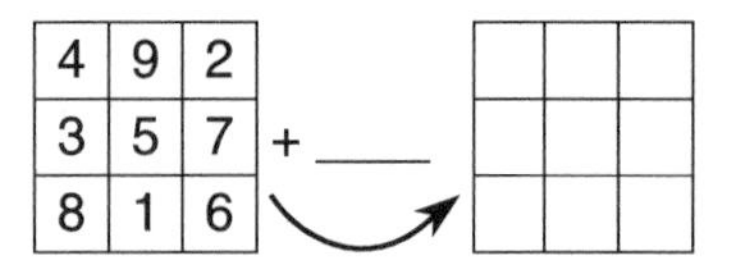


Is this also a magic square? ________

If so, what is the magic sum? ________

d. Take the number you chose for $D$ and divide each term of the magic square by it. Write your answers as fractions.

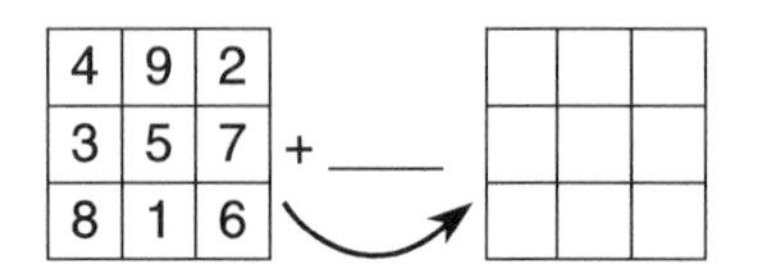


Is this also a magic square? ________

If so, what is the magic sum? ________

Name ______________________ Date ______________________

Altering Magic Squares (cont.)

e. Do you think if you first multiply each term of a magic square by the same number and then add another number to the answer you will still have a magic square? Try it.

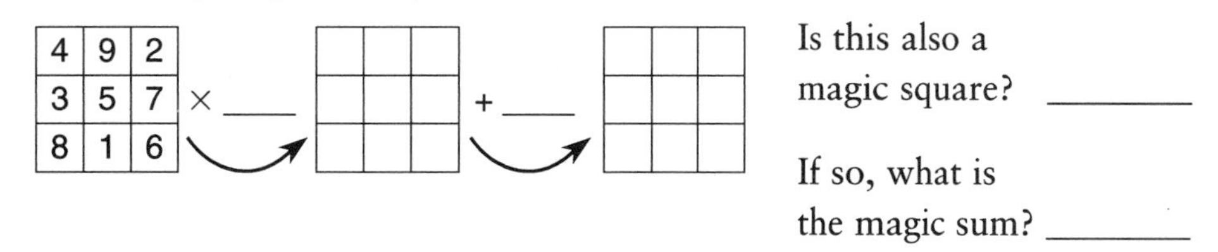


Is this also a magic square? ________

If so, what is the magic sum? ________

f. Square each term of this magic square.

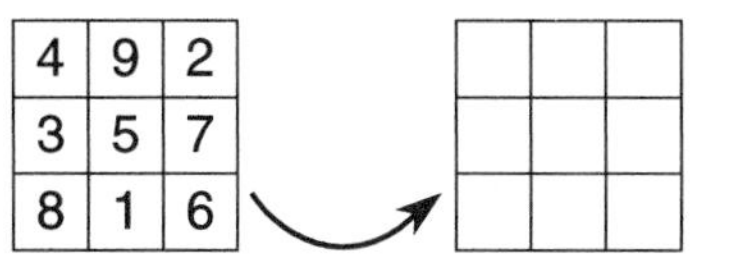


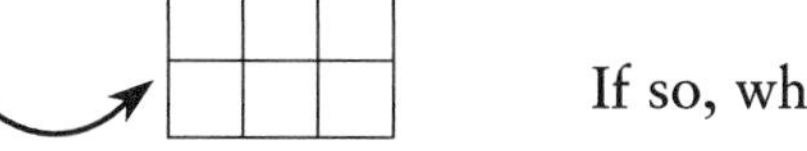

Is this also a magic square? ________

If so, what is the magic sum? ________

3. Look at the center number and the magic sum for each of the magic squares that you created in Problem 2. Do they follow the rule that the magic sum equals 3 times the center number? If not, which ones do not? ________________

**Bonus**

Here is another way to create a magic square.

A. Choose any three numbers for $X$, $Y$, and $Z$ and substitute them in the expressions at the right. For example, try $X = 5$, $Y = 7$, and $Z = 9$.

| $X - Y$ | $X + Y - Z$ | $X + Z$ |
|---|---|---|
| $X + Y + Z$ | $X$ | $X - Y - Z$ |
| $X - Z$ | $X + Z - Y$ | $X + Y$ |

What is the magic sum? ________

B. Choose your own values for $X$, $Y$, and $Z$.

$X =$ _____ $Y =$ _____ $Z =$ _____

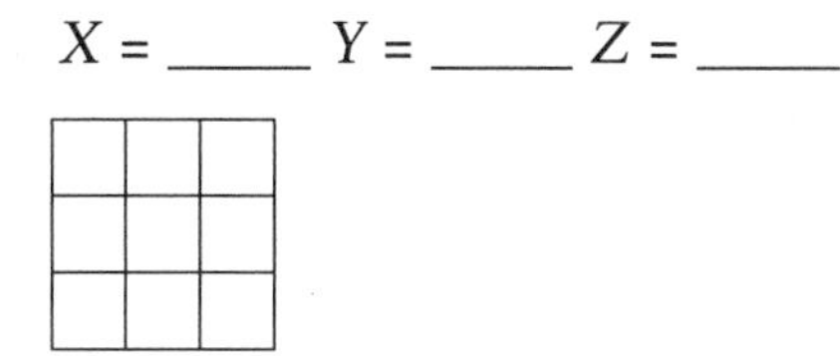

What is the magic sum? ________

C. Does the same rule of 3 times the middle number hold for these magic squares? Why or why not?

________________________________________

________________________________________

# Melancholia
## artist: Albrecht Dürer

# Alphamagic Squares

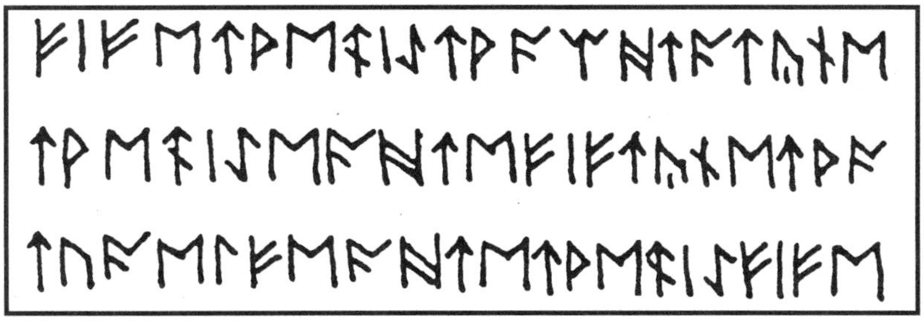

| 5 | 22 | 18 |
|---|---|---|
| 28 | 15 | 2 |
| 12 | 8 | 25 |

→

| five | twenty-two | eighteen |
|---|---|---|
| twenty-eight | fifteen | two |
| twelve | eight | twenty-five |

→

| 4 | 9 | 8 |
|---|---|---|
| 11 | 7 | 3 |
| 6 | 5 | 10 |

The recent deciphering of this fifth-century runic inscription led to the discovery of a new class of magic squares. The inscription consists of numbers that fill a 3-by-3 square. Each column, row, and diagonal adds to 45. When the number in each space is replaced by the number of letters in the word for the number, a new magic square is created—one that uses all the numbers from 3 to 11. It works in both the original language and in modern English.

# Muhammad ibn Muhammad

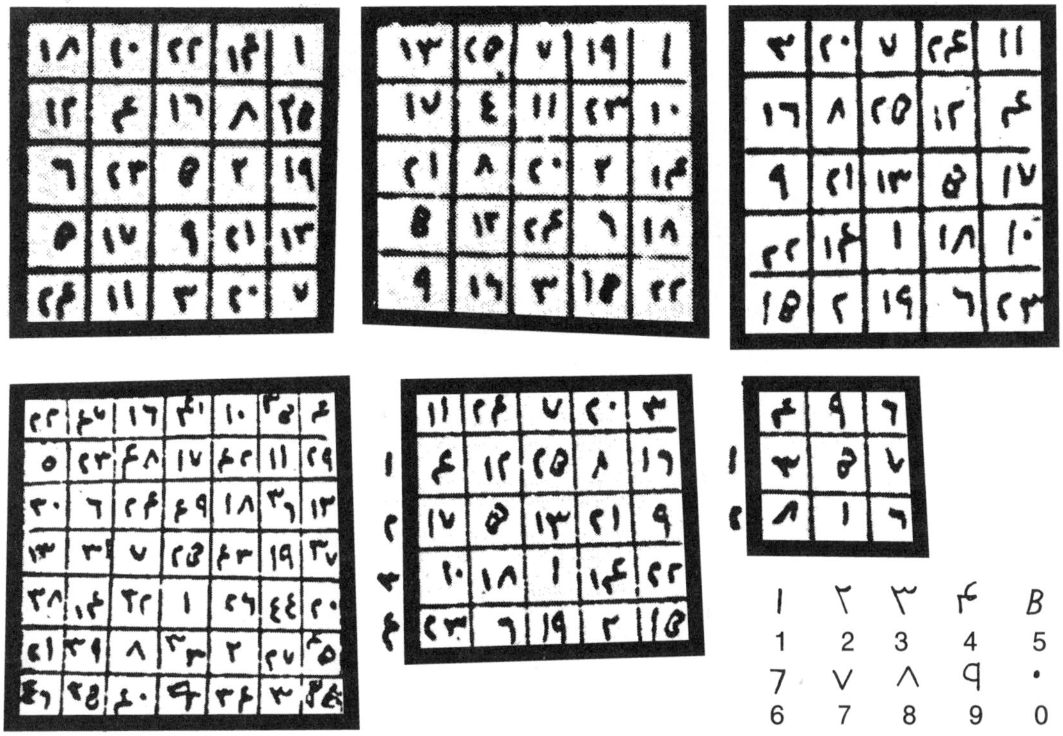

1 2 3 4 5

6 7 8 9 0

Name ______________________ Date ______________________

# Concentric Magic Squares

An *even* magic square has an even number of cells.

1. Here is an even *concentric* magic square for you to complete. It does not have a center number, but the rules for the diagonal corners still apply.

   a. What is the sum of the diagonal corners of the 4-by-4 magic square? ______

   b. What is the sum of the diagonal corners of the 6-by-6 magic square? ______

   c. What is the magic sum of the 4-by-4 magic square? ______

   d. What is the magic sum of the 6-by-6 magic square? ______

| | | | | | |
|---|---|---|---|---|---|
| 31 | | 28 | | 33 | 1 |
| | 23 | | 22 | 11 | |
| | | 20 | | | 34 |
| 32 | | | 17 | 24 | |
| | 26 | | 19 | | 30 |
| 36 | | | 29 | | |

2. Use this model to make your own concentric magic square. Choose values for $A$, $B$, $C$, $D$, and $E$ to substitute in the expressions below. Use the blank square on page 137.

| | | | | |
|---|---|---|---|---|
| $A + D$ | $A + D + E$ | $A - B - D$ | $A + B - D$ | $A - E$ |
| $A - C - D$ | $A - B$ | $A + B - C$ | $A + C$ | $A + C + D$ |
| $A + D - E$ | $A + B + C$ | $A$ | $A - B - C$ | $A - D + E$ |
| $A + C - D$ | $A - C$ | $A - B + C$ | $A + B$ | $A - C + D$ |
| $A + E$ | $A - D - E$ | $A + B + D$ | $A - B + D$ | $A - D$ |

$A$ = _____ $B$ = _____ $C$ = _____ $D$ = _____ $E$ = _____

Name ______________________________ Date ______________________________

Concentric Magic Squares (cont.)

**3. a.** What is the magic sum of your 3–by-3 magic square? ______

**b.** What is the magic sum of your 5-by-5 magic square? ______

**c.** What is the sum of each of the diagonal corner pairs of your 3-by-3 magic square? ______

| | | | | |
|---|---|---|---|---|
| | | | | |
| | | | | |
| | | | | |
| | | | | |
| | | | | |

**d.** How does this relate to the center number?

______________________________________________

**e.** What is the sum of each of the diagonal corner pairs of your 5-by-5 magic square? ______________________

**f.** How does this relate to the center number?

______________________________________________

**4. a.** Look at the general formula for a concentric magic square above. Will the sum of the diagonal corners always be twice the center number? Why or why not?

______________________________________________

______________________________________________

**b.** Will the magic sum always be 3 times the center number for the 3-by-3 square and 5 times the center number for the 5-by-5 square? Why or why not?

______________________________________________

______________________________________________

Name ______________________ Date ______________________

# Chinese Rod Numerals

The Chinese developed five different ways to write numbers. You can learn to read and write the Chinese numerals that were originally used more than 2,000 years ago and were still used up until the 19th century. In the Tang Dynasty (618–907), if you were an official you would be required to carry a little bag of bamboo or wooden sticks called *zhou* (counting pieces). When computing, the officials placed the sticks on a counting board called a *suan ban* that looked something like a checkerboard. Later, after the abacus was invented, the Chinese also called the abacus a *suan ban*.

Here are the first five Chinese numerals: 𝍠 𝍡 𝍢 𝍣 𝍤 (1 2 3 4 5) and the next four: 𝍥 𝍦 𝍧 𝍨 (6 7 8 9)

1. Why do you think 𝍥 stands for 6? ______________
2. Why do you think 𝍧 stands for 8? ______________
3. Using zhou, 10 is 𝍩 and 20 is 𝍪 . Use toothpicks as zhou to make 30, 40, and 50. Write your numerals. ______________
4. Using zhou, 60 is 𝍮 and 70 is 𝍯 . Write the numerals for 80 and 90. ______________
5. The symbols for 40 and 9 were combined to make 49: 𝍬𝍨 . Write the numerals for 67 and 88. ______________

The Chinese used symbols to write larger numbers too. Here is how they wrote 345,721: 𝍫𝍣𝍭𝍦𝍪𝍠 (3 4 5 7 2 1)

6. Which place values were written the same way as

   a. the ones? ______________  b. the tens? ______________

In the eighth century, Xiàhóu Yáng wrote the poem at the right in his *Mathematical Manual*. Xiàhóu Yáng's poem should tell you the answer to the two questions about writing place values. If you made a mistake, go back and correct your answers now.

*Units stand vertical, tens are horizontal,*
*Hundreds stand, thousands lie down.*
*Thousands and tens look the same,*
*Ten thousands and hundreds look alike.*
*Once bigger than six, Five is on top;*
*Six does not accumulate,*
*Five does not stand alone.*

The other thing you should know is that the Chinese would push the numbers together when writing them down, so 345,721 would actually look like this:

Name ________________________ Date ________________________

Chinese Rod Numerals (cont.)

7. Write 234,563. ____________

8. Write a number in rod numerals and have your partner translate it for you.

About 1,700 years ago, long before people in the Western world knew how to write with decimals, the Chinese understood how to write and began to compute with decimal fractions on their suan ban. When they did not have a digit in a place in the number, they left the spot blank on the suan ban. When the Hindu symbol for the blank spot, what we call "zero," became known and accepted in China 700 years ago, the Chinese could write any number. So 3,045 was written: ≡O≡||||

9. Write 504 and 1,001. ____________

During the Yuan Dynasty (1280–1368), when Kublai Khan was the ruler, the Chinese also wrote decimal numbers with the rod numerals. Look carefully at these two examples:

O≡|||| .3 4

OOO⊥═|⊢ .0 0 7 2 1

10. a. How did the Chinese write zero? The decimal point? ____________

b. How do you think they could tell the decimal point from the zero?

____________

11. What do you think might be a problem if you used the same symbol to represent both a zero and a decimal point when writing mixed numbers?

____________

12. In 0.34, the 3 is in the tenths place. Which symbols did the Chinese use, the same as the ones or the tens? ____________

The Chinese used the same symbols for the fractional part of the number as for the whole part. So to indicate the tens or tenths, they used the horizontal numbers. To indicate the ones, hundreds, or hundredths, they used the vertical numbers.

13. List five different values ⊥ can have when writing with rod numerals.

____________

14. Write 0.9201 and 0.0505. ____________

One problem with using the same symbol for the zero and decimal point is deciding what a zero means in the middle of a number. The Chinese realized this was a problem and so if they wanted to write a mixed number such as 23.45 they would not use the O for the decimal point. Instead they would insert the character *yu* which meant "remainder." Why do you think they chose this word?

Name ______________________ Date ______________________

Chinese Rod Numerals (cont.)

Now you are ready to try translating a real historical document.

**A Translation**

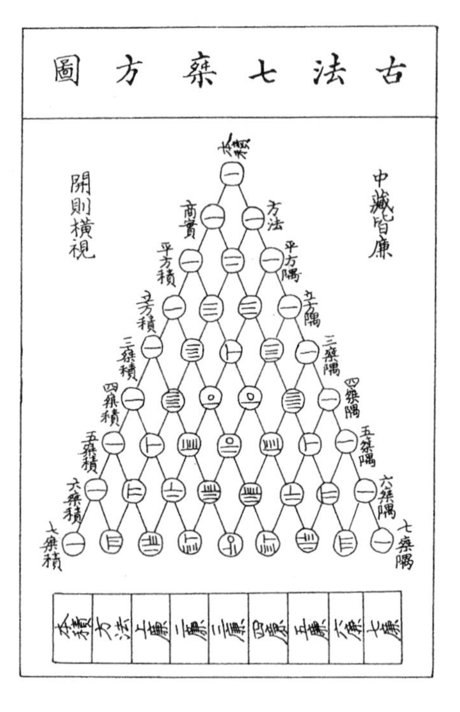


In 1303, Chu Shih-Chieh included the triangle at the left in his book *Precious Mirror of the Four Elements*. He said it really was an old method used in algebra by Chia Hsien around 1100. It looks very similar to the rod numerals that you have been writing. In fact, it is almost the same if you rotate some of the numbers.

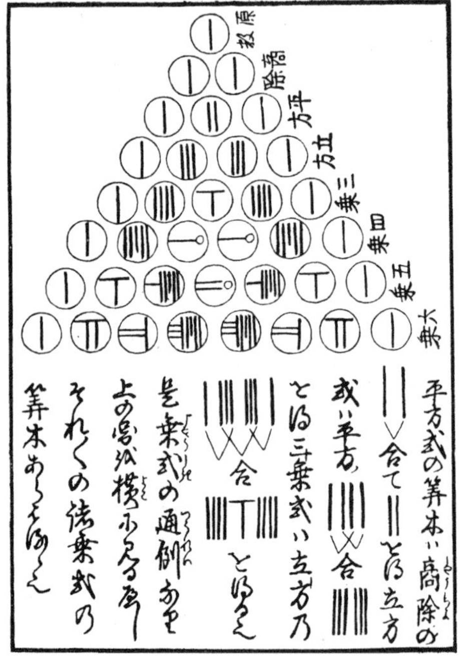

The Japanese also used Chinese rod numerals. In 1781, Murai wrote *Arithmetic for the Young*, and he included the same triangle written in the rod numerals as you know them. His triangle is shown at the right.

**15.** Translate the triangle into our numerals. Then study the pattern of the numbers in the triangle and then write the next two lines of the triangle.

**16.** Study your translation of the number triangle. Find three other patterns in the triangle and describe them.

______________________

______________________

______________________

______________________

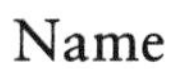

Name ______________________ Date ______________________

# The World Series and Pascal

Imagine that Hypatia's Hot Hitters and The Batting Bernoulli Brothers are playing the baseball World Series this year. It is a best-of-7 series of games. This means that the first team to win more than half of the 7 games wins the series.

1. What is the least number of games they must play? The greatest number of games? ____________

2. The first 4 games have already been played, and Hypatia's Hot Hitters have won 3 games and lost 1 game. What do you think is the probability that Hypatia's team will win the World Series? ____________

We can model the playing of the rest of the series by tossing a coin. For example, can we say "heads" means a win for Hypatia's Hot Hitters and "tails" means a loss.

3. What is the least number of tosses that could determine the series results? The greatest number? ____________

4. a. How many more wins do Hypatia's Hot Hitters need to win the series? ____________

   b. How many more wins do The Batting Bernoulli Brothers need to win the series? ____________

5. With your partner, try playing the World Series eight times. For each series, record each of the coin tosses (game results) and which team won the series.

6. What fraction of the time did Hypatia's Hot Hitters win the series? ____________

7. The Chevalier de Méré wrote the mathematician Blaise Pascal (1623–1662) a letter inquiring how to fairly divide the prize if a game is stopped before it is over. Imagine you have been playing a series of games in a sports tournament and the winner is the first person to win 4 games. The prize for the winner of the tournament is $80. The game is stopped when you have 1 point and your opponent has 3. How should you fairly divide the prize? Your opponent might say, "I've got 3 points and need only 1 more to win, so I should get $80." You might say, "Wait a minute! I have 1 point, so I could still win the tournament. Your plan is not fair." How do you think the prize should be divided?

   ______________________________________________

8. Explain your answer. How is this problem related to the World Series question?

   ______________________________________________

   ______________________________________________

Name ______________________ Date ______________________

# Math Detective: How Did They Do That?

You are math detectives trying to figure out how several ancient cultures multiplied. In each case, study the multiplication example for 237 × 672. When you know how to multiply as in the example, show how to multiply 129 × 1,482. Be ready to explain the process to your classmates.

**1. a.** Ancient Egyptian Multiplication

| 237 | × 672 |
|---|---|
| ✓ 1 | 672 |
| 2 | 1,344 |
| ✓ 4 | 2,688 |
| ✓ 8 | 5,376 |
| 16 | 10,752 |
| ✓ 32 | 21,504 |
| ✓ 64 | 43,008 |
| ✓ 128 | 86,016 |

Product: 159, 264

129 × 1,482

**b.** Explain why you think this method of multiplication is easier or harder than the algorithm for multiplication that you have learned.

______________________________________________

______________________________________________

**2. a.** Russian Peasant Multiplication

| 237 × 672 | |
|---|---|
| 237 | 672 |
| ~~118~~ | ~~1,344~~ |
| 59 | 2,688 |
| 29 | 5,376 |
| ~~14~~ | ~~10,752~~ |
| 7 | 21,504 |
| 3 | 43,008 |
| 1 | 86,016 |

Product: 159,264

129 × 1,482

**b.** Explain why you think this method of multiplication is easier or harder than the algorithm for multiplication that you have learned.

______________________________________________

______________________________________________

Name ____________________ Date ____________________

**Math Detective: How Did They Do That? (cont.)**

3. **a.** Lattice (or Gelosia) Multiplication

**237 × 672** **129 × 1,482**

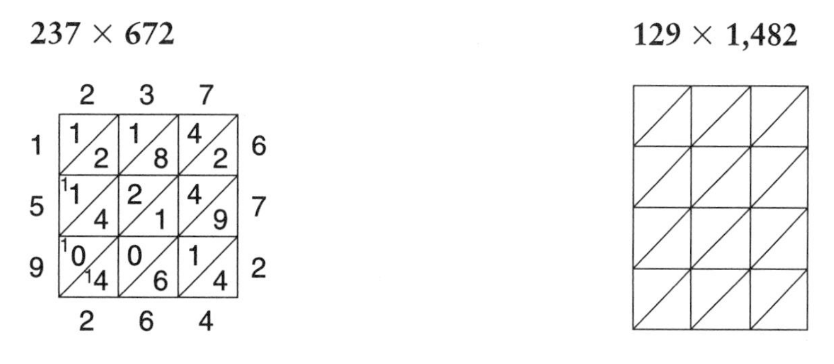

Product: 15,264

**b.** Explain why you think this method of multiplication is easier or harder than the algorithm for multiplication that you have learned.

_______________________________________________

_______________________________________________

4. **a.** Sacchieri Multiplication

**237 × 672** **129 × 1,482**

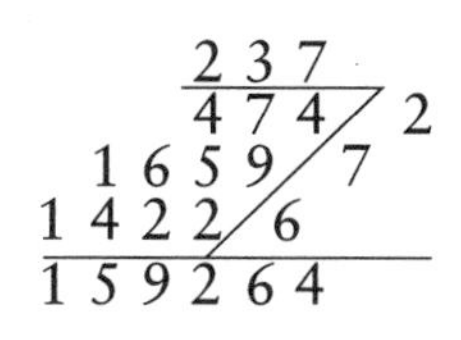


Product: 159,264

**b.** Explain why you think this method of multiplication is easier or harder than the algorithm for multiplication that you have learned.

_______________________________________________

_______________________________________________

Name ______________________ Date ______________________

Math Detective: How Did They Do That? (cont.)

5. a. Hindu Multiplication

237 × 672      129 × 1,482

```
    6 7 2
  2 3 7
-------
1 4 2 2
  1 6 5 9
      4 7 4
---------
1 5 9 2 6 4
```

Product: 159,264

b. Explain why you think this method of multiplication is easier or harder than the algorithm for multiplication that you have learned.

______________________________________________

______________________________________________

Name ______________________ Date ______________________

Activity

# Egyptian Unit Fractions

More than 3,500 years ago, the Egyptians computed with fractions; however, their fractions were different from ours in that they used only fractions with a numerator of 1.

The Egyptians wrote whole numbers using the following hieroglyphics:

𓏺 = 1   𓎆 = 10   𓍢 = 100   𓆼 = 1,000   𓂭 = 10,000

Their system was additive, using at most nine of any symbol. For example,

324 was written 𓏺𓏺𓏺𓏺𓎆𓎆𓍢𓍢𓍢.

1,205 was written 𓏺𓏺𓏺𓏺𓏺𓍢𓍢𓆼.

To write a unit fraction, the Egyptians wrote the symbol 𓂋, meaning "mouth," over what we call the denominator.

$\frac{1}{5}$ = 𓂋𓏺𓏺𓏺𓏺𓏺 and $\frac{1}{324}$ = 𓂋𓏺𓏺𓏺𓏺𓎆𓎆𓍢𓍢𓍢

To write a fraction other than a unit fraction, they wrote unit fractions whose sum was the desired fraction.

$\frac{3}{4}$ is 𓂋𓏺𓏺 𓂋𓏺𓏺𓏺𓏺, because $\frac{1}{2} + \frac{1}{4} = \frac{3}{4}$.

1. Find the total value for each Egyptian fraction.

a. 𓂋𓎆𓎆 ____________

b. 𓂋𓏺𓏺𓏺𓏺𓏺 𓂋𓏺𓏺𓏺𓏺𓏺𓏺𓏺𓏺𓏺 ____________

c. 𓂋𓏺𓏺𓏺 𓂋𓎆𓎆 ____________

d. 𓂋𓏺𓏺𓏺𓏺𓏺𓎆𓎆 𓂋𓏺𓏺𓏺𓏺𓏺𓎆 ____________

e. 𓂋𓆼𓆼 𓂋𓆼 ____________

f. 𓂋𓏺𓏺𓎆𓎆𓂭𓂭𓂭𓂭 𓂋𓏺𓏺 ____________

g. 𓂋𓆼𓂭 𓂋𓏺𓏺 ____________

2. Write each fraction using Egyptian hieroglyphics.

a. $\frac{1}{641}$

b. $\frac{1}{231}$

c. $\frac{1}{22{,}031}$

d. $\frac{11}{24}$ (Hint: $\frac{11}{24} = \frac{1}{3} +$ ____ )

e. $\frac{11}{18}$ (Hint: Think of the factors of the denominator.)

f. $\frac{17}{72}$

Name ______________________________ Date ______________________________

Egyptian Unit Fractions (cont.)

3. Sometimes there is more than one way to write a fraction as a sum of unit fractions. For example:

   $\frac{2}{35} = \frac{1}{21} + \frac{1}{105}$ $\quad \frac{2}{35} = \frac{1}{30} + \frac{1}{42}$ $\quad \frac{2}{35} = \frac{1}{20} + \frac{1}{140}$

   Find two different ways to represent $\frac{5}{12}$.
   What are they? ______________________________

**Bonus**

From Problem 3, you know there can be more than one way to represent a fraction using unit fractions. No one who is alive today spoke with the ancient Egyptians and they did not leave specific directions on how to determine which combination of unit fractions to use. Figuring out ways to generate unit fractions for any fraction is a problem that interested some mathematicians. J.J. Sylvester (1814–1897) developed a method to generate unit fractions.

Start with a fraction, for example $\frac{9}{24}$.

**Step 1:** Subtract the greatest fraction less than the given fraction. $\frac{1}{2}$ is greater than $\frac{9}{24}$, and $\frac{1}{3}$ is the greatest unit fraction less than $\frac{9}{24}$, so subtract $\frac{1}{3}$.

$\frac{9}{24} - \frac{1}{3} = \frac{9}{24} - \frac{8}{24} = \frac{1}{24}$, so $\frac{9}{24} = \frac{1}{3} + \frac{1}{24}$.

**Step 2:** If the result of Step 1 does not result in only unit fractions, repeat the process with the fraction that is *not* a unit fraction.

Step 1 worked for $\frac{9}{24}$, so we did not need to go onto Step 2. However, look at $\frac{13}{20}$.

$\frac{1}{2}$ is the greatest unit fraction less than $\frac{13}{20}$, so subtract $\frac{1}{2}$.

$\frac{13}{20} - \frac{1}{2} = \frac{13}{20} - \frac{10}{20} = \frac{3}{20}$, so $\frac{13}{20} = \frac{1}{2} + \frac{3}{20}$.

But $\frac{3}{20}$ is not a unit fraction, so repeat the process. The greatest unit fraction less than $\frac{3}{20}$ is $\frac{1}{7}$, so subtract $\frac{1}{7}$.

$\frac{3}{20} - \frac{1}{7} = \frac{21}{140} - \frac{20}{140} = \frac{1}{140}$, so $\frac{3}{20} = \frac{1}{7} + \frac{1}{140}$, and $\frac{13}{20} = \frac{1}{2} + \frac{3}{20} = \frac{1}{2} + \frac{1}{7} + \frac{1}{140}$.

Use Sylvester's Rule to convert each fraction to a unit fraction.

**A.** $\frac{7}{24}$ ______________________ **B.** $\frac{17}{36}$ ______________________

Name ______________________ Date ______________________

Activity

# Eye-of-Horus Fractions

Horus was the son of the Egyptian gods Osiris and Isis. Osiris, the Judge of the Dead, had been murdered by his brother Set. When Horus grew up, he set out to avenge the death of his father by his uncle Set. In one of their savage battles, Horus lost his eye; it was cut into 6 pieces. Finally the other gods intervened, made Horus the god protecting the pharaohs, and made Set the God of Barbarians and Lord of Evil. Thoth, the God of Magic and Learning, collected the pieces of Horus's eye, and, using magic, restored it and gave it back to Horus. The Eye of Horus became the symbol of wholeness, health, total vision, abundance, and fertility.

The ancient Egyptians had a special set of fractions to be used when measuring grain. They measured grain in *hekats*; a hekat is about $\frac{1}{8}$ of a bushel in our measurements. These symbols were based on the Eye of Horus.

$\frac{1}{8}$ $\frac{1}{4}$ $\frac{1}{16}$ $\frac{1}{2}$ $\frac{1}{32}$ $\frac{1}{64}$

$\frac{1}{2}$ $\frac{1}{4}$ $\frac{1}{8}$ $\frac{1}{16}$ $\frac{1}{32}$ $\frac{1}{64}$

Once an apprentice scribe noticed that the sum of the fractions that make up the Eye of Horus fractions is not 1. He was told that Thoth would always supply the missing part if he put himself under the protection of Thoth.

1. What is the value of the missing part of the Eye of Horus? ______________

The Egyptians used only unit fractions, in which the numerator is 1, and never repeated the same fraction. So $\frac{3}{8}$ would be represented as ○∫ , because $\frac{3}{8} = \frac{1}{4} + \frac{1}{8}$.

2. Write each fraction using Eye-of-Horus fractions.

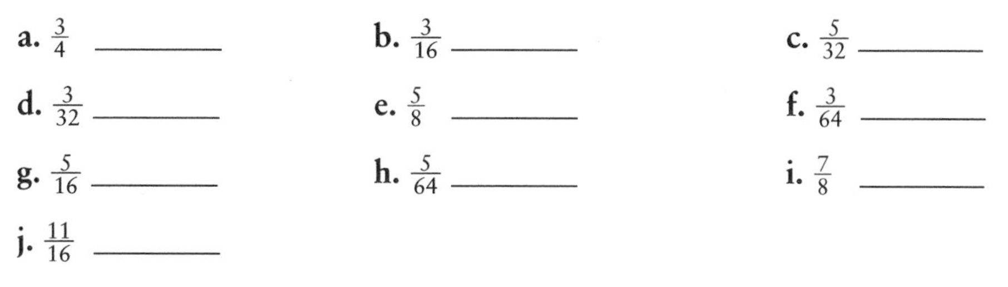

a. $\frac{3}{4}$ ________ b. $\frac{3}{16}$ ________ c. $\frac{5}{32}$ ________

d. $\frac{3}{32}$ ________ e. $\frac{5}{8}$ ________ f. $\frac{3}{64}$ ________

g. $\frac{5}{16}$ ________ h. $\frac{5}{64}$ ________ i. $\frac{7}{8}$ ________

j. $\frac{11}{16}$ ________

**Bonus**

Can any fraction be written using Eye of Horus fractions? If you think that the answer is *yes*, explain why. If you think that the answer is *no*, give an example and show why the fraction cannot be written this way.

______________________________________________

______________________________________________

Name ______________________________ Date ______________________________

# Writing Decimals Through the Years

Tell what decimal number each notation represents.

| | Notation | Source | Answer |
|---|---|---|---|
| **1.** | 163'35 | al-Uglidīsī<br>Damascus, 952 | ________ |
| **2.** | ○⊥\|\|\|\| | Yuan Dynasty<br>China, 1280–1368 | ________ |
| **3.** | Sah-hah<br>3 141592635898732 | al-Kāshī<br>Samarkand, early 1400s | ________ |
| **4.** | 393 \| 75 | Christoff Rudolff<br>Vienna, 1530 | ________ |
| **5.** | 141,421 $\underline{356,24}$ | Francois Viète<br>France, 1579 | ________ |
| **6.** | **314,159**,265,36 | Francois Viète<br>France, 1579 | ________ |
| **7.** | 3 ⓪ 1 ① 4 ② | Simon Stevin<br>Belgium, 1585 | ________ |
| **8.** | 0 i ii iii iv v vi<br>123.4.5.9.8.7.2 | Johann H. Beyer<br>Frankfurt, 1603 | ________ |
| **9.** | 8 79$\overset{\vee}{8}$ | Johann H. Beyer<br>Frankfurt, 1603 | ________ |
| **10.** | 017 | Bartholomacus Pitiscus<br>Heidelberg, 1608 | ________ |
| **11.** | 13 \| 00024 | Bartholomacus Pitiscus<br>Heidelberg, 1612 | ________ |
| **12.** | I II III IIII<br>1994,9 1 6 0 | John Napier<br>Edinburgh, 1617 | ________ |
| **13.** | 001414 | Joost Bürgi<br>Prag, 1620 | ________ |
| **14.** | 14$\underset{o}{1}$4 | Joost Bürgi<br>Prag, 1623 | ________ |
| **15.** | 3 \| 1.2.3.4.5.<br>3 \| 22916 | John Johnson<br>1623 | ________ |
| **16.** | $5^{\underline{9321}}$ | Henry Briggs<br>London, 1624 | ________ |
| **17.** | 693② | Wilhelm Von Kulcheim<br>Bremen, 1629 | ________ |
| **18.** | 1,532 | A. Girard<br>Amsterdam, 1629 | ________ |

Name ______________________ Date ______________________

Writing Decimals Through the Years (cont.)

| | | | |
|---|---|---|---|
| **19.** | 39(063 | Joach Stegman<br>Rakow, 1630 | ____________ |
| **20.** | $2^{\underline{15}}$ | William Oughtred<br>England, 1631 | ____________ |
| **21.** | .25 | John Kersey<br>1650 | ____________ |
| **22.** | $16\,|\,\dot{7}\dot{2}\dot{4}\dot{9}$ | Robert Jager<br>London, 1651 | ____________ |
| **23.** | 3:04 | Richard Balam<br>London, 1653 | ____________ |
| **24.** | 58,5① | Francisci à Schoute<br>Leyden, 1657 | ____________ |
| **25.** | $31.^{\underline{008}}$ | Samuel Foster<br>London, 1659 | ____________ |
| **26.** | $25.\overset{i}{8}\overset{ii}{0}\overset{iii}{0}\overset{iv}{7}\overset{v}{9}$ | Andrea Tacquet<br>Antwerp, 1665 | ____________ |
| **27.** | 12[345 | N. Mercator<br>1668 | ____________ |
| **28.** | 92=123,345 | Johann Caramuel<br>Companiae, 1670 | ____________ |
| **29.** | 22=3 | Johann Caramuel<br>Companiae, 1670 | ____________ |
| **30.** | $27209779\overset{vi}{2}$ | Jean Prestet<br>Paris, 1689 | ____________ |
| **31.** | $645.\,\frac{879}{1000}$ | Tobias Beutel<br>Leipzig, 1690 | ____________ |
| **32.** | 30‚24 | William Molyneux<br>London, 1692 | ____________ |
| **33.** | 0;9985 | G. Whiston<br>Cambridge, 1707 | ____________ |
| **34.** | $4.\overset{I}{2}\overset{IV}{5}$ | Paolino Chelucci<br>Rome, 1738 | ____________ |
| **35.** | $32.\overset{I}{6}\overset{II}{3}\overset{III}{4}$ | L' Abbé Deidier<br>Paris, 1739 | ____________ |
| **36.** | (4) 2677 | H. Sherwin<br>London, 1741 | ____________ |
| **37.** | 2'5 | Luis Monsante<br>Lima, 1872 | ____________ |
| **38.** | $2_{\blacktriangle}5$ | A.F. Vallin<br>Madrid, 1889 | ____________ |

Name ______________________ Date ______________________

# To Repeat or Not Repeat, That Is the Question

Every fraction can be converted to a decimal. Fractions have either nonrepeating, or *terminating*, decimals or infinitely repeating, or *nonterminating*, decimals.

1. Use your calculator to decide in which category each fraction belongs.
   $\frac{1}{2}, \frac{1}{3}, \frac{1}{4}, \frac{1}{5}, \frac{1}{6}, \frac{1}{7}, \frac{1}{8}, \frac{1}{9}, \frac{1}{10}, \frac{1}{11}, \frac{1}{12}$

   Nonrepeating ______________________

   Repeating ______________________

2. Write the denominator for each fraction in Problem 1 in prime factored form.

   ______________________

   ______________________

3. What do you notice about the denominators of the numbers in the nonrepeating category?

   ______________________

4. Predict which of the following fractions is a nonrepeating decimal. Then check to see if you were correct.

   a. $\frac{1}{15}$ ______________ b. $\frac{1}{16}$ ______________

   c. $\frac{1}{20}$ ______________ d. $\frac{1}{24}$ ______________

   e. $\frac{1}{30}$ ______________ f. $\frac{1}{40}$ ______________

5. Try to write a rule to use to tell whether a fraction will be repeating or not before you actually check it by dividing on your calculator.

   ______________________

   ______________________

6. Why do you think this rule applies?

   ______________________

   ______________________

7. Write 60 in prime factored form. ______________________

Name ______________________ Date ______________________

# Divide Like a Babylonian

Five thousand years ago, in the valleys of the Tigris and Euphrates Rivers, lived the people who developed the first known writing system. They wrote by making wedge-shaped marks in clay with a stylus. People have found mathematical texts that are 4,000 years old. The Babylonians understood how to calculate using *sexigesimals*, a base-60 system that included fractions written in what we call "decimal form." Their methods of addition, subtraction, and multiplication are similar to ours. However, the Babylonians had a different way of dividing; they changed the division problems to multiplication problems.

In order to divide like a Babylonian, you need to create a reciprocal table using decimals. For example: The reciprocal of 5 is $\frac{1}{5} = 0.2$.

**1.** Complete these tables by giving each reciprocal in decimal form.

| | Number | Reciprocal |
|---|---|---|
| | 5 | 0.2 |
| **a.** | 2 | |
| **b.** | 4 | |
| **c.** | 8 | |

| | Number | Reciprocal |
|---|---|---|
| **d.** | 10 | |
| **e.** | 25 | |
| **f.** | 50 | |
| **g.** | 125 | |

To divide by 5, the Babylonians multiplied by its reciprocal, 0.2.
So, $2{,}785 \div 5 = 2{,}785 \times 0.2 = 557$.

**2.** Which do you think is generally easier, dividing by 5 or multiplying by 0.2? Remember, there were no calculators then. ______________________

Divide the Babylonian way, and show your work.

**3.** $2{,}745 \div 25$ ____________

**4.** $3{,}257 \div 50$ ____________

**5.** $18{,}848 \div 8$ ____________

Name ______________________ Date ______________________

# An Old-Time Toy: The Tower Puzzle

If you were born 100 years ago, you might have played with a "new" puzzle that was first sold as a toy in 1883. Even though you are not that old you still might have tried this puzzle.

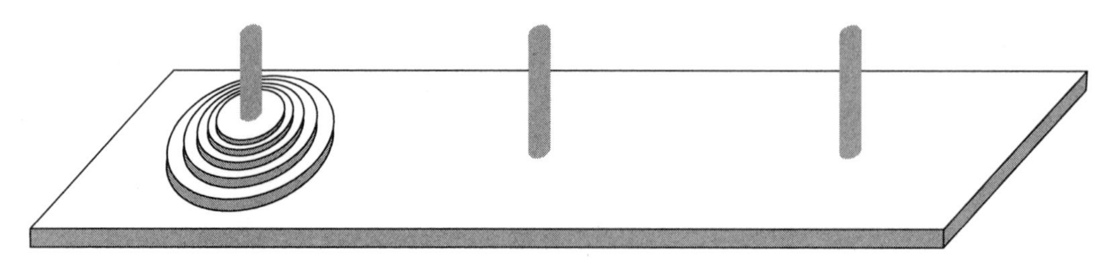

### Trying the Tower Puzzle

The goal is to move all the disks from one dowel to another, *but*

**a.** You may move only one disk at a time.

**b.** You may never put a larger disk on top of a smaller disk.

**c.** You may move a disk only if it is the top one. You can not take a disk from below another and move it someplace else.

Try the puzzle using the disks your teacher gives you.

### Investigating the Tower Puzzle

Work with a partner to find some of the patterns in this puzzle and to find the least number of moves necessary to transfer the disks.

1. What is the least number of moves to transfer the given number of disks from one dowel to another?

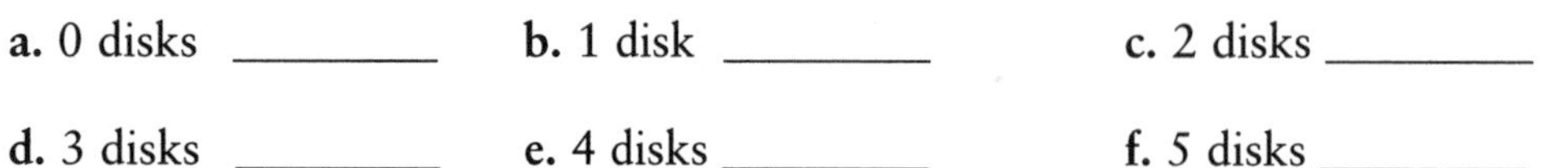

**a.** 0 disks ________ **b.** 1 disk ________ **c.** 2 disks ________

**d.** 3 disks ________ **e.** 4 disks ________ **f.** 5 disks ________

**g.** 10 disks ________

2. What patterns do you notice in the number of moves in Problem 1?

______________________________________________

______________________________________________

Name ______________________ Date ______________________



3. Is there any pattern with the colors of the disks? Try moving the disks from one dowel to another again. This time watch the colors. What happens? Try to state a rule based on color that will help give the least number of moves.

______________________

______________________

4. Keep track of which disk is moved when transferring disks from one tower to another. For example, if disk A is moved and then disk B, record *AB*.

   a. 1 disk ______________________

   b. 2 disks ______________________

   c. 3 disks ______________________

   d. 4 disks ______________________

   e. 5 disks ______________________

   f. 6 disks ______________________

5. What do you notice about the patterns of the disk moving in Problem 4?

______________________

______________________

6. Try moving 4 disks again. Use this table to keep track of the total number of moves for each disk.

7. Try moving 5 disks again. Use this table to keep track of the total number of moves for each disk.

8. What pattern do you notice for the number of moves for each disk?

______________________

______________________

Name ______________________ Date ______________________



### Further Investigating the Tower Puzzle

9. Suppose you wanted the tower to be transferred to a specific different tower. Propose a rule as to where to put the first disk, and then check your rule. If your rule does not work for each of the various size stacks of disks, revise your rule and check it again. What is your rule?

______________________________________________

______________________________________________

The following is a legend about the tower puzzle.

> "In the great temple at Benares beneath the dome which marks the center of the world, rests a brass plate in which are fixed three diamond needles, each a cubit high and as thick as the body of a bee. On one of these needles, at the creation, God placed sixty-four disks of pure gold, the largest disk resting on the brass plate and the others getting smaller and smaller up to the top one. This is the Tower of Brahma. Day and night unceasingly, the priests transfer the disks from one diamond needle to another, according to the fixed and immutable laws of Brahma, which require that the priest on duty must not move more than one disk at a time and that he must place this disk on a needle so that there is never a smaller disk below it. When the sixty-four disks shall have been thus transferred from the needle on which, at the creation, God placed them, to one of the other needles, tower, temple, and Brahmans alike will crumble into dust, and with a thunderclap, the world will vanish."

10. If these priests are working in shifts, day and night, unceasingly transferring a disk every second, are we in danger that the world will come to an end? Why or why not?

______________________________________________

______________________________________________

# The Tower Puzzle Disks A

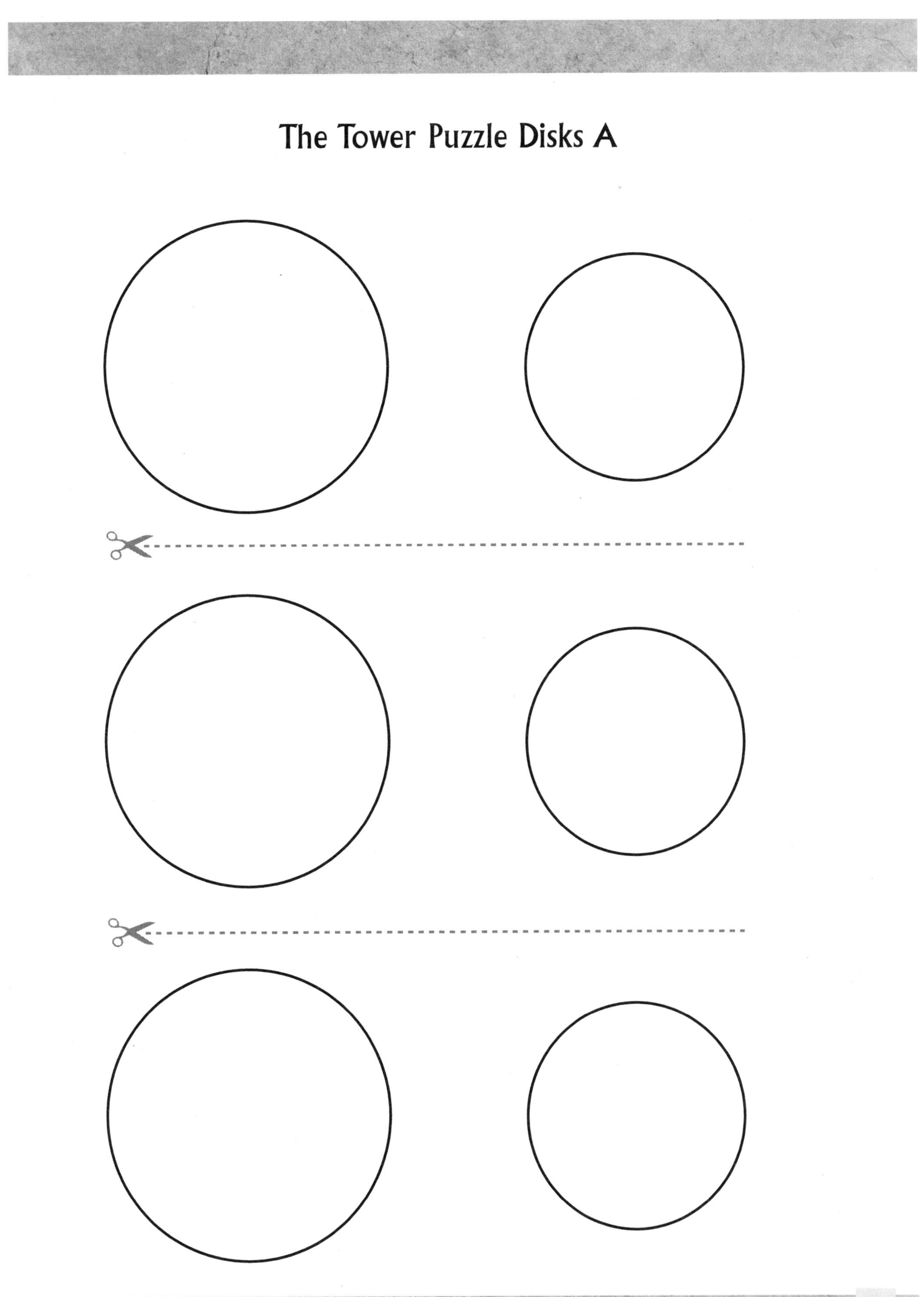

# The Tower Puzzle Disks B

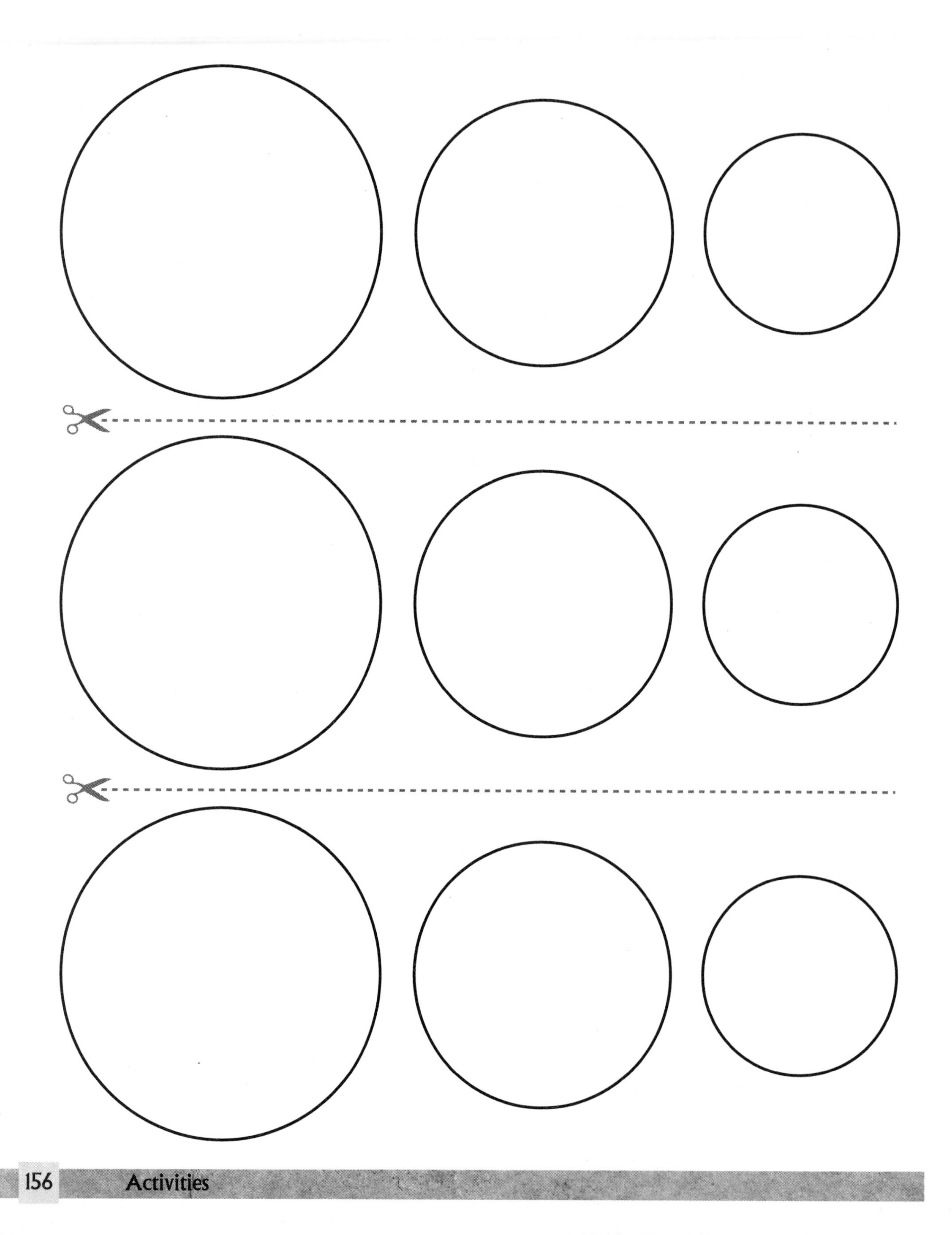

Name ________________________ Date ________________________

# Mersenne Primes and Perfect Numbers

Friar Marin Mersenne founded an informal social group that met at his monastery from 1635 to 1648 and discussed the latest developments in mathematics and science. Among the regular visitors to these sessions were Étienne Pascal and his son Blaise, as well as René Descartes. Mersenne also corresponded with famous mathematicians from all over Europe. A prime number that can be written as $2^n - 1$ when $n \geq 1$ is called a *Mersenne prime.*

In June, 1640, Pierre Fermat wrote Mersenne a letter in which he said that if $2^n - 1$ is a prime number, then $n$ is a prime number.

1. With a partner check these numbers to see if the following is true: If $n$ is a prime number, then $2^n - 1$ is a prime number.

| | $n$ | Is $n$ a Prime? | $2^n - 1$ | Is $2^n - 1$ a Prime? List Its Factors. |
|---|---|---|---|---|
| a. | 1 | | | |
| b. | 2 | | | |
| c. | 3 | | | |
| d. | 4 | | | |
| e. | 5 | | | |
| f. | 6 | | | |
| g. | 7 | | | |
| h. | 8 | | | |
| i. | 9 | | | |
| j. | 10 | | | |
| k. | 11 | | | |

2. Study your table. Is there any prime number that does *not* give a Mersenne prime? If so, what is it? ____________________

You should have found that "If $n$ is a prime number, then $2^n - 1$ is a prime number" is not the same as "If $2^n - 1$ is a prime number, then $n$ is a prime number." Edouard Lucas, the inventor of the Tower Puzzle, was interested in Mersenne primes. He showed that $2^{127} - 1$ is a prime. But the fact that 127 is a prime number did not guarantee that the 39-digit number $2^{127} - 1$ is prime. It was not until 1952 that a computer found a greater Mersenne prime, $2^{2,281} - 1$.

Name ______________________ Date ______________________



Long before Mersenne lived, people were interested in numbers of the form of $2^n - 1$. About 300 B.C.E., Euclid wrote *The Elements*. Most people think the book was only about geometry, but Euclid was also interested in number theory and wrote about perfect numbers.

A *perfect number* is one whose sum of its proper factors is equal to the number itself. For example, 4 is *not* a perfect number because the proper factors of 4 are 1 and 2, and $1 + 2 = 3$.

3. Check 5, 6, and 8. Are any of these perfect numbers? If so, which ones? ______________

Euclid claimed: If $2^n - 1$ is a prime number, then $(2^{n-1})(2^n - 1)$ is a perfect number.

4. Use the Mersenne primes you found in the first table to find four perfect numbers. Then prove that they are perfect.

| $n$ | $(2^{n-1})(2^n - 1)$ | List of Factors | Sum of Proper Factors |
|---|---|---|---|
| | | | |
| | | | |
| | | | |
| | | | |
| | | | |
| | | | |
| | | | |
| | | | |
| | | | |
| | | | |
| | | | |

______________________________________________

______________________________________________

______________________________________________

______________________________________________

Name ______________________ Date ______________________

# Chess

Indian legend tells the story of how the scholar Sessa Ben Dahir, the inventor of chess, presented his new game to King Shirhan of India, who was amazed by his ingenuity in creating a game with so many possible moves. The king wanted to generously reward Sessa and asked what he wanted. Sessa requested grains of wheat to cover the checkerboard. In the first square would be 1 grain; the second, 2; the third, 4; the fourth, 8; and so on, until all squares were covered. The king found this to be a very modest request and immediately sent his vizier to bring the bag of wheat. King Shirhan probably did not realize that there about $10^{10^{50}}$ possible moves in chess.

1. Do you think this request made by the inventor of chess was modest? Why or why not?

   ______________________

   ______________________

2. How many grains of wheat will be on the 10th square? ______________________

   How many grains will be on the 20th square? ______________________

3. Is there an easier way to write the number of grains that are on each of these squares? What is it? ______________________

4. Find the total number of grains on the first 10 squares. ______________________

   On the first 20 squares. ______________________

5. Use exponents to write the total number of grains on the first 10 squares. ______________________

6. Use exponents to write the number of grains on the final square of the checkerboard. ______________________

7. Use exponents to write the total number of grains on the entire checkerboard. ______________________

8. Do you think you could put that many grains of wheat on a checkerboard? ______________________

9. Could Sessa carry his reward home with him in a bag? Why or why not?

   ______________________

Name ______________________ Date ______________________

Activity

# Chess Epilogue

The king's vizier went to the royal reckoners to find out how much wheat was actually needed. Calculations continued for days. The king could not understand why such a simple request took so long and felt his reckoners must be incompetent. He dismissed them and hired a new set of reckoners who also progressed quite slowly with the calculations. The chief reckoner finally went to King Shirhan and apologetically explained that it would be impossible for the king to reward Sessa as agreed. It would take 18,446,744,073,709,551,615 grains of wheat.

1. Write in words the number of grains of wheat Sessa requested as his reward.

______________________________________________

______________________________________________

2. Round the number of grains to the leading digit and write the number in scientific notation. __________

3. If there are about $5 \times 10^6$ grains of wheat in a bushel, about how many bushels of wheat did King Shirhan need? __________

4. Chess probably dates from seventh-century India. At that time, the world wheat production was only a fraction of today's production. In 1991, the annual world wheat production was about $2 \times 10^{10}$ bushels. At this annual rate of production, how many years would it take to produce enough wheat to pay off Sessa? __________

5. King Shirhan was distressed; how could he honor his promise to Sessa? If he emptied all of the storehouses in the world, he would still not have enough wheat. In fact, the wheat Sessa requested would cover the earth's surface 1 inch deep! His chief reckoner made a suggestion: Have Sessa count out his own reward and let him keep whatever he can count. Was this a good suggestion? Why or why not?

______________________________________________

6. Assuming that Sessa counts unceasingly at a rate of 1 grain per second, 24 hours per day, how many grains could he count in 60 years? __________

7. Round your answer in Problem 6 to the leading digit. Use rounded numbers to figure out what fraction of the total amount of the reward this is. __________

Name ______________________________ Date ______________________________

# Exploring the Perpetual Calendar

If asked, you could easily tell someone your birthday; you have probably even celebrated it each year. That has not always been true for children. As a young boy in the 1700s, Carl Gauss asked his mother what was date of his birth. She knew what year he was born but not the date. However, she did remember that it was close to Easter. Easter, a Christian holiday, has a variable date that is related to Passover, a Jewish holiday. So in 1802, Gauss created a special perpetual calendar that would give him the date of Easter for any year. As a result of Gauss's research, we know that he was born on April 30, 1777.

General perpetual calendars can be used to find what day of the week any date is for any given year. Your copy of the perpetual calendar is only one form that you might find; some are more complicated to use but span more centuries. This perpetual calendar was not developed by Gauss, but you can use it to find the day for any date from 1800 to 2063.

1. Study the perpetual calendar your teacher gives you, and figure out how to use it. Find the day of birth for each of your family members.

______________________________

______________________________

______________________________

2. What patterns do you see in the calendar?

______________________________

______________________________

______________________________

3. Pose a problem that could be solved by using this calendar; then solve it.

______________________________

______________________________

______________________________

______________________________

______________________________

# Perpetual Calendar

| | | | | | | | |
|---|---|---|---|---|---|---|---|
| 1800 . . . .4 | 1837 . . . .1 | 1874 . . . .5 | 1911 . . . .1 | 1948 . . .12 | 1985 . . . .3 | 2022 . . . .7 | 2043 . . . .5 |
| 1801 . . . .5 | 1838 . . . .2 | 1875 . . . .6 | 1912 . . . .9 | 1949 . . . .7 | 1986 . . . .4 | 2023 . . . .1 | 2044 . . .13 |
| 1802 . . . .6 | 1839 . . . .3 | 1876 . . .14 | 1913 . . . .4 | 1950 . . . .1 | 1987 . . . .5 | 2024 . . . .9 | 2045 . . . .1 |
| 1803 . . . .7 | 1840 . . .11 | 1877 . . . .2 | 1914 . . . .5 | 1951 . . . .2 | 1988 . . .13 | 2025 . . . .4 | 2046 . . . .2 |
| 1804 . . . .8 | 1841 . . . .6 | 1878 . . . .3 | 1915 . . . .6 | 1952 . . .10 | 1989 . . . .1 | 2026 . . . .5 | 2047 . . . .3 |
| 1805 . . . .3 | 1842 . . . .7 | 1879 . . . .4 | 1916 . . .14 | 1953 . . . .5 | 1990 . . . .2 | 2027 . . . .6 | 2048 . . .11 |
| 1806 . . . .4 | 1843 . . . .1 | 1880 . . .12 | 1917 . . . .2 | 1954 . . . .6 | 1991 . . . .3 | 2028 . . .14 | 2049 . . . .6 |
| 1807 . . . .5 | 1844 . . . .9 | 1881 . . . .7 | 1918 . . . .3 | 1955 . . . .7 | 1992 . . .11 | 2029 . . . .2 | 2050 . . . .7 |
| 1808 . . .13 | 1845 . . . .4 | 1882 . . . .1 | 1919 . . . .4 | 1956 . . . .8 | 1993 . . . .6 | 2030 . . . .3 | 2051 . . . .1 |
| 1809 . . . .1 | 1846 . . . .5 | 1883 . . . .2 | 1920 . . .12 | 1957 . . . .3 | 1994 . . . .7 | 2031 . . . .4 | 2052 . . . .9 |
| 1810 . . . .2 | 1847 . . . .6 | 1884 . . .10 | 1921 . . . .7 | 1958 . . . .4 | 1995 . . . .1 | 2032 . . .12 | 2053 . . . .4 |
| 1811 . . . .3 | 1848 . . .14 | 1885 . . . .5 | 1922 . . . .1 | 1959 . . . .5 | 1996 . . . .9 | 2033 . . . .7 | 2054 . . . .5 |
| 1812 . . .11 | 1849 . . . .2 | 1886 . . . .6 | 1923 . . . .2 | 1960 . . .13 | 1997 . . . .4 | 2034 . . . .1 | 2055 . . . .6 |
| 1813 . . . .6 | 1850 . . . .3 | 1887 . . . .7 | 1924 . . .10 | 1961 . . . .1 | 1998 . . . .5 | 2035 . . . .2 | 2056 . . .14 |
| 1814 . . . .7 | 1851 . . . .4 | 1888 . . . .8 | 1925 . . . .5 | 1962 . . . .2 | 1999 . . . .6 | 2036 . . .10 | 2057 . . . .2 |
| 1815 . . . .1 | 1852 . . .12 | 1889 . . . .3 | 1926 . . . .6 | 1963 . . . .3 | 2000 . . .14 | 2037 . . . .5 | 2058 . . . .3 |
| 1816 . . . .9 | 1853 . . . .7 | 1890 . . . .4 | 1927 . . . .7 | 1964 . . .11 | 2001 . . . .2 | 2038 . . . .6 | 2059 . . . .4 |
| 1817 . . . .4 | 1854 . . . .1 | 1891 . . . .5 | 1928 . . . .8 | 1965 . . . .6 | 2002 . . . .3 | 2039 . . . .7 | 2060 . . .12 |
| 1818 . . . .5 | 1855 . . . .2 | 1892 . . .13 | 1929 . . . .3 | 1966 . . . .7 | 2003 . . . .4 | 2040 . . . .8 | 2061 . . . .7 |
| 1819 . . . .6 | 1856 . . .10 | 1893 . . . .1 | 1930 . . . .4 | 1967 . . . .1 | 2004 . . .12 | 2041 . . . .3 | 2062 . . . .1 |
| 1820 . . .14 | 1857 . . . .5 | 1894 . . . .2 | 1931 . . . .5 | 1968 . . . .9 | 2005 . . . .7 | 2042 . . . .4 | 2063 . . . .2 |
| 1821 . . . .2 | 1858 . . . .6 | 1895 . . . .3 | 1932 . . .13 | 1969 . . . .4 | 2006 . . . .1 | | |
| 1822 . . . .3 | 1859 . . . .7 | 1896 . . .11 | 1933 . . . .1 | 1970 . . . .5 | 2007 . . . .2 | | |
| 1823 . . . .4 | 1860 . . . .8 | 1897 . . . .6 | 1934 . . . .2 | 1971 . . . .6 | 2008 . . .10 | | |
| 1824 . . .12 | 1861 . . . .3 | 1898 . . . .7 | 1935 . . . .3 | 1972 . . .14 | 2009 . . . .5 | | |
| 1825 . . . .7 | 1862 . . . .4 | 1899 . . . .1 | 1936 . . .11 | 1973 . . . .2 | 2010 . . . .6 | | |
| 1826 . . . .1 | 1863 . . . .5 | 1900 . . . .2 | 1937 . . . .6 | 1974 . . . .3 | 2011 . . . .7 | | |
| 1827 . . . .2 | 1864 . . .13 | 1901 . . . .3 | 1938 . . . .7 | 1975 . . . .4 | 2012 . . . .8 | | |
| 1828 . . .10 | 1865 . . . .1 | 1902 . . . .4 | 1939 . . . .1 | 1976 . . .12 | 2013 . . . .3 | | |
| 1829 . . . .5 | 1866 . . . .2 | 1903 . . . .5 | 1940 . . . .9 | 1977 . . . .7 | 2014 . . . .4 | | |
| 1830 . . . .6 | 1867 . . . .3 | 1904 . . .13 | 1941 . . . .4 | 1978 . . . .1 | 2015 . . . .5 | | |
| 1831 . . . .7 | 1868 . . .11 | 1905 . . . .1 | 1942 . . . .5 | 1979 . . . .2 | 2016 . . .13 | | |
| 1832 . . . .8 | 1869 . . . .6 | 1906 . . . .2 | 1943 . . . .6 | 1980 . . .10 | 2017 . . . .1 | | |
| 1833 . . . .3 | 1870 . . . .7 | 1907 . . . .3 | 1944 . . .14 | 1981 . . . .5 | 2018 . . . .2 | | |
| 1834 . . . .4 | 1871 . . . .1 | 1908 . . .11 | 1945 . . . .2 | 1982 . . . .6 | 2019 . . . .3 | | |
| 1835 . . . .5 | 1872 . . . .9 | 1909 . . . .6 | 1946 . . . .3 | 1983 . . . .7 | 2020 . . .11 | | |
| 1836 . . .13 | 1873 . . . .4 | 1910 . . . .7 | 1947 . . . .4 | 1984 . . . .8 | 2021 . . . .6 | | |

**DIRECTIONS:**
The number given with each year in the key above is number of calendar to use for that year.

## 1

**JANUARY**

| S | M | T | W | T | F | S |
|---|---|---|---|---|---|---|
| 1 | 2 | 3 | 4 | 5 | 6 | 7 |
| 8 | 9 | 10 | 11 | 12 | 13 | 14 |
| 15 | 16 | 17 | 18 | 19 | 20 | 21 |
| 22 | 23 | 24 | 25 | 26 | 27 | 28 |
| 29 | 30 | 31 | | | | |

**FEBRUARY**

| S | M | T | W | T | F | S |
|---|---|---|---|---|---|---|
| | | | 1 | 2 | 3 | 4 |
| 5 | 6 | 7 | 8 | 9 | 10 | 11 |
| 12 | 13 | 14 | 15 | 16 | 17 | 18 |
| 19 | 20 | 21 | 22 | 23 | 24 | 25 |
| 26 | 27 | 28 | | | | |

**MARCH**

| S | M | T | W | T | F | S |
|---|---|---|---|---|---|---|
| | | | 1 | 2 | 3 | 4 |
| 5 | 6 | 7 | 8 | 9 | 10 | 11 |
| 12 | 13 | 14 | 15 | 16 | 17 | 18 |
| 19 | 20 | 21 | 22 | 23 | 24 | 25 |
| 26 | 27 | 28 | 29 | 30 | 31 | |

**APRIL**

| S | M | T | W | T | F | S |
|---|---|---|---|---|---|---|
| | | | | | | 1 |
| 2 | 3 | 4 | 5 | 6 | 7 | 8 |
| 9 | 10 | 11 | 12 | 13 | 14 | 15 |
| 16 | 17 | 18 | 19 | 20 | 21 | 22 |
| 23 | 24 | 25 | 26 | 27 | 28 | 29 |
| 30 | | | | | | |

**MAY**

| S | M | T | W | T | F | S |
|---|---|---|---|---|---|---|
| | 1 | 2 | 3 | 4 | 5 | 6 |
| 7 | 8 | 9 | 10 | 11 | 12 | 13 |
| 14 | 15 | 16 | 17 | 18 | 19 | 20 |
| 21 | 22 | 23 | 24 | 25 | 26 | 27 |
| 28 | 29 | 30 | 31 | | | |

**JUNE**

| S | M | T | W | T | F | S |
|---|---|---|---|---|---|---|
| | | | | 1 | 2 | 3 |
| 4 | 5 | 6 | 7 | 8 | 9 | 10 |
| 11 | 12 | 13 | 14 | 15 | 16 | 17 |
| 18 | 19 | 20 | 21 | 22 | 23 | 24 |
| 25 | 26 | 27 | 28 | 29 | 30 | |

**JULY**

| S | M | T | W | T | F | S |
|---|---|---|---|---|---|---|
| | | | | | | 1 |
| 2 | 3 | 4 | 5 | 6 | 7 | 8 |
| 9 | 10 | 11 | 12 | 13 | 14 | 15 |
| 16 | 17 | 18 | 19 | 20 | 21 | 22 |
| 23 | 24 | 25 | 26 | 27 | 28 | 29 |
| 30 | 31 | | | | | |

**AUGUST**

| S | M | T | W | T | F | S |
|---|---|---|---|---|---|---|
| | | 1 | 2 | 3 | 4 | 5 |
| 6 | 7 | 8 | 9 | 10 | 11 | 12 |
| 13 | 14 | 15 | 16 | 17 | 18 | 19 |
| 20 | 21 | 22 | 23 | 24 | 25 | 26 |
| 27 | 28 | 29 | 30 | 31 | | |

**SEPTEMBER**

| S | M | T | W | T | F | S |
|---|---|---|---|---|---|---|
| | | | | | 1 | 2 |
| 3 | 4 | 5 | 6 | 7 | 8 | 9 |
| 10 | 11 | 12 | 13 | 14 | 15 | 16 |
| 17 | 18 | 19 | 20 | 21 | 22 | 23 |
| 24 | 25 | 26 | 27 | 28 | 29 | 30 |

**OCTOBER**

| S | M | T | W | T | F | S |
|---|---|---|---|---|---|---|
| 1 | 2 | 3 | 4 | 5 | 6 | 7 |
| 8 | 9 | 10 | 11 | 12 | 13 | 14 |
| 15 | 16 | 17 | 18 | 19 | 20 | 21 |
| 22 | 23 | 24 | 25 | 26 | 27 | 28 |
| 29 | 30 | 31 | | | | |

**NOVEMBER**

| S | M | T | W | T | F | S |
|---|---|---|---|---|---|---|
| | | | 1 | 2 | 3 | 4 |
| 5 | 6 | 7 | 8 | 9 | 10 | 11 |
| 12 | 13 | 14 | 15 | 16 | 17 | 18 |
| 19 | 20 | 21 | 22 | 23 | 24 | 25 |
| 26 | 27 | 28 | 29 | 30 | | |

**DECEMBER**

| S | M | T | W | T | F | S |
|---|---|---|---|---|---|---|
| | | | | | 1 | 2 |
| 3 | 4 | 5 | 6 | 7 | 8 | 9 |
| 10 | 11 | 12 | 13 | 14 | 15 | 16 |
| 17 | 18 | 19 | 20 | 21 | 22 | 23 |
| 24 | 25 | 26 | 27 | 28 | 29 | 30 |
| 31 | | | | | | |

## 2

**JANUARY**

| S | M | T | W | T | F | S |
|---|---|---|---|---|---|---|
| | 1 | 2 | 3 | 4 | 5 | 6 |
| 7 | 8 | 9 | 10 | 11 | 12 | 13 |
| 14 | 15 | 16 | 17 | 18 | 19 | 20 |
| 21 | 22 | 23 | 24 | 25 | 26 | 27 |
| 28 | 29 | 30 | 31 | | | |

**FEBRUARY**

| S | M | T | W | T | F | S |
|---|---|---|---|---|---|---|
| | | | | 1 | 2 | 3 |
| 4 | 5 | 6 | 7 | 8 | 9 | 10 |
| 11 | 12 | 13 | 14 | 15 | 16 | 17 |
| 18 | 19 | 20 | 21 | 22 | 23 | 24 |
| 25 | 26 | 27 | 28 | | | |

**MARCH**

| S | M | T | W | T | F | S |
|---|---|---|---|---|---|---|
| | | | | 1 | 2 | 3 |
| 4 | 5 | 6 | 7 | 8 | 9 | 10 |
| 11 | 12 | 13 | 14 | 15 | 16 | 17 |
| 18 | 19 | 20 | 21 | 22 | 23 | 24 |
| 25 | 26 | 27 | 28 | 29 | 30 | 31 |

**APRIL**

| S | M | T | W | T | F | S |
|---|---|---|---|---|---|---|
| 1 | 2 | 3 | 4 | 5 | 6 | 7 |
| 8 | 9 | 10 | 11 | 12 | 13 | 14 |
| 15 | 16 | 17 | 18 | 19 | 20 | 21 |
| 22 | 23 | 24 | 25 | 26 | 27 | 28 |
| 29 | 30 | | | | | |

**MAY**

| S | M | T | W | T | F | S |
|---|---|---|---|---|---|---|
| | | 1 | 2 | 3 | 4 | 5 |
| 6 | 7 | 8 | 9 | 10 | 11 | 12 |
| 13 | 14 | 15 | 16 | 17 | 18 | 19 |
| 20 | 21 | 22 | 23 | 24 | 25 | 26 |
| 27 | 28 | 29 | 30 | 31 | | |

**JUNE**

| S | M | T | W | T | F | S |
|---|---|---|---|---|---|---|
| | | | | | 1 | 2 |
| 3 | 4 | 5 | 6 | 7 | 8 | 9 |
| 10 | 11 | 12 | 13 | 14 | 15 | 16 |
| 17 | 18 | 19 | 20 | 21 | 22 | 23 |
| 24 | 25 | 26 | 27 | 28 | 29 | 30 |

**JULY**

| S | M | T | W | T | F | S |
|---|---|---|---|---|---|---|
| 1 | 2 | 3 | 4 | 5 | 6 | 7 |
| 8 | 9 | 10 | 11 | 12 | 13 | 14 |
| 15 | 16 | 17 | 18 | 19 | 20 | 21 |
| 22 | 23 | 24 | 25 | 26 | 27 | 28 |
| 29 | 30 | 31 | | | | |

**AUGUST**

| S | M | T | W | T | F | S |
|---|---|---|---|---|---|---|
| | | | 1 | 2 | 3 | 4 |
| 5 | 6 | 7 | 8 | 9 | 10 | 11 |
| 12 | 13 | 14 | 15 | 16 | 17 | 18 |
| 19 | 20 | 21 | 22 | 23 | 24 | 25 |
| 26 | 27 | 28 | 29 | 30 | 31 | |

**SEPTEMBER**

| S | M | T | W | T | F | S |
|---|---|---|---|---|---|---|
| | | | | | | 1 |
| 2 | 3 | 4 | 5 | 6 | 7 | 8 |
| 9 | 10 | 11 | 12 | 13 | 14 | 15 |
| 16 | 17 | 18 | 19 | 20 | 21 | 22 |
| 23 | 24 | 25 | 26 | 27 | 28 | 29 |
| 30 | | | | | | |

**OCTOBER**

| S | M | T | W | T | F | S |
|---|---|---|---|---|---|---|
| | 1 | 2 | 3 | 4 | 5 | 6 |
| 7 | 8 | 9 | 10 | 11 | 12 | 13 |
| 14 | 15 | 16 | 17 | 18 | 19 | 20 |
| 21 | 22 | 23 | 24 | 25 | 26 | 27 |
| 28 | 29 | 30 | 31 | | | |

**NOVEMBER**

| S | M | T | W | T | F | S |
|---|---|---|---|---|---|---|
| | | | | 1 | 2 | 3 |
| 4 | 5 | 6 | 7 | 8 | 9 | 10 |
| 11 | 12 | 13 | 14 | 15 | 16 | 17 |
| 18 | 19 | 20 | 21 | 22 | 23 | 24 |
| 25 | 26 | 27 | 28 | 29 | 30 | |

**DECEMBER**

| S | M | T | W | T | F | S |
|---|---|---|---|---|---|---|
| | | | | | | 1 |
| 2 | 3 | 4 | 5 | 6 | 7 | 8 |
| 9 | 10 | 11 | 12 | 13 | 14 | 15 |
| 16 | 17 | 18 | 19 | 20 | 21 | 22 |
| 23 | 24 | 25 | 26 | 27 | 28 | 29 |
| 30 | 31 | | | | | |

# Perpetual Calendar

## 3

**JANUARY**

| S | M | T | W | T | F | S |
|---|---|---|---|---|---|---|
|  |  | 1 | 2 | 3 | 4 | 5 |
| 6 | 7 | 8 | 9 | 10 | 11 | 12 |
| 13 | 14 | 15 | 16 | 17 | 18 | 19 |
| 20 | 21 | 22 | 23 | 24 | 25 | 26 |
| 27 | 28 | 29 | 30 | 31 |  |  |

**FEBRUARY**

| S | M | T | W | T | F | S |
|---|---|---|---|---|---|---|
|  |  |  |  |  | 1 | 2 |
| 3 | 4 | 5 | 6 | 7 | 8 | 9 |
| 10 | 11 | 12 | 13 | 14 | 15 | 16 |
| 17 | 18 | 19 | 20 | 21 | 22 | 23 |
| 24 | 25 | 26 | 27 | 28 |  |  |

**MARCH**

| S | M | T | W | T | F | S |
|---|---|---|---|---|---|---|
|  |  |  |  |  | 1 | 2 |
| 3 | 4 | 5 | 6 | 7 | 8 | 9 |
| 10 | 11 | 12 | 13 | 14 | 15 | 16 |
| 17 | 18 | 19 | 20 | 21 | 22 | 23 |
| 24 | 25 | 26 | 27 | 28 | 29 | 30 |
| 31 |  |  |  |  |  |  |

**APRIL**

| S | M | T | W | T | F | S |
|---|---|---|---|---|---|---|
|  | 1 | 2 | 3 | 4 | 5 | 6 |
| 7 | 8 | 9 | 10 | 11 | 12 | 13 |
| 14 | 15 | 16 | 17 | 18 | 19 | 20 |
| 21 | 22 | 23 | 24 | 25 | 26 | 27 |
| 28 | 29 | 30 |  |  |  |  |

**MAY**

| S | M | T | W | T | F | S |
|---|---|---|---|---|---|---|
|  |  |  | 1 | 2 | 3 | 4 |
| 5 | 6 | 7 | 8 | 9 | 10 | 11 |
| 12 | 13 | 14 | 15 | 16 | 17 | 18 |
| 19 | 20 | 21 | 22 | 23 | 24 | 25 |
| 26 | 27 | 28 | 29 | 30 | 31 |  |

**JUNE**

| S | M | T | W | T | F | S |
|---|---|---|---|---|---|---|
|  |  |  |  |  |  | 1 |
| 2 | 3 | 4 | 5 | 6 | 7 | 8 |
| 9 | 10 | 11 | 12 | 13 | 14 | 15 |
| 16 | 17 | 18 | 19 | 20 | 21 | 22 |
| 23 | 24 | 25 | 26 | 27 | 28 | 29 |
| 30 |  |  |  |  |  |  |

**JULY**

| S | M | T | W | T | F | S |
|---|---|---|---|---|---|---|
|  | 1 | 2 | 3 | 4 | 5 | 6 |
| 7 | 8 | 9 | 10 | 11 | 12 | 13 |
| 14 | 15 | 16 | 17 | 18 | 19 | 20 |
| 21 | 22 | 23 | 24 | 25 | 26 | 27 |
| 28 | 29 | 30 | 31 |  |  |  |

**AUGUST**

| S | M | T | W | T | F | S |
|---|---|---|---|---|---|---|
|  |  |  |  | 1 | 2 | 3 |
| 4 | 5 | 6 | 7 | 8 | 9 | 10 |
| 11 | 12 | 13 | 14 | 15 | 16 | 17 |
| 18 | 19 | 20 | 21 | 22 | 23 | 24 |
| 25 | 26 | 27 | 28 | 29 | 30 | 31 |

**SEPTEMBER**

| S | M | T | W | T | F | S |
|---|---|---|---|---|---|---|
| 1 | 2 | 3 | 4 | 5 | 6 | 7 |
| 8 | 9 | 10 | 11 | 12 | 13 | 14 |
| 15 | 16 | 17 | 18 | 19 | 20 | 21 |
| 22 | 23 | 24 | 25 | 26 | 27 | 28 |
| 29 | 30 |  |  |  |  |  |

**OCTOBER**

| S | M | T | W | T | F | S |
|---|---|---|---|---|---|---|
|  |  | 1 | 2 | 3 | 4 | 5 |
| 6 | 7 | 8 | 9 | 10 | 11 | 12 |
| 13 | 14 | 15 | 16 | 17 | 18 | 19 |
| 20 | 21 | 22 | 23 | 24 | 25 | 26 |
| 27 | 28 | 29 | 30 | 31 |  |  |

**NOVEMBER**

| S | M | T | W | T | F | S |
|---|---|---|---|---|---|---|
|  |  |  |  |  | 1 | 2 |
| 3 | 4 | 5 | 6 | 7 | 8 | 9 |
| 10 | 11 | 12 | 13 | 14 | 15 | 16 |
| 17 | 18 | 19 | 20 | 21 | 22 | 23 |
| 24 | 25 | 26 | 27 | 28 | 29 | 30 |

**DECEMBER**

| S | M | T | W | T | F | S |
|---|---|---|---|---|---|---|
| 1 | 2 | 3 | 4 | 5 | 6 | 7 |
| 8 | 9 | 10 | 11 | 12 | 13 | 14 |
| 15 | 16 | 17 | 18 | 19 | 20 | 21 |
| 22 | 23 | 24 | 25 | 26 | 27 | 28 |
| 29 | 30 | 31 |  |  |  |  |

## 4

**JANUARY**

| S | M | T | W | T | F | S |
|---|---|---|---|---|---|---|
|  |  |  | 1 | 2 | 3 | 4 |
| 5 | 6 | 7 | 8 | 9 | 10 | 11 |
| 12 | 13 | 14 | 15 | 16 | 17 | 18 |
| 19 | 20 | 21 | 22 | 23 | 24 | 25 |
| 26 | 27 | 28 | 29 | 30 | 31 |  |

**FEBRUARY**

| S | M | T | W | T | F | S |
|---|---|---|---|---|---|---|
|  |  |  |  |  |  | 1 |
| 2 | 3 | 4 | 5 | 6 | 7 | 8 |
| 9 | 10 | 11 | 12 | 13 | 14 | 15 |
| 16 | 17 | 18 | 19 | 20 | 21 | 22 |
| 23 | 24 | 25 | 26 | 27 | 28 |  |

**MARCH**

| S | M | T | W | T | F | S |
|---|---|---|---|---|---|---|
|  |  |  |  |  |  | 1 |
| 2 | 3 | 4 | 5 | 6 | 7 | 8 |
| 9 | 10 | 11 | 12 | 13 | 14 | 15 |
| 16 | 17 | 18 | 19 | 20 | 21 | 22 |
| 23 | 24 | 25 | 26 | 27 | 28 | 29 |
| 30 | 31 |  |  |  |  |  |

**APRIL**

| S | M | T | W | T | F | S |
|---|---|---|---|---|---|---|
|  |  | 1 | 2 | 3 | 4 | 5 |
| 6 | 7 | 8 | 9 | 10 | 11 | 12 |
| 13 | 14 | 15 | 16 | 17 | 18 | 19 |
| 20 | 21 | 22 | 23 | 24 | 25 | 26 |
| 27 | 28 | 29 | 30 |  |  |  |

**MAY**

| S | M | T | W | T | F | S |
|---|---|---|---|---|---|---|
|  |  |  |  | 1 | 2 | 3 |
| 4 | 5 | 6 | 7 | 8 | 9 | 10 |
| 11 | 12 | 13 | 14 | 15 | 16 | 17 |
| 18 | 19 | 20 | 21 | 22 | 23 | 24 |
| 25 | 26 | 27 | 28 | 29 | 30 | 31 |

**JUNE**

| S | M | T | W | T | F | S |
|---|---|---|---|---|---|---|
| 1 | 2 | 3 | 4 | 5 | 6 | 7 |
| 8 | 9 | 10 | 11 | 12 | 13 | 14 |
| 15 | 16 | 17 | 18 | 19 | 20 | 21 |
| 22 | 23 | 24 | 25 | 26 | 27 | 28 |
| 29 | 30 |  |  |  |  |  |

**JULY**

| S | M | T | W | T | F | S |
|---|---|---|---|---|---|---|
|  |  | 1 | 2 | 3 | 4 | 5 |
| 6 | 7 | 8 | 9 | 10 | 11 | 12 |
| 13 | 14 | 15 | 16 | 17 | 18 | 19 |
| 20 | 21 | 22 | 23 | 24 | 25 | 26 |
| 27 | 28 | 29 | 30 | 31 |  |  |

**AUGUST**

| S | M | T | W | T | F | S |
|---|---|---|---|---|---|---|
|  |  |  |  |  | 1 | 2 |
| 3 | 4 | 5 | 6 | 7 | 8 | 9 |
| 10 | 11 | 12 | 13 | 14 | 15 | 16 |
| 17 | 18 | 19 | 20 | 21 | 22 | 23 |
| 24 | 25 | 26 | 27 | 28 | 29 | 30 |
| 31 |  |  |  |  |  |  |

**SEPTEMBER**

| S | M | T | W | T | F | S |
|---|---|---|---|---|---|---|
|  | 1 | 2 | 3 | 4 | 5 | 6 |
| 7 | 8 | 9 | 10 | 11 | 12 | 13 |
| 14 | 15 | 16 | 17 | 18 | 19 | 20 |
| 21 | 22 | 23 | 24 | 25 | 26 | 27 |
| 28 | 29 | 30 |  |  |  |  |

**OCTOBER**

| S | M | T | W | T | F | S |
|---|---|---|---|---|---|---|
|  |  |  | 1 | 2 | 3 | 4 |
| 5 | 6 | 7 | 8 | 9 | 10 | 11 |
| 12 | 13 | 14 | 15 | 16 | 17 | 18 |
| 19 | 20 | 21 | 22 | 23 | 24 | 25 |
| 26 | 27 | 28 | 29 | 30 | 31 |  |

**NOVEMBER**

| S | M | T | W | T | F | S |
|---|---|---|---|---|---|---|
|  |  |  |  |  |  | 1 |
| 2 | 3 | 4 | 5 | 6 | 7 | 8 |
| 9 | 10 | 11 | 12 | 13 | 14 | 15 |
| 16 | 17 | 18 | 19 | 20 | 21 | 22 |
| 23 | 24 | 25 | 26 | 27 | 28 | 29 |
| 30 |  |  |  |  |  |  |

**DECEMBER**

| S | M | T | W | T | F | S |
|---|---|---|---|---|---|---|
|  | 1 | 2 | 3 | 4 | 5 | 6 |
| 7 | 8 | 9 | 10 | 11 | 12 | 13 |
| 14 | 15 | 16 | 17 | 18 | 19 | 20 |
| 21 | 22 | 23 | 24 | 25 | 26 | 27 |
| 28 | 29 | 30 | 31 |  |  |  |

## 5

**JANUARY**

| S | M | T | W | T | F | S |
|---|---|---|---|---|---|---|
|  |  |  |  | 1 | 2 | 3 |
| 4 | 5 | 6 | 7 | 8 | 9 | 10 |
| 11 | 12 | 13 | 14 | 15 | 16 | 17 |
| 18 | 19 | 20 | 21 | 22 | 23 | 24 |
| 25 | 26 | 27 | 28 | 29 | 30 | 31 |

**FEBRUARY**

| S | M | T | W | T | F | S |
|---|---|---|---|---|---|---|
| 1 | 2 | 3 | 4 | 5 | 6 | 7 |
| 8 | 9 | 10 | 11 | 12 | 13 | 14 |
| 15 | 16 | 17 | 18 | 19 | 20 | 21 |
| 22 | 23 | 24 | 25 | 26 | 27 | 28 |

**MARCH**

| S | M | T | W | T | F | S |
|---|---|---|---|---|---|---|
| 1 | 2 | 3 | 4 | 5 | 6 | 7 |
| 8 | 9 | 10 | 11 | 12 | 13 | 14 |
| 15 | 16 | 17 | 18 | 19 | 20 | 21 |
| 22 | 23 | 24 | 25 | 26 | 27 | 28 |
| 29 | 30 | 31 |  |  |  |  |

**APRIL**

| S | M | T | W | T | F | S |
|---|---|---|---|---|---|---|
|  |  |  | 1 | 2 | 3 | 4 |
| 5 | 6 | 7 | 8 | 9 | 10 | 11 |
| 12 | 13 | 14 | 15 | 16 | 17 | 18 |
| 19 | 20 | 21 | 22 | 23 | 24 | 25 |
| 26 | 27 | 28 | 29 | 30 |  |  |

**MAY**

| S | M | T | W | T | F | S |
|---|---|---|---|---|---|---|
|  |  |  |  |  | 1 | 2 |
| 3 | 4 | 5 | 6 | 7 | 8 | 9 |
| 10 | 11 | 12 | 13 | 14 | 15 | 16 |
| 17 | 18 | 19 | 20 | 21 | 22 | 23 |
| 24 | 25 | 26 | 27 | 28 | 29 | 30 |
| 31 |  |  |  |  |  |  |

**JUNE**

| S | M | T | W | T | F | S |
|---|---|---|---|---|---|---|
|  | 1 | 2 | 3 | 4 | 5 | 6 |
| 7 | 8 | 9 | 10 | 11 | 12 | 13 |
| 14 | 15 | 16 | 17 | 18 | 19 | 20 |
| 21 | 22 | 23 | 24 | 25 | 26 | 27 |
| 28 | 29 | 30 |  |  |  |  |

**JULY**

| S | M | T | W | T | F | S |
|---|---|---|---|---|---|---|
|  |  |  | 1 | 2 | 3 | 4 |
| 5 | 6 | 7 | 8 | 9 | 10 | 11 |
| 12 | 13 | 14 | 15 | 16 | 17 | 18 |
| 19 | 20 | 21 | 22 | 23 | 24 | 25 |
| 26 | 27 | 28 | 29 | 30 | 31 |  |

**AUGUST**

| S | M | T | W | T | F | S |
|---|---|---|---|---|---|---|
|  |  |  |  |  |  | 1 |
| 2 | 3 | 4 | 5 | 6 | 7 | 8 |
| 9 | 10 | 11 | 12 | 13 | 14 | 15 |
| 16 | 17 | 18 | 19 | 20 | 21 | 22 |
| 23 | 24 | 25 | 26 | 27 | 28 | 29 |
| 30 | 31 |  |  |  |  |  |

**SEPTEMBER**

| S | M | T | W | T | F | S |
|---|---|---|---|---|---|---|
|  |  | 1 | 2 | 3 | 4 | 5 |
| 6 | 7 | 8 | 9 | 10 | 11 | 12 |
| 13 | 14 | 15 | 16 | 17 | 18 | 19 |
| 20 | 21 | 22 | 23 | 24 | 25 | 26 |
| 27 | 28 | 29 | 30 |  |  |  |

**OCTOBER**

| S | M | T | W | T | F | S |
|---|---|---|---|---|---|---|
|  |  |  |  | 1 | 2 | 3 |
| 4 | 5 | 6 | 7 | 8 | 9 | 10 |
| 11 | 12 | 13 | 14 | 15 | 16 | 17 |
| 18 | 19 | 20 | 21 | 22 | 23 | 24 |
| 25 | 26 | 27 | 28 | 29 | 30 | 31 |

**NOVEMBER**

| S | M | T | W | T | F | S |
|---|---|---|---|---|---|---|
| 1 | 2 | 3 | 4 | 5 | 6 | 7 |
| 8 | 9 | 10 | 11 | 12 | 13 | 14 |
| 15 | 16 | 17 | 18 | 19 | 20 | 21 |
| 22 | 23 | 24 | 25 | 26 | 27 | 28 |
| 29 | 30 |  |  |  |  |  |

**DECEMBER**

| S | M | T | W | T | F | S |
|---|---|---|---|---|---|---|
|  |  | 1 | 2 | 3 | 4 | 5 |
| 6 | 7 | 8 | 9 | 10 | 11 | 12 |
| 13 | 14 | 15 | 16 | 17 | 18 | 19 |
| 20 | 21 | 22 | 23 | 24 | 25 | 26 |
| 27 | 28 | 29 | 30 | 31 |  |  |

## 6

**JANUARY**

| S | M | T | W | T | F | S |
|---|---|---|---|---|---|---|
|  |  |  |  |  | 1 | 2 |
| 3 | 4 | 5 | 6 | 7 | 8 | 9 |
| 10 | 11 | 12 | 13 | 14 | 15 | 16 |
| 17 | 18 | 19 | 20 | 21 | 22 | 23 |
| 24 | 25 | 26 | 27 | 28 | 29 | 30 |
| 31 |  |  |  |  |  |  |

**FEBRUARY**

| S | M | T | W | T | F | S |
|---|---|---|---|---|---|---|
|  | 1 | 2 | 3 | 4 | 5 | 6 |
| 7 | 8 | 9 | 10 | 11 | 12 | 13 |
| 14 | 15 | 16 | 17 | 18 | 19 | 20 |
| 21 | 22 | 23 | 24 | 25 | 26 | 27 |
| 28 |  |  |  |  |  |  |

**MARCH**

| S | M | T | W | T | F | S |
|---|---|---|---|---|---|---|
|  | 1 | 2 | 3 | 4 | 5 | 6 |
| 7 | 8 | 9 | 10 | 11 | 12 | 13 |
| 14 | 15 | 16 | 17 | 18 | 19 | 20 |
| 21 | 22 | 23 | 24 | 25 | 26 | 27 |
| 28 | 29 | 30 | 31 |  |  |  |

**APRIL**

| S | M | T | W | T | F | S |
|---|---|---|---|---|---|---|
|  |  |  |  | 1 | 2 | 3 |
| 4 | 5 | 6 | 7 | 8 | 9 | 10 |
| 11 | 12 | 13 | 14 | 15 | 16 | 17 |
| 18 | 19 | 20 | 21 | 22 | 23 | 24 |
| 25 | 26 | 27 | 28 | 29 | 30 |  |

**MAY**

| S | M | T | W | T | F | S |
|---|---|---|---|---|---|---|
|  |  |  |  |  |  | 1 |
| 2 | 3 | 4 | 5 | 6 | 7 | 8 |
| 9 | 10 | 11 | 12 | 13 | 14 | 15 |
| 16 | 17 | 18 | 19 | 20 | 21 | 22 |
| 23 | 24 | 25 | 26 | 27 | 28 | 29 |
| 30 | 31 |  |  |  |  |  |

**JUNE**

| S | M | T | W | T | F | S |
|---|---|---|---|---|---|---|
|  |  | 1 | 2 | 3 | 4 | 5 |
| 6 | 7 | 8 | 9 | 10 | 11 | 12 |
| 13 | 14 | 15 | 16 | 17 | 18 | 19 |
| 20 | 21 | 22 | 23 | 24 | 25 | 26 |
| 27 | 28 | 29 | 30 |  |  |  |

**JULY**

| S | M | T | W | T | F | S |
|---|---|---|---|---|---|---|
|  |  |  |  | 1 | 2 | 3 |
| 4 | 5 | 6 | 7 | 8 | 9 | 10 |
| 11 | 12 | 13 | 14 | 15 | 16 | 17 |
| 18 | 19 | 20 | 21 | 22 | 23 | 24 |
| 25 | 26 | 27 | 28 | 29 | 30 | 31 |

**AUGUST**

| S | M | T | W | T | F | S |
|---|---|---|---|---|---|---|
| 1 | 2 | 3 | 4 | 5 | 6 | 7 |
| 8 | 9 | 10 | 11 | 12 | 13 | 14 |
| 15 | 16 | 17 | 18 | 19 | 20 | 21 |
| 22 | 23 | 24 | 25 | 26 | 27 | 28 |
| 29 | 30 | 31 |  |  |  |  |

**SEPTEMBER**

| S | M | T | W | T | F | S |
|---|---|---|---|---|---|---|
|  |  |  | 1 | 2 | 3 | 4 |
| 5 | 6 | 7 | 8 | 9 | 10 | 11 |
| 12 | 13 | 14 | 15 | 16 | 17 | 18 |
| 19 | 20 | 21 | 22 | 23 | 24 | 25 |
| 26 | 27 | 28 | 29 | 30 |  |  |

**OCTOBER**

| S | M | T | W | T | F | S |
|---|---|---|---|---|---|---|
|  |  |  |  |  | 1 | 2 |
| 3 | 4 | 5 | 6 | 7 | 8 | 9 |
| 10 | 11 | 12 | 13 | 14 | 15 | 16 |
| 17 | 18 | 19 | 20 | 21 | 22 | 23 |
| 24 | 25 | 26 | 27 | 28 | 29 | 30 |
| 31 |  |  |  |  |  |  |

**NOVEMBER**

| S | M | T | W | T | F | S |
|---|---|---|---|---|---|---|
|  | 1 | 2 | 3 | 4 | 5 | 6 |
| 7 | 8 | 9 | 10 | 11 | 12 | 13 |
| 14 | 15 | 16 | 17 | 18 | 19 | 20 |
| 21 | 22 | 23 | 24 | 25 | 26 | 27 |
| 28 | 29 | 30 |  |  |  |  |

**DECEMBER**

| S | M | T | W | T | F | S |
|---|---|---|---|---|---|---|
|  |  |  | 1 | 2 | 3 | 4 |
| 5 | 6 | 7 | 8 | 9 | 10 | 11 |
| 12 | 13 | 14 | 15 | 16 | 17 | 18 |
| 19 | 20 | 21 | 22 | 23 | 24 | 25 |
| 26 | 27 | 28 | 29 | 30 | 31 |  |

## 7

**JANUARY**

| S | M | T | W | T | F | S |
|---|---|---|---|---|---|---|
|  |  |  |  |  |  | 1 |
| 2 | 3 | 4 | 5 | 6 | 7 | 8 |
| 9 | 10 | 11 | 12 | 13 | 14 | 15 |
| 16 | 17 | 18 | 19 | 20 | 21 | 22 |
| 23 | 24 | 25 | 26 | 27 | 28 | 29 |
| 30 | 31 |  |  |  |  |  |

**FEBRUARY**

| S | M | T | W | T | F | S |
|---|---|---|---|---|---|---|
|  |  | 1 | 2 | 3 | 4 | 5 |
| 6 | 7 | 8 | 9 | 10 | 11 | 12 |
| 13 | 14 | 15 | 16 | 17 | 18 | 19 |
| 20 | 21 | 22 | 23 | 24 | 25 | 26 |
| 27 | 28 |  |  |  |  |  |

**MARCH**

| S | M | T | W | T | F | S |
|---|---|---|---|---|---|---|
|  |  | 1 | 2 | 3 | 4 | 5 |
| 6 | 7 | 8 | 9 | 10 | 11 | 12 |
| 13 | 14 | 15 | 16 | 17 | 18 | 19 |
| 20 | 21 | 22 | 23 | 24 | 25 | 26 |
| 27 | 28 | 29 | 30 | 31 |  |  |

**APRIL**

| S | M | T | W | T | F | S |
|---|---|---|---|---|---|---|
|  |  |  |  |  | 1 | 2 |
| 3 | 4 | 5 | 6 | 7 | 8 | 9 |
| 10 | 11 | 12 | 13 | 14 | 15 | 16 |
| 17 | 18 | 19 | 20 | 21 | 22 | 23 |
| 24 | 25 | 26 | 27 | 28 | 29 | 30 |

**MAY**

| S | M | T | W | T | F | S |
|---|---|---|---|---|---|---|
| 1 | 2 | 3 | 4 | 5 | 6 | 7 |
| 8 | 9 | 10 | 11 | 12 | 13 | 14 |
| 15 | 16 | 17 | 18 | 19 | 20 | 21 |
| 22 | 23 | 24 | 25 | 26 | 27 | 28 |
| 29 | 30 | 31 |  |  |  |  |

**JUNE**

| S | M | T | W | T | F | S |
|---|---|---|---|---|---|---|
|  |  |  | 1 | 2 | 3 | 4 |
| 5 | 6 | 7 | 8 | 9 | 10 | 11 |
| 12 | 13 | 14 | 15 | 16 | 17 | 18 |
| 19 | 20 | 21 | 22 | 23 | 24 | 25 |
| 26 | 27 | 28 | 29 | 30 |  |  |

**JULY**

| S | M | T | W | T | F | S |
|---|---|---|---|---|---|---|
|  |  |  |  |  | 1 | 2 |
| 3 | 4 | 5 | 6 | 7 | 8 | 9 |
| 10 | 11 | 12 | 13 | 14 | 15 | 16 |
| 17 | 18 | 19 | 20 | 21 | 22 | 23 |
| 24 | 25 | 26 | 27 | 28 | 29 | 30 |
| 31 |  |  |  |  |  |  |

**AUGUST**

| S | M | T | W | T | F | S |
|---|---|---|---|---|---|---|
|  | 1 | 2 | 3 | 4 | 5 | 6 |
| 7 | 8 | 9 | 10 | 11 | 12 | 13 |
| 14 | 15 | 16 | 17 | 18 | 19 | 20 |
| 21 | 22 | 23 | 24 | 25 | 26 | 27 |
| 28 | 29 | 30 | 31 |  |  |  |

**SEPTEMBER**

| S | M | T | W | T | F | S |
|---|---|---|---|---|---|---|
|  |  |  |  | 1 | 2 | 3 |
| 4 | 5 | 6 | 7 | 8 | 9 | 10 |
| 11 | 12 | 13 | 14 | 15 | 16 | 17 |
| 18 | 19 | 20 | 21 | 22 | 23 | 24 |
| 25 | 26 | 27 | 28 | 29 | 30 |  |

**OCTOBER**

| S | M | T | W | T | F | S |
|---|---|---|---|---|---|---|
|  |  |  |  |  |  | 1 |
| 2 | 3 | 4 | 5 | 6 | 7 | 8 |
| 9 | 10 | 11 | 12 | 13 | 14 | 15 |
| 16 | 17 | 18 | 19 | 20 | 21 | 22 |
| 23 | 24 | 25 | 26 | 27 | 28 | 29 |
| 30 | 31 |  |  |  |  |  |

**NOVEMBER**

| S | M | T | W | T | F | S |
|---|---|---|---|---|---|---|
|  |  | 1 | 2 | 3 | 4 | 5 |
| 6 | 7 | 8 | 9 | 10 | 11 | 12 |
| 13 | 14 | 15 | 16 | 17 | 18 | 19 |
| 20 | 21 | 22 | 23 | 24 | 25 | 26 |
| 27 | 28 | 29 | 30 |  |  |  |

**DECEMBER**

| S | M | T | W | T | F | S |
|---|---|---|---|---|---|---|
|  |  |  |  | 1 | 2 | 3 |
| 4 | 5 | 6 | 7 | 8 | 9 | 10 |
| 11 | 12 | 13 | 14 | 15 | 16 | 17 |
| 18 | 19 | 20 | 21 | 22 | 23 | 24 |
| 25 | 26 | 27 | 28 | 29 | 30 | 31 |

## 8

**JANUARY**

| S | M | T | W | T | F | S |
|---|---|---|---|---|---|---|
| 1 | 2 | 3 | 4 | 5 | 6 | 7 |
| 8 | 9 | 10 | 11 | 12 | 13 | 14 |
| 15 | 16 | 17 | 18 | 19 | 20 | 21 |
| 22 | 23 | 24 | 25 | 26 | 27 | 28 |
| 29 | 30 | 31 |  |  |  |  |

**FEBRUARY**

| S | M | T | W | T | F | S |
|---|---|---|---|---|---|---|
|  |  |  | 1 | 2 | 3 | 4 |
| 5 | 6 | 7 | 8 | 9 | 10 | 11 |
| 12 | 13 | 14 | 15 | 16 | 17 | 18 |
| 19 | 20 | 21 | 22 | 23 | 24 | 25 |
| 26 | 27 | 28 | 29 |  |  |  |

**MARCH**

| S | M | T | W | T | F | S |
|---|---|---|---|---|---|---|
|  |  |  |  | 1 | 2 | 3 |
| 4 | 5 | 6 | 7 | 8 | 9 | 10 |
| 11 | 12 | 13 | 14 | 15 | 16 | 17 |
| 18 | 19 | 20 | 21 | 22 | 23 | 24 |
| 25 | 26 | 27 | 28 | 29 | 30 | 31 |

**APRIL**

| S | M | T | W | T | F | S |
|---|---|---|---|---|---|---|
| 1 | 2 | 3 | 4 | 5 | 6 | 7 |
| 8 | 9 | 10 | 11 | 12 | 13 | 14 |
| 15 | 16 | 17 | 18 | 19 | 20 | 21 |
| 22 | 23 | 24 | 25 | 26 | 27 | 28 |
| 29 | 30 |  |  |  |  |  |

**MAY**

| S | M | T | W | T | F | S |
|---|---|---|---|---|---|---|
|  |  | 1 | 2 | 3 | 4 | 5 |
| 6 | 7 | 8 | 9 | 10 | 11 | 12 |
| 13 | 14 | 15 | 16 | 17 | 18 | 19 |
| 20 | 21 | 22 | 23 | 24 | 25 | 26 |
| 27 | 28 | 29 | 30 | 31 |  |  |

**JUNE**

| S | M | T | W | T | F | S |
|---|---|---|---|---|---|---|
|  |  |  |  |  | 1 | 2 |
| 3 | 4 | 5 | 6 | 7 | 8 | 9 |
| 10 | 11 | 12 | 13 | 14 | 15 | 16 |
| 17 | 18 | 19 | 20 | 21 | 22 | 23 |
| 24 | 25 | 26 | 27 | 28 | 29 | 30 |

**JULY**

| S | M | T | W | T | F | S |
|---|---|---|---|---|---|---|
| 1 | 2 | 3 | 4 | 5 | 6 | 7 |
| 8 | 9 | 10 | 11 | 12 | 13 | 14 |
| 15 | 16 | 17 | 18 | 19 | 20 | 21 |
| 22 | 23 | 24 | 25 | 26 | 27 | 28 |
| 29 | 30 | 31 |  |  |  |  |

**AUGUST**

| S | M | T | W | T | F | S |
|---|---|---|---|---|---|---|
|  |  |  | 1 | 2 | 3 | 4 |
| 5 | 6 | 7 | 8 | 9 | 10 | 11 |
| 12 | 13 | 14 | 15 | 16 | 17 | 18 |
| 19 | 20 | 21 | 22 | 23 | 24 | 25 |
| 26 | 27 | 28 | 29 | 30 | 31 |  |

**SEPTEMBER**

| S | M | T | W | T | F | S |
|---|---|---|---|---|---|---|
|  |  |  |  |  |  | 1 |
| 2 | 3 | 4 | 5 | 6 | 7 | 8 |
| 9 | 10 | 11 | 12 | 13 | 14 | 15 |
| 16 | 17 | 18 | 19 | 20 | 21 | 22 |
| 23 | 24 | 25 | 26 | 27 | 28 | 29 |
| 30 |  |  |  |  |  |  |

**OCTOBER**

| S | M | T | W | T | F | S |
|---|---|---|---|---|---|---|
|  | 1 | 2 | 3 | 4 | 5 | 6 |
| 7 | 8 | 9 | 10 | 11 | 12 | 13 |
| 14 | 15 | 16 | 17 | 18 | 19 | 20 |
| 21 | 22 | 23 | 24 | 25 | 26 | 27 |
| 28 | 29 | 30 | 31 |  |  |  |

**NOVEMBER**

| S | M | T | W | T | F | S |
|---|---|---|---|---|---|---|
|  |  |  |  | 1 | 2 | 3 |
| 4 | 5 | 6 | 7 | 8 | 9 | 10 |
| 11 | 12 | 13 | 14 | 15 | 16 | 17 |
| 18 | 19 | 20 | 21 | 22 | 23 | 24 |
| 25 | 26 | 27 | 28 | 29 | 30 |  |

**DECEMBER**

| S | M | T | W | T | F | S |
|---|---|---|---|---|---|---|
|  |  |  |  |  |  | 1 |
| 2 | 3 | 4 | 5 | 6 | 7 | 8 |
| 9 | 10 | 11 | 12 | 13 | 14 | 15 |
| 16 | 17 | 18 | 19 | 20 | 21 | 22 |
| 23 | 24 | 25 | 26 | 27 | 28 | 29 |
| 30 | 31 |  |  |  |  |  |

# Perpetual Calendar

## 9

### JANUARY

| S | M | T | W | T | F | S |
|---|---|---|---|---|---|---|
| | 1 | 2 | 3 | 4 | 5 | 6 |
| 7 | 8 | 9 | 10 | 11 | 12 | 13 |
| 14 | 15 | 16 | 17 | 18 | 19 | 20 |
| 21 | 22 | 23 | 24 | 25 | 26 | 27 |
| 28 | 29 | 30 | 31 | | | |

### FEBRUARY

| S | M | T | W | T | F | S |
|---|---|---|---|---|---|---|
| | | | | 1 | 2 | 3 |
| 4 | 5 | 6 | 7 | 8 | 9 | 10 |
| 11 | 12 | 13 | 14 | 15 | 16 | 17 |
| 18 | 19 | 20 | 21 | 22 | 23 | 24 |
| 25 | 26 | 27 | 28 | 29 | | |

### MARCH

| S | M | T | W | T | F | S |
|---|---|---|---|---|---|---|
| | | | | | 1 | 2 |
| 3 | 4 | 5 | 6 | 7 | 8 | 9 |
| 10 | 11 | 12 | 13 | 14 | 15 | 16 |
| 17 | 18 | 19 | 20 | 21 | 22 | 23 |
| 24 | 25 | 26 | 27 | 28 | 29 | 30 |
| 31 | | | | | | |

### APRIL

| S | M | T | W | T | F | S |
|---|---|---|---|---|---|---|
| | 1 | 2 | 3 | 4 | 5 | 6 |
| 7 | 8 | 9 | 10 | 11 | 12 | 13 |
| 14 | 15 | 16 | 17 | 18 | 19 | 20 |
| 21 | 22 | 23 | 24 | 25 | 26 | 27 |
| 28 | 29 | 30 | | | | |

### MAY

| S | M | T | W | T | F | S |
|---|---|---|---|---|---|---|
| | | | 1 | 2 | 3 | 4 |
| 5 | 6 | 7 | 8 | 9 | 10 | 11 |
| 12 | 13 | 14 | 15 | 16 | 17 | 18 |
| 19 | 20 | 21 | 22 | 23 | 24 | 25 |
| 26 | 27 | 28 | 29 | 30 | 31 | |

### JUNE

| S | M | T | W | T | F | S |
|---|---|---|---|---|---|---|
| | | | | | | 1 |
| 2 | 3 | 4 | 5 | 6 | 7 | 8 |
| 9 | 10 | 11 | 12 | 13 | 14 | 15 |
| 16 | 17 | 18 | 19 | 20 | 21 | 22 |
| 23 | 24 | 25 | 26 | 27 | 28 | 29 |
| 30 | | | | | | |

### JULY

| S | M | T | W | T | F | S |
|---|---|---|---|---|---|---|
| | 1 | 2 | 3 | 4 | 5 | 6 |
| 7 | 8 | 9 | 10 | 11 | 12 | 13 |
| 14 | 15 | 16 | 17 | 18 | 19 | 20 |
| 21 | 22 | 23 | 24 | 25 | 26 | 27 |
| 28 | 29 | 30 | 31 | | | |

### AUGUST

| S | M | T | W | T | F | S |
|---|---|---|---|---|---|---|
| | | | | 1 | 2 | 3 |
| 4 | 5 | 6 | 7 | 8 | 9 | 10 |
| 11 | 12 | 13 | 14 | 15 | 16 | 17 |
| 18 | 19 | 20 | 21 | 22 | 23 | 24 |
| 25 | 26 | 27 | 28 | 29 | 30 | 31 |

### SEPTEMBER

| S | M | T | W | T | F | S |
|---|---|---|---|---|---|---|
| 1 | 2 | 3 | 4 | 5 | 6 | 7 |
| 8 | 9 | 10 | 11 | 12 | 13 | 14 |
| 15 | 16 | 17 | 18 | 19 | 20 | 21 |
| 22 | 23 | 24 | 25 | 26 | 27 | 28 |
| 29 | 30 | | | | | |

### OCTOBER

| S | M | T | W | T | F | S |
|---|---|---|---|---|---|---|
| | | 1 | 2 | 3 | 4 | 5 |
| 6 | 7 | 8 | 9 | 10 | 11 | 12 |
| 13 | 14 | 15 | 16 | 17 | 18 | 19 |
| 20 | 21 | 22 | 23 | 24 | 25 | 26 |
| 27 | 28 | 29 | 30 | 31 | | |

### NOVEMBER

| S | M | T | W | T | F | S |
|---|---|---|---|---|---|---|
| | | | | | 1 | 2 |
| 3 | 4 | 5 | 6 | 7 | 8 | 9 |
| 10 | 11 | 12 | 13 | 14 | 15 | 16 |
| 17 | 18 | 19 | 20 | 21 | 22 | 23 |
| 24 | 25 | 26 | 27 | 28 | 29 | 30 |

### DECEMBER

| S | M | T | W | T | F | S |
|---|---|---|---|---|---|---|
| 1 | 2 | 3 | 4 | 5 | 6 | 7 |
| 8 | 9 | 10 | 11 | 12 | 13 | 14 |
| 15 | 16 | 17 | 18 | 19 | 20 | 21 |
| 22 | 23 | 24 | 25 | 26 | 27 | 28 |
| 29 | 30 | 31 | | | | |

## 10

### JANUARY

| S | M | T | W | T | F | S |
|---|---|---|---|---|---|---|
| | | 1 | 2 | 3 | 4 | 5 |
| 6 | 7 | 8 | 9 | 10 | 11 | 12 |
| 13 | 14 | 15 | 16 | 17 | 18 | 19 |
| 20 | 21 | 22 | 23 | 24 | 25 | 26 |
| 27 | 28 | 29 | 30 | 31 | | |

### FEBRUARY

| S | M | T | W | T | F | S |
|---|---|---|---|---|---|---|
| | | | | | 1 | 2 |
| 3 | 4 | 5 | 6 | 7 | 8 | 9 |
| 10 | 11 | 12 | 13 | 14 | 15 | 16 |
| 17 | 18 | 19 | 20 | 21 | 22 | 23 |
| 24 | 25 | 26 | 27 | 28 | 29 | |

### MARCH

| S | M | T | W | T | F | S |
|---|---|---|---|---|---|---|
| | | | | | | 1 |
| 2 | 3 | 4 | 5 | 6 | 7 | 8 |
| 9 | 10 | 11 | 12 | 13 | 14 | 15 |
| 16 | 17 | 18 | 19 | 20 | 21 | 22 |
| 23 | 24 | 25 | 26 | 27 | 28 | 29 |
| 30 | 31 | | | | | |

### APRIL

| S | M | T | W | T | F | S |
|---|---|---|---|---|---|---|
| | | 1 | 2 | 3 | 4 | 5 |
| 6 | 7 | 8 | 9 | 10 | 11 | 12 |
| 13 | 14 | 15 | 16 | 17 | 18 | 19 |
| 20 | 21 | 22 | 23 | 24 | 25 | 26 |
| 27 | 28 | 29 | 30 | | | |

### MAY

| S | M | T | W | T | F | S |
|---|---|---|---|---|---|---|
| | | | | 1 | 2 | 3 |
| 4 | 5 | 6 | 7 | 8 | 9 | 10 |
| 11 | 12 | 13 | 14 | 15 | 16 | 17 |
| 18 | 19 | 20 | 21 | 22 | 23 | 24 |
| 25 | 26 | 27 | 28 | 29 | 30 | 31 |

### JUNE

| S | M | T | W | T | F | S |
|---|---|---|---|---|---|---|
| 1 | 2 | 3 | 4 | 5 | 6 | 7 |
| 8 | 9 | 10 | 11 | 12 | 13 | 14 |
| 15 | 16 | 17 | 18 | 19 | 20 | 21 |
| 22 | 23 | 24 | 25 | 26 | 27 | 28 |
| 29 | 30 | | | | | |

### JULY

| S | M | T | W | T | F | S |
|---|---|---|---|---|---|---|
| | | 1 | 2 | 3 | 4 | 5 |
| 6 | 7 | 8 | 9 | 10 | 11 | 12 |
| 13 | 14 | 15 | 16 | 17 | 18 | 19 |
| 20 | 21 | 22 | 23 | 24 | 25 | 26 |
| 27 | 28 | 29 | 30 | 31 | | |

### AUGUST

| S | M | T | W | T | F | S |
|---|---|---|---|---|---|---|
| | | | | | 1 | 2 |
| 3 | 4 | 5 | 6 | 7 | 8 | 9 |
| 10 | 11 | 12 | 13 | 14 | 15 | 16 |
| 17 | 18 | 19 | 20 | 21 | 22 | 23 |
| 24 | 25 | 26 | 27 | 28 | 29 | 30 |
| 31 | | | | | | |

### SEPTEMBER

| S | M | T | W | T | F | S |
|---|---|---|---|---|---|---|
| | 1 | 2 | 3 | 4 | 5 | 6 |
| 7 | 8 | 9 | 10 | 11 | 12 | 13 |
| 14 | 15 | 16 | 17 | 18 | 19 | 20 |
| 21 | 22 | 23 | 24 | 25 | 26 | 27 |
| 28 | 29 | 30 | | | | |

### OCTOBER

| S | M | T | W | T | F | S |
|---|---|---|---|---|---|---|
| | | | 1 | 2 | 3 | 4 |
| 5 | 6 | 7 | 8 | 9 | 10 | 11 |
| 12 | 13 | 14 | 15 | 16 | 17 | 18 |
| 19 | 20 | 21 | 22 | 23 | 24 | 25 |
| 26 | 27 | 28 | 29 | 30 | 31 | |

### NOVEMBER

| S | M | T | W | T | F | S |
|---|---|---|---|---|---|---|
| | | | | | | 1 |
| 2 | 3 | 4 | 5 | 6 | 7 | 8 |
| 9 | 10 | 11 | 12 | 13 | 14 | 15 |
| 16 | 17 | 18 | 19 | 20 | 21 | 22 |
| 23 | 24 | 25 | 26 | 27 | 28 | 29 |
| 30 | | | | | | |

### DECEMBER

| S | M | T | W | T | F | S |
|---|---|---|---|---|---|---|
| | 1 | 2 | 3 | 4 | 5 | 6 |
| 7 | 8 | 9 | 10 | 11 | 12 | 13 |
| 14 | 15 | 16 | 17 | 18 | 19 | 20 |
| 21 | 22 | 23 | 24 | 25 | 26 | 27 |
| 28 | 29 | 30 | 31 | | | |

## 11

### JANUARY

| S | M | T | W | T | F | S |
|---|---|---|---|---|---|---|
| | | | 1 | 2 | 3 | 4 |
| 5 | 6 | 7 | 8 | 9 | 10 | 11 |
| 12 | 13 | 14 | 15 | 16 | 17 | 18 |
| 19 | 20 | 21 | 22 | 23 | 24 | 25 |
| 26 | 27 | 28 | 29 | 30 | 31 | |

### FEBRUARY

| S | M | T | W | T | F | S |
|---|---|---|---|---|---|---|
| | | | | | | 1 |
| 2 | 3 | 4 | 5 | 6 | 7 | 8 |
| 9 | 10 | 11 | 12 | 13 | 14 | 15 |
| 16 | 17 | 18 | 19 | 20 | 21 | 22 |
| 23 | 24 | 25 | 26 | 27 | 28 | 29 |

### MARCH

| S | M | T | W | T | F | S |
|---|---|---|---|---|---|---|
| 1 | 2 | 3 | 4 | 5 | 6 | 7 |
| 8 | 9 | 10 | 11 | 12 | 13 | 14 |
| 15 | 16 | 17 | 18 | 19 | 20 | 21 |
| 22 | 23 | 24 | 25 | 26 | 27 | 28 |
| 29 | 30 | 31 | | | | |

### APRIL

| S | M | T | W | T | F | S |
|---|---|---|---|---|---|---|
| | | | 1 | 2 | 3 | 4 |
| 5 | 6 | 7 | 8 | 9 | 10 | 11 |
| 12 | 13 | 14 | 15 | 16 | 17 | 18 |
| 19 | 20 | 21 | 22 | 23 | 24 | 25 |
| 26 | 27 | 28 | 29 | 30 | | |

### MAY

| S | M | T | W | T | F | S |
|---|---|---|---|---|---|---|
| | | | | | 1 | 2 |
| 3 | 4 | 5 | 6 | 7 | 8 | 9 |
| 10 | 11 | 12 | 13 | 14 | 15 | 16 |
| 17 | 18 | 19 | 20 | 21 | 22 | 23 |
| 24 | 25 | 26 | 27 | 28 | 29 | 30 |
| 31 | | | | | | |

### JUNE

| S | M | T | W | T | F | S |
|---|---|---|---|---|---|---|
| | 1 | 2 | 3 | 4 | 5 | 6 |
| 7 | 8 | 9 | 10 | 11 | 12 | 13 |
| 14 | 15 | 16 | 17 | 18 | 19 | 20 |
| 21 | 22 | 23 | 24 | 25 | 26 | 27 |
| 28 | 29 | 30 | | | | |

### JULY

| S | M | T | W | T | F | S |
|---|---|---|---|---|---|---|
| | | | 1 | 2 | 3 | 4 |
| 5 | 6 | 7 | 8 | 9 | 10 | 11 |
| 12 | 13 | 14 | 15 | 16 | 17 | 18 |
| 19 | 20 | 21 | 22 | 23 | 24 | 25 |
| 26 | 27 | 28 | 29 | 30 | 31 | |

### AUGUST

| S | M | T | W | T | F | S |
|---|---|---|---|---|---|---|
| | | | | | | 1 |
| 2 | 3 | 4 | 5 | 6 | 7 | 8 |
| 9 | 10 | 11 | 12 | 13 | 14 | 15 |
| 16 | 17 | 18 | 19 | 20 | 21 | 22 |
| 23 | 24 | 25 | 26 | 27 | 28 | 29 |
| 30 | 31 | | | | | |

### SEPTEMBER

| S | M | T | W | T | F | S |
|---|---|---|---|---|---|---|
| | | 1 | 2 | 3 | 4 | 5 |
| 6 | 7 | 8 | 9 | 10 | 11 | 12 |
| 13 | 14 | 15 | 16 | 17 | 18 | 19 |
| 20 | 21 | 22 | 23 | 24 | 25 | 26 |
| 27 | 28 | 29 | 30 | | | |

### OCTOBER

| S | M | T | W | T | F | S |
|---|---|---|---|---|---|---|
| | | | | 1 | 2 | 3 |
| 4 | 5 | 6 | 7 | 8 | 9 | 10 |
| 11 | 12 | 13 | 14 | 15 | 16 | 17 |
| 18 | 19 | 20 | 21 | 22 | 23 | 24 |
| 25 | 26 | 27 | 28 | 29 | 30 | 31 |

### NOVEMBER

| S | M | T | W | T | F | S |
|---|---|---|---|---|---|---|
| 1 | 2 | 3 | 4 | 5 | 6 | 7 |
| 8 | 9 | 10 | 11 | 12 | 13 | 14 |
| 15 | 16 | 17 | 18 | 19 | 20 | 21 |
| 22 | 23 | 24 | 25 | 26 | 27 | 28 |
| 29 | 30 | | | | | |

### DECEMBER

| S | M | T | W | T | F | S |
|---|---|---|---|---|---|---|
| | | 1 | 2 | 3 | 4 | 5 |
| 6 | 7 | 8 | 9 | 10 | 11 | 12 |
| 13 | 14 | 15 | 16 | 17 | 18 | 19 |
| 20 | 21 | 22 | 23 | 24 | 25 | 26 |
| 27 | 28 | 29 | 30 | 31 | | |

## 12

### JANUARY

| S | M | T | W | T | F | S |
|---|---|---|---|---|---|---|
| | | | | 1 | 2 | 3 |
| 4 | 5 | 6 | 7 | 8 | 9 | 10 |
| 11 | 12 | 13 | 14 | 15 | 16 | 17 |
| 18 | 19 | 20 | 21 | 22 | 23 | 24 |
| 25 | 26 | 27 | 28 | 29 | 30 | 31 |

### FEBRUARY

| S | M | T | W | T | F | S |
|---|---|---|---|---|---|---|
| 1 | 2 | 3 | 4 | 5 | 6 | 7 |
| 8 | 9 | 10 | 11 | 12 | 13 | 14 |
| 15 | 16 | 17 | 18 | 19 | 20 | 21 |
| 22 | 23 | 24 | 25 | 26 | 27 | 28 |
| 29 | | | | | | |

### MARCH

| S | M | T | W | T | F | S |
|---|---|---|---|---|---|---|
| | 1 | 2 | 3 | 4 | 5 | 6 |
| 7 | 8 | 9 | 10 | 11 | 12 | 13 |
| 14 | 15 | 16 | 17 | 18 | 19 | 20 |
| 21 | 22 | 23 | 24 | 25 | 26 | 27 |
| 28 | 29 | 30 | 31 | | | |

### APRIL

| S | M | T | W | T | F | S |
|---|---|---|---|---|---|---|
| | | | | 1 | 2 | 3 |
| 4 | 5 | 6 | 7 | 8 | 9 | 10 |
| 11 | 12 | 13 | 14 | 15 | 16 | 17 |
| 18 | 19 | 20 | 21 | 22 | 23 | 24 |
| 25 | 26 | 27 | 28 | 29 | 30 | |

### MAY

| S | M | T | W | T | F | S |
|---|---|---|---|---|---|---|
| | | | | | | 1 |
| 2 | 3 | 4 | 5 | 6 | 7 | 8 |
| 9 | 10 | 11 | 12 | 13 | 14 | 15 |
| 16 | 17 | 18 | 19 | 20 | 21 | 22 |
| 23 | 24 | 25 | 26 | 27 | 28 | 29 |
| 30 | 31 | | | | | |

### JUNE

| S | M | T | W | T | F | S |
|---|---|---|---|---|---|---|
| | | 1 | 2 | 3 | 4 | 5 |
| 6 | 7 | 8 | 9 | 10 | 11 | 12 |
| 13 | 14 | 15 | 16 | 17 | 18 | 19 |
| 20 | 21 | 22 | 23 | 24 | 25 | 26 |
| 27 | 28 | 29 | 30 | | | |

### JULY

| S | M | T | W | T | F | S |
|---|---|---|---|---|---|---|
| | | | | 1 | 2 | 3 |
| 4 | 5 | 6 | 7 | 8 | 9 | 10 |
| 11 | 12 | 13 | 14 | 15 | 16 | 17 |
| 18 | 19 | 20 | 21 | 22 | 23 | 24 |
| 25 | 26 | 27 | 28 | 29 | 30 | 31 |

### AUGUST

| S | M | T | W | T | F | S |
|---|---|---|---|---|---|---|
| 1 | 2 | 3 | 4 | 5 | 6 | 7 |
| 8 | 9 | 10 | 11 | 12 | 13 | 14 |
| 15 | 16 | 17 | 18 | 19 | 20 | 21 |
| 22 | 23 | 24 | 25 | 26 | 27 | 28 |
| 29 | 30 | 31 | | | | |

### SEPTEMBER

| S | M | T | W | T | F | S |
|---|---|---|---|---|---|---|
| | | | 1 | 2 | 3 | 4 |
| 5 | 6 | 7 | 8 | 9 | 10 | 11 |
| 12 | 13 | 14 | 15 | 16 | 17 | 18 |
| 19 | 20 | 21 | 22 | 23 | 24 | 25 |
| 26 | 27 | 28 | 29 | 30 | | |

### OCTOBER

| S | M | T | W | T | F | S |
|---|---|---|---|---|---|---|
| | | | | | 1 | 2 |
| 3 | 4 | 5 | 6 | 7 | 8 | 9 |
| 10 | 11 | 12 | 13 | 14 | 15 | 16 |
| 17 | 18 | 19 | 20 | 21 | 22 | 23 |
| 24 | 25 | 26 | 27 | 28 | 29 | 30 |
| 31 | | | | | | |

### NOVEMBER

| S | M | T | W | T | F | S |
|---|---|---|---|---|---|---|
| | 1 | 2 | 3 | 4 | 5 | 6 |
| 7 | 8 | 9 | 10 | 11 | 12 | 13 |
| 14 | 15 | 16 | 17 | 18 | 19 | 20 |
| 21 | 22 | 23 | 24 | 25 | 26 | 27 |
| 28 | 29 | 30 | | | | |

### DECEMBER

| S | M | T | W | T | F | S |
|---|---|---|---|---|---|---|
| | | | 1 | 2 | 3 | 4 |
| 5 | 6 | 7 | 8 | 9 | 10 | 11 |
| 12 | 13 | 14 | 15 | 16 | 17 | 18 |
| 19 | 20 | 21 | 22 | 23 | 24 | 25 |
| 26 | 27 | 28 | 29 | 30 | 31 | |

## 13

### JANUARY

| S | M | T | W | T | F | S |
|---|---|---|---|---|---|---|
| | | | | | 1 | 2 |
| 3 | 4 | 5 | 6 | 7 | 8 | 9 |
| 10 | 11 | 12 | 13 | 14 | 15 | 16 |
| 17 | 18 | 19 | 20 | 21 | 22 | 23 |
| 24 | 25 | 26 | 27 | 28 | 29 | 30 |
| 31 | | | | | | |

### FEBRUARY

| S | M | T | W | T | F | S |
|---|---|---|---|---|---|---|
| | 1 | 2 | 3 | 4 | 5 | 6 |
| 7 | 8 | 9 | 10 | 11 | 12 | 13 |
| 14 | 15 | 16 | 17 | 18 | 19 | 20 |
| 21 | 22 | 23 | 24 | 25 | 26 | 27 |
| 28 | 29 | | | | | |

### MARCH

| S | M | T | W | T | F | S |
|---|---|---|---|---|---|---|
| | | 1 | 2 | 3 | 4 | 5 |
| 6 | 7 | 8 | 9 | 10 | 11 | 12 |
| 13 | 14 | 15 | 16 | 17 | 18 | 19 |
| 20 | 21 | 22 | 23 | 24 | 25 | 26 |
| 27 | 28 | 29 | 30 | 31 | | |

### APRIL

| S | M | T | W | T | F | S |
|---|---|---|---|---|---|---|
| | | | | | 1 | 2 |
| 3 | 4 | 5 | 6 | 7 | 8 | 9 |
| 10 | 11 | 12 | 13 | 14 | 15 | 16 |
| 17 | 18 | 19 | 20 | 21 | 22 | 23 |
| 24 | 25 | 26 | 27 | 28 | 29 | 30 |

### MAY

| S | M | T | W | T | F | S |
|---|---|---|---|---|---|---|
| 1 | 2 | 3 | 4 | 5 | 6 | 7 |
| 8 | 9 | 10 | 11 | 12 | 13 | 14 |
| 15 | 16 | 17 | 18 | 19 | 20 | 21 |
| 22 | 23 | 24 | 25 | 26 | 27 | 28 |
| 29 | 30 | 31 | | | | |

### JUNE

| S | M | T | W | T | F | S |
|---|---|---|---|---|---|---|
| | | | 1 | 2 | 3 | 4 |
| 5 | 6 | 7 | 8 | 9 | 10 | 11 |
| 12 | 13 | 14 | 15 | 16 | 17 | 18 |
| 19 | 20 | 21 | 22 | 23 | 24 | 25 |
| 26 | 27 | 28 | 29 | 30 | | |

### JULY

| S | M | T | W | T | F | S |
|---|---|---|---|---|---|---|
| | | | | | 1 | 2 |
| 3 | 4 | 5 | 6 | 7 | 8 | 9 |
| 10 | 11 | 12 | 13 | 14 | 15 | 16 |
| 17 | 18 | 19 | 20 | 21 | 22 | 23 |
| 24 | 25 | 26 | 27 | 28 | 29 | 30 |
| 31 | | | | | | |

### AUGUST

| S | M | T | W | T | F | S |
|---|---|---|---|---|---|---|
| | 1 | 2 | 3 | 4 | 5 | 6 |
| 7 | 8 | 9 | 10 | 11 | 12 | 13 |
| 14 | 15 | 16 | 17 | 18 | 19 | 20 |
| 21 | 22 | 23 | 24 | 25 | 26 | 27 |
| 28 | 29 | 30 | 31 | | | |

### SEPTEMBER

| S | M | T | W | T | F | S |
|---|---|---|---|---|---|---|
| | | | | 1 | 2 | 3 |
| 4 | 5 | 6 | 7 | 8 | 9 | 10 |
| 11 | 12 | 13 | 14 | 15 | 16 | 17 |
| 18 | 19 | 20 | 21 | 22 | 23 | 24 |
| 25 | 26 | 27 | 28 | 29 | 30 | |

### OCTOBER

| S | M | T | W | T | F | S |
|---|---|---|---|---|---|---|
| | | | | | | 1 |
| 2 | 3 | 4 | 5 | 6 | 7 | 8 |
| 9 | 10 | 11 | 12 | 13 | 14 | 15 |
| 16 | 17 | 18 | 19 | 20 | 21 | 22 |
| 23 | 24 | 25 | 26 | 27 | 28 | 29 |
| 30 | 31 | | | | | |

### NOVEMBER

| S | M | T | W | T | F | S |
|---|---|---|---|---|---|---|
| | | 1 | 2 | 3 | 4 | 5 |
| 6 | 7 | 8 | 9 | 10 | 11 | 12 |
| 13 | 14 | 15 | 16 | 17 | 18 | 19 |
| 20 | 21 | 22 | 23 | 24 | 25 | 26 |
| 27 | 28 | 29 | 30 | | | |

### DECEMBER

| S | M | T | W | T | F | S |
|---|---|---|---|---|---|---|
| | | | | 1 | 2 | 3 |
| 4 | 5 | 6 | 7 | 8 | 9 | 10 |
| 11 | 12 | 13 | 14 | 15 | 16 | 17 |
| 18 | 19 | 20 | 21 | 22 | 23 | 24 |
| 25 | 26 | 27 | 28 | 29 | 30 | 31 |

## 14

### JANUARY

| S | M | T | W | T | F | S |
|---|---|---|---|---|---|---|
| | | | | | | 1 |
| 2 | 3 | 4 | 5 | 6 | 7 | 8 |
| 9 | 10 | 11 | 12 | 13 | 14 | 15 |
| 16 | 17 | 18 | 19 | 20 | 21 | 22 |
| 23 | 24 | 25 | 26 | 27 | 28 | 29 |
| 30 | 31 | | | | | |

### FEBRUARY

| S | M | T | W | T | F | S |
|---|---|---|---|---|---|---|
| | | 1 | 2 | 3 | 4 | 5 |
| 6 | 7 | 8 | 9 | 10 | 11 | 12 |
| 13 | 14 | 15 | 16 | 17 | 18 | 19 |
| 20 | 21 | 22 | 23 | 24 | 25 | 26 |
| 27 | 28 | 29 | | | | |

### MARCH

| S | M | T | W | T | F | S |
|---|---|---|---|---|---|---|
| | | | 1 | 2 | 3 | 4 |
| 5 | 6 | 7 | 8 | 9 | 10 | 11 |
| 12 | 13 | 14 | 15 | 16 | 17 | 18 |
| 19 | 20 | 21 | 22 | 23 | 24 | 25 |
| 26 | 27 | 28 | 29 | 30 | 31 | |

### APRIL

| S | M | T | W | T | F | S |
|---|---|---|---|---|---|---|
| | | | | | | 1 |
| 2 | 3 | 4 | 5 | 6 | 7 | 8 |
| 9 | 10 | 11 | 12 | 13 | 14 | 15 |
| 16 | 17 | 18 | 19 | 20 | 21 | 22 |
| 23 | 24 | 25 | 26 | 27 | 28 | 29 |
| 30 | | | | | | |

### MAY

| S | M | T | W | T | F | S |
|---|---|---|---|---|---|---|
| | 1 | 2 | 3 | 4 | 5 | 6 |
| 7 | 8 | 9 | 10 | 11 | 12 | 13 |
| 14 | 15 | 16 | 17 | 18 | 19 | 20 |
| 21 | 22 | 23 | 24 | 25 | 26 | 27 |
| 28 | 29 | 30 | 31 | | | |

### JUNE

| S | M | T | W | T | F | S |
|---|---|---|---|---|---|---|
| | | | | 1 | 2 | 3 |
| 4 | 5 | 6 | 7 | 8 | 9 | 10 |
| 11 | 12 | 13 | 14 | 15 | 16 | 17 |
| 18 | 19 | 20 | 21 | 22 | 23 | 24 |
| 25 | 26 | 27 | 28 | 29 | 30 | |

### JULY

| S | M | T | W | T | F | S |
|---|---|---|---|---|---|---|
| | | | | | | 1 |
| 2 | 3 | 4 | 5 | 6 | 7 | 8 |
| 9 | 10 | 11 | 12 | 13 | 14 | 15 |
| 16 | 17 | 18 | 19 | 20 | 21 | 22 |
| 23 | 24 | 25 | 26 | 27 | 28 | 29 |
| 30 | 31 | | | | | |

### AUGUST

| S | M | T | W | T | F | S |
|---|---|---|---|---|---|---|
| | | 1 | 2 | 3 | 4 | 5 |
| 6 | 7 | 8 | 9 | 10 | 11 | 12 |
| 13 | 14 | 15 | 16 | 17 | 18 | 19 |
| 20 | 21 | 22 | 23 | 24 | 25 | 26 |
| 27 | 28 | 29 | 30 | 31 | | |

### SEPTEMBER

| S | M | T | W | T | F | S |
|---|---|---|---|---|---|---|
| | | | | | 1 | 2 |
| 3 | 4 | 5 | 6 | 7 | 8 | 9 |
| 10 | 11 | 12 | 13 | 14 | 15 | 16 |
| 17 | 18 | 19 | 20 | 21 | 22 | 23 |
| 24 | 25 | 26 | 27 | 28 | 29 | 30 |

### OCTOBER

| S | M | T | W | T | F | S |
|---|---|---|---|---|---|---|
| 1 | 2 | 3 | 4 | 5 | 6 | 7 |
| 8 | 9 | 10 | 11 | 12 | 13 | 14 |
| 15 | 16 | 17 | 18 | 19 | 20 | 21 |
| 22 | 23 | 24 | 25 | 26 | 27 | 28 |
| 29 | 30 | 31 | | | | |

### NOVEMBER

| S | M | T | W | T | F | S |
|---|---|---|---|---|---|---|
| | | | 1 | 2 | 3 | 4 |
| 5 | 6 | 7 | 8 | 9 | 10 | 11 |
| 12 | 13 | 14 | 15 | 16 | 17 | 18 |
| 19 | 20 | 21 | 22 | 23 | 24 | 25 |
| 26 | 27 | 28 | 29 | 30 | | |

### DECEMBER

| S | M | T | W | T | F | S |
|---|---|---|---|---|---|---|
| | | | | | 1 | 2 |
| 3 | 4 | 5 | 6 | 7 | 8 | 9 |
| 10 | 11 | 12 | 13 | 14 | 15 | 16 |
| 17 | 18 | 19 | 20 | 21 | 22 | 23 |
| 24 | 25 | 26 | 27 | 28 | 29 | 30 |
| 31 | | | | | | |

Name ______________________ Date ______________________

# Time Travel Historical News Service, Part 1

Choose 10 historical events that occurred in the nineteenth and twentieth centuries. For each, find the date on which the event occurred, and then use your perpetual calendar to find out on which day of the week it occurred. Work independently so that there is the least possible duplication of dates.

**1.**

| | Event | Date | Day of the Week |
|---|---|---|---|
| a. | | | |
| b. | | | |
| c. | | | |
| d. | | | |
| e. | | | |
| f. | | | |
| g. | | | |
| h. | | | |
| i. | | | |
| j. | | | |

**2.** Which days of the week had the most events and which had the fewest?

______________________________________________

______________________________________________

**3.** If you had investigated more historical events, say 100 instead of 10, do you think you would have the same day of the week with the most events? Why or why not?

______________________________________________

______________________________________________

______________________________________________

Name ______________________ Date ______________________

# Time Travel Historical News Service, Part 2

1. Use your data on what days of the week historical events occurred to fill in the table with the number of events that occurred on each day of the week.

| Sunday | Monday | Tuesday | Wednesday | Thursday | Friday | Saturday |
|---|---|---|---|---|---|---|
| | | | | | | |

2. Do you think that including the events of your group mates will change which day of the week has the most historical events? Why?

______________________

3. Use the data from your entire group to fill in the table with the number of events that occurred on each day of the week.

| Sunday | Monday | Tuesday | Wednesday | Thursday | Friday | Saturday |
|---|---|---|---|---|---|---|
| | | | | | | |

4. Do you think that including the events of all of your classmates will change which day of the week has the most historical events? Why?

______________________

5. Write one sticky note for each historical event. Include the date, day, and event. Check within your group to make sure no one else has also included that event. Add your notes to the class graph. Record the results from the class graph in this table.

| Sunday | Monday | Tuesday | Wednesday | Thursday | Friday | Saturday |
|---|---|---|---|---|---|---|
| | | | | | | |

6. Which two days of the week did the most recorded historical events occur? ______________________

7. Which two days of the week did the fewest recorded historical events occur? ______________________

8. Imagine you are the news director for "Time Travel, Historical News Service," which provides on-the-spot reporting for things that happened in the past. Write a letter to your station manager explaining why you should or should not have the same number of reporters working on weekend days as on weekdays.

Name ______________________________ Date ______________________________

# Friday the 13th

Many people are suspicious about Friday the 13th.

1. Are there any Friday the 13ths this year? ______________

2. What are the most and the fewest Friday the 13ths that any year could have? ______________

3. What is the probability that the 13th of the month will occur on a Friday? How do you know?

______________________________________________

______________________________________________

______________________________________________

4. Which day of the week is the 13th most likely to be? Explain your answer.

______________________________________________

______________________________________________

______________________________________________

Name ______________________ Date ______________________

# Birthday Parties

Grace Murray Hopper, a talented mathematician who helped create the computer programming language COBOL, became a rear admiral in the U.S. Navy at the age of 82. She was born on a Sunday, and coincidentally her 50th birthday was also on a Sunday.

1. What day of the week were you born? ______________

2. What day of the week will be your 50th birthday? ______________

3. Survey ten people. Do *not* include yourself or anyone one else in your grade at school. To avoid duplication of data, do not survey anyone that a classmate has surveyed. Ask each person in your survey for his or her date of birth. For each person, look up the day of birth and day of 50th birthday.

4. What percent of the people you surveyed celebrated (or will celebrate) their 50th birthday on the same day of the week as their birth day? ______________

Name ______________________ Date ______________________

# Birthday Parties, the Sequel

We started to investigate the probability of someone having his or her 50th birthday on the same day of the week as his or her birth day.

1. From your survey of 10 people, what would you predict is the percent of people who would have the same day of the week for their birth and their 50th birthday? ________

2. From the survey done by the math class, what would you predict is the percent of people who would have the same day of the week for their birth and their 50th birthday? ________

Both of these predictions are examples of *experimental probability*. Now we will look at *theoretical probability*.

Use the *Perpetual Calendar* to fill out the table on page 170. Use the data in your table to answer the following questions.

3. Based on the data you collected, what percent of the time would you expect someone to have his or her 50th birthday on the same day of the week that he or she was born? ________

4. Consider the years in which the members of your class were born. Look at the data for those years and predict whether you would expect those people to have their 50th birthday on the same day as their birth day. ________

5. Why did you eliminate that data from your data collecting for the experimental probability?

______________________________________________

6. Why did you initially choose 28 consecutive years to evaluate when figuring this probability?

______________________________________________

7. Summarize the rule to tell whether someone will have his or her 50th birthday on the same day of the week as the day of his or her birth.

______________________________________________

______________________________________________

Name ______________________ Date ______________________

Birthday Parties, the Sequel (cont.)

| BirthYear | Fifty Years Later | | | | Totals | |
|---|---|---|---|---|---|---|
| | Days Before Feb. 29 | | Days After Feb. 28 | | Yes | No |
| | Yes | or No | Yes | or No | | |
| 1901 | | | | | | |
| 1902 | | | | | | |
| 1903 | | | | | | |
| 1904 | | | | | | |
| 1905 | | | | | | |
| 1906 | | | | | | |
| 1907 | | | | | | |
| 1908 | | | | | | |
| 1909 | | | | | | |
| 1910 | | | | | | |
| 1911 | | | | | | |
| 1912 | | | | | | |
| 1913 | | | | | | |
| 1914 | | | | | | |
| 1915 | | | | | | |
| 1916 | | | | | | |
| 1917 | | | | | | |
| 1918 | | | | | | |
| 1919 | | | | | | |
| 1920 | | | | | | |
| 921 | | | | | | |
| 1922 | | | | | | |
| 1923 | | | | | | |
| 1924 | | | | | | |
| 1925 | | | | | | |
| 1926 | | | | | | |
| 1927 | | | | | | |
| 1928 | | | | | | |

Total yes days _____ Total no days _____

# Acknowledgments

**Photos**
All photos © Pearson Learning unless otherwise noted. Front cover: *t., b.m.* Palmer/Kane, Inc./The Stock Market; *b.r.* Laurie Platt Winfrey, Inc. Back cover: Palmer/Kane, Inc./The Stock Market. 134: The Bridgeman Art Library.

**Cover Illustrations**
Chinese version of Pascal's Triangle from *A History of Chinese Mathematics* by Jean Claude Martzloff. © 1997 Springer-Verlag (54749-5).

Multiplication *per gelosia* of 534 by 342 and the rod-numeral system example from *From One To Zero: A Universal History of Numbers,* written and illustrated by Georges Ifrah. © 1985 Viking Penguin Inc. Also in *The Universal History of Numbers from prehistory to the invention of the computer,* written and illustrated by Georges Ifrah. New enlarged and revised edition, © John Wiley & Sons. Used by permission of the author.

**Interior Illustrations**
84: Excerpt from "The Purcell Catch" from *The Catch Club or Merry Companions Being a Choice Collection of the Most Diversity Catches for Three and Four Voices.* © 1965 Da Capo Press. 90: Chronogram examples from *From One To Zero: A Universal History of Numbers,* written and illustrated by Georges Ifrah. © 1985 Viking Penguin Inc. Also in *The Universal History of Numbers from prehistory to the invention of the computer,* written and illustrated by Georges Ifrah. New enlarged and revised edition, © John Wiley & Sons. Used by permission of the author. 131: C.A. Browne's 27X27 Magic Squares from *The Wonders of Magic Squares* by Jim Moran. © 1982 Vintage Books. 135: Muhammad ibn Muhammad illustrations from *Africa Counts* by Claudia Zaslavsky. © 1973 Prindle, Weber & Schmidt. 135: Alphamagic Squares from "Games Mathematicians Play" by Ivars Peterson. 140: Pascal's Triangle by Murai from *A History of Japanese Mathematics* by Eugene David and Yoshio Mikami. © 1914 The Open Court Publishing Company. 140: Chinese version of Pascal's Triangle from *A History of Chinese Mathematics* by Jean Claude Martzloff. © 1997 Springer-Verlag (54749-5). Note: Every effort has been made to locate the copyright owner of material reprinted in this book. Omissions brought to our attention will be corrected in subsequent editions.